Challenging Modern

Questioning Einstein's Relativity Theories

Al Kelly

BrownWalker Press
Boca Raton • 2005

Challenging Modern Physics: Questioning Einstein's Relativity Theories

Previous editions under the title *Universal Theory of Relativity* were lodged in the copyright libraries of the U.K. and Ireland from April 1993 to February 1996. This was done to establish ownership of the ideas in this book.

BrownWalker Press
Boca Raton, Florida
USA • 2005

ISBN: 1-58112-437-6 (paper)
ISBN: 1-58112-438-4 (ebook)

BrownWalker.com

Challenging Modern Physics

Connie Sharr (nee HARFORD) June 07
From the late Al Kelly
Trinity College
originally - Walterstown, Navan Co Meath

Acknowledgments

To the late Professor Séamus Timoney of University College Dublin, who said he did not believe in Special Relativity and encouraged me to investigate it. To my son Piaras for the lengthy correspondence and hours of debate. To my son Gavin, who translated the original Sagnac and other French and German papers. To Barbara Melchiori, who translated the Italian De Pretto paper. To Ria, who supplied cups of tea at late hours, and to Simon, Gemma, Louise (who suggested the name 'Full Stop' for the postulate in chapter 10) and Donnacha for their active support. To Sr. Bernadette Kelly and Angela Caffrey for editorial suggestions; to Gráinne O'Donovan, who edited the final text so excellently. To Dr. Finbar Callanan and Patrick Purcell, successive Directors General of the Institution of Engineers of Ireland and to the late Dr. Christine Somers, Director of Education with the Institution, all of whom had the courage to publish the seven monographs that form the basis of this book. To my nephew Ian Duffy for helping to publicise those monographs. To an anonymous central European professor of physics who discussed the Sagnac effect at length and encouraged me to publish. To an anonymous Irish friend who debated with vigour many of the ideas in this book and, in several cases, corrected my line of thinking.

Dublin 2005

There was a young lady named Bright,
Whose speed was far faster than light.
She went out one day,
In a relative way
And returned on the previous night.

Reginald Buller (1913)

Contents

When in doubt, make a fool of yourself. There is a microscopically thin line between being brilliantly creative and acting like the most gigantic idiot. So what the hell, leap.

Cynthia Heimel

Preface

No theory can ever be proven; it can only be falsified. The well-known *'all swans are white'* proverb was falsified when the first flock of black swans was discovered in Australia. Each theory stands as the best available until someone devises a theory that better fits experimental evidence.

Newton's Laws held for 300 years until Einstein came along with his 'special theory of relativity'. Experiments carried out since the launch of Einstein's theory in 1905 show anomalies. This book sets out a different explanation of the behaviour of light, which dispels those particular anomalies.

The book starts with a standard explanation of the special theory of relativity to acquaint the reader with the claims of that theory. Some problems with the theory are next described; these are euphemistically named 'paradoxes'. It is shown that Einstein was not the first to derive the famous equation $E = mc^2$, which has become synonymous with his name. Next, experimental evidence that cannot be explained by Special Relativity is given. In the light of this evidence, the two basic postulates of the special theory on the behaviour of light are shown to be untenable. A new theory is then developed, which conforms to the experimental evidence. This theory is simple; it requires no exotic concepts such as the slowing of time with speed, which are required by the special theory.

Novel experiments on the relative motion of magnets and conductors are described. These were undertaken because the movement of a conductor near the stationary pole of a magnet and the movement of that pole near a stationary conductor did not always give the same result. This result was claimed to be in contradiction to relativity theory, which requires that it is solely the relative motion of the magnet and conductor that matters. However, in the event, it is another basic law of physics that is shown to be in need of revision (Faraday's Law) – the experimental results are shown not to contradict relativity theory.

The Big Bang theory of the beginning of the universe is questioned and an alternative proposed. The source of much of the mysterious missing 'dark matter', which has been sought for decades by astronomers, is located. An explanation of the peculiar shapes of some galaxies is proffered.

It will be seen that everyday phenomena such as light and gravity are not yet properly understood. Perhaps this book will spur the reader to solve some of the unexplained mysteries of nature.

The general reader can skip the occasional mathematics without losing the trend of the debate. The conclusions drawn are also, in each instance, stated in words. In relation to the important aspects of the theory proposed in this book, there will be some repetition to ensure that the reader has grasped the kernel of the proposed theory.

1

There is not a single concept of which I am convinced that it will survive, and I am unsure whether I am on the right way at all.

Albert Einstein (1949)

Chapter 1

Special Theory of Relativity

Before Relativity

Before Einstein propounded the theory of Special Relativity, there were unexplained problems created by the assumption that light was behaving in the same way as sound. Sound travels through different media, such as the air. However, because it travels through (or piggybacks on) the air, the speed of sound, as measured by an observer, will vary depending on (a) the velocity of the air and the direction in which the air is travelling, and (b) any motion of the observer in relation to the source of the sound.

It was naturally assumed that light also travelled through a medium called 'ether'. Otherwise, the light coming from the stars would be travelling through 'nothing', which seemed an unacceptable proposition. It was also assumed that the measured velocity of light relative to an observer should vary in a similar manner to sound.

But then one famous experiment upset that notion.

The Michelson and Morley Experiment

Let us reflect on the famous 1887 Michelson and Morley[1] experiment. If there were an ether, the time measured for light emitted upon earth to travel at right angles to the direction of the motion of the earth on its orbit around the sun should prove different from the time for light to travel in the same direction as the motion of the earth upon its orbit. A test of this would confirm the motion of the earth and the existence of the ether.

Michelson later explained the experiment to his children as recorded by his daughter Dorothy Michelson (1973) as follows[2]:

> *Suppose we have a river of width w (say 100 feet) and two swimmers who swim at the same speed v (say, 5 feet per second). The river is flowing at a steady rate, say 3 feet per second. The swimmers race in the following way: they both start at the same point on the bank. One swims directly across the river to the closest point on the opposite bank, then turns around and swims back. The other stays on one side of the river, swimming upstream a distance (measured along the bank) exactly equal to the width of the river, and then swims back to the start. Who wins?*
>
> *Consider the swimmer going upstream and back. Going 100 feet upstream, the speed relative to the bank is only 2 feet per second, so that takes 50 seconds. Coming back the speed is 8 feet per second, so it takes 12.5 seconds for a total of*

---

[1] References are listed alphabetically at the end of the book.
[2] SI units are used throughout but here we quote directly from the paper.

62.5 seconds.

Now consider the cross stream swimmer. It won't do to aim at the opposite bank – the flow will carry the swimmer downstream. To succeed in going directly across, the swimmer must aim upstream at the correct angle. The swimmer is going at 5 feet per second at an angle relative to the river and being carried downstream at 3 feet per second. In one second the swimmer will move 4 feet across (right angled triangle is 3, 4, and 5). So at a crossing rate of 4 feet per second the swimmer gets across in 25 seconds and back in the same time – total 50 seconds. The cross stream swimmer wins.

Michelson's idea was to construct a similar race for light pulses, with the ether playing the part of the river.

The prevailing theory was that the ether formed an absolute reference with respect to which the universe was stationary. An observer on earth would picture himself or herself as stationary. To this observer, the stationary ether would appear to be moving.

Taking the speed of the earth moving on its orbit as v km/s, to the observer in the laboratory, the ether flow would appear as v in the opposite direction. The speed of light is c km/s and the ether flow is v km/s through the laboratory.

Two light signals were sent out, one in the direction of the motion of the earth on its orbit around the sun and the other at right angles to that direction. These two signals are depicted in the two sketches in figure 1. If the apparatus were at rest in the supposed ether, the two light signals would come back at the same instant. If not, the effect of the ether would be that the two signals would not come back at the same time.

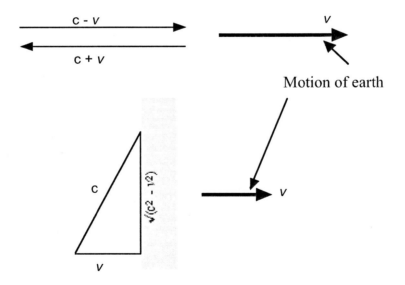

Figure 1: The Michelson and Morley Experiment

The earth's movement, which corresponds to the swimmer going with and against the flow in Michelson's explanation to his children, is in the direction of v. The ether flow in relation to the earth is therefore v to the left. In the top sketch, the speed of the light pulse going out and back in a straight line to the right for a distance L is $c - v$ on the outward journey and $c + v$ on the return journey, where v is the velocity of the earth relative to the supposed ether and c is the speed of light. Therefore, the time taken for the total journey would be:

$$[L/(c - v)] + [L/(c + v)] = [2Lc/(c^2 - v^2)]$$

The situation where the light signal is sent at right angles to the direction of the orbital motion of the earth is shown in the lower sketch of figure 1. This corresponds to the cross-stream swimmer. The result is different from the top sketch. Considering the right-angled triangle, the vertical component is $\sqrt{(c^2 - v^2)}$. The time for the double journey is:

$$2L/\sqrt{(c^2 - v^2)}$$

Because the times for the double journey in the two cases are different, it was foreseen that this difference could be used to determine the movement of the earth through the supposed ether. However, to Michelson and Morley's great surprise, no difference was detected.

While the experiment is always referred to as the Michelson and Morley experiment, Michelson alone had done an earlier test in 1881, where he proved the same result to an accuracy of one in two. The later more famous experiment was to an accuracy of one in forty, which was considered to be of sufficient accuracy to be generally accepted.

We need not go into the details of the apparatus, which had to detect one-millionth of a millionth of a second of time difference. Suffice it to say that it was based on measuring the difference in the interference fringes in continuous light sent in the two directions – the light should return at different times and thus set up these 'fringes' of light. The development of this method of measurement was a pioneering effort by Michelson, who had been a master in the U.S.A. navy. Many trials were made, but no difference in the time taken could be seen within the accuracy of the test equipment. He made the whole apparatus so that it could be rotated to find the maximum effect. The equipment was sufficiently accurate to detect one-tenth of the expected result. Thirteen tests culminating in an accuracy of 1:375 in 1930 are listed in Shankland (1955). Later, Jaseja et al. (1964) carried out a test to an accuracy of 1:1000. Any theory proposed must conform to this result. An even more accurate test that brings in another (startling) complication will be discussed later.

The Jaseja et al. test was 25 times more accurate than the Michelson and Morley test. We can therefore conclude that the speed of light is the same to very great accuracy in the direction of the orbital movement of the earth around the sun as the speed of light at right angles to that direction.

The Michelson and Morley experiment is renowned as the most famous test to have got a zero result. The result was so amazing that it was immediately known throughout the scientific world.

This puzzle led to some proposals that, in retrospect, seem bizarre. One suggestion was that the earth's movement through the ether was exactly balanced by some other movement of the solar system as a whole. Another was that the ether was dragged along by the earth when near the earth's surface. The Irish scientist Stokes had proposed in 1864 that a 'jelly-ether' existed, and this earlier idea persisted into the last century as a possible explanation (Wilson, 1987).

One explanation, proposed independently by the Irish scientist Fitzgerald in 1889 and the Dutch scientist Lorentz in 1892, required objects to contract in the direction of their motion (a fairly unlikely occurrence). This is known as the 'Lorentz-Fitzgerald contraction'. Fitzgerald wrote to Lorentz in November 1894 as follows:

> *A couple of years after Michelson's results were published, as well as I recollect, I wrote a letter to 'Science' the American paper that has recently become defunct, explaining my view, but I do not know if they ever published it, for I did not see the journal for some time afterwards. I am pretty sure that your publication is then prior to any of my printed publications for I have looked up several places where I thought I might have mentioned it but cannot find that I did.*

Fitzgerald also commented in that letter, *"I have been rather laughed at for my view over here."* The original letter to *Science* was dated May 2nd 1889 and actually appeared in *Science* in the issue dated May 24th. The letter went from Trinity College Dublin to Cork, 150 miles away, and then by tender to an ocean-going ship that sailed to New York, U.S.A. The letter was published 22 days later. The fact that the letter was actually published lay dormant until 1967, when it was discovered by Brush. What an efficient postal service, editorial review and publication organisation existed then!

The French scientist Poincaré had earlier concluded in 1899 that the movement of the earth with respect to an ether was *in principle* undetectable.

On occasions, such as in a letter written in 1952 (French, 1968), Einstein stated that he did not know of the Michelson and Morley experiment before 1905, when he published his famous paper launching his theory on relativity. The 1887 paper by Michelson and Morley referenced sources in German, Dutch and French, indicating that the findings would be known all over Europe. In 1922, Einstein had suggested that the test was the trigger to his relativity theory (see Highfield and Carter, 1993), and Einstein freely referred to Michelson and Morley in his 1916 book. There is other evidence that Einstein knew about the Michelson and Morley test as early as 1899.

Have Patience

Remember that in the 1930s there were reputed to be only three persons in the world who professed to understand and believe in Special Relativity; at least one of those (Einstein) is now dead. So do not be disheartened if you find the next few pages of this book abstruse or confusing. Unfortunately, we have to forge through the fog of Special Relativity to emerge into the sunlight of the later chapters; it is a purgatory that must be suffered before getting to the heaven of clarity and common sense. Remember this when you are tempted early on to throw the whole thing in the waste paper basket. Understanding clearly what is being claimed is quite different from believing that it is true. No apology is made to those who profess to believe in Special Relativity.

Special Theory of Relativity

Einstein set out two postulates in his special theory of relativity, which he launched in a paper in 1905. The theory is referred to as Special Relativity (SR for short) throughout this book.

The first postulate is that the *"laws of electrodynamics and optics will be valid for all frames of reference for which the equations of mechanics hold good"*. The second postulate states that *"light is always propagated in empty space with a definite velocity c which is independent of the state of motion of the emitting body"*. From these two postulates, Einstein concluded that:

1. *The laws by which the states of physical systems undergo changes are not affected, whether these changes of state be referred to the one or the other of two systems of co-ordinates in uniform translatory motion.*
2. *Any ray of light moves in the 'stationary' system of co-ordinates with the determined velocity c, whether the ray be emitted by a stationary or by a moving body.*

Based on the above postulates of SR, Einstein derived two requirements relating to the behaviour of light. The first states that *"light is always propagated in empty space with a definite velocity c which is independent of the state of motion of the emitting body"*. This first requirement says that light (just like sound in still air) is not affected by the speed of the emitting source. If a flash of light emanates from an aeroplane, the light flash goes out in relation to the spot at which the aeroplane was when the flash was let off; the speed of the light going out from that spot does not have the speed of the aeroplane added to its speed. There is really nothing unexpected about this.

The second requirement claims that *"light moves in the 'stationary' system of co-ordinates with the determined velocity c, whether the ray be emitted by a stationary or by a moving body"*. This requirement says that the speed of the light will be found to have the same value whether measured by a stationary observer at the spot where the light flash emanates or by an observer who is moving off at a uniform speed relative to that spot. The whole of SR is based upon this claim. If the reader fully accepts the claim, the rest of the theory follows logically. If, on the other hand, the reader is sceptical of such a claim, then read on!

This second requirement is a rather startling claim. In this respect, light should not behave like sound in still air. The measured speed of sound is directly affected by the speed of the observer in relation to the point of emission of the sound pulse. This is a well-known phenomenon. Additionally, the movement of the air through which the sound pulse moves has to be added to the speed of the sound in relation to the observer.

It is immediately obvious that this second proposal by Einstein fits the Michelson and Morley result, where the speed of the light was measured as the same whether going with the orbital motion of the earth around the sun or at right angles to that direction. Einstein's proposal meant that, in such a test, you could never get any answer except the constant speed of light.

The speed of light in a vacuum is about 300,000 km/s (= c). In air, it is slightly less (0.9997c). The speed c is usually used for the speed of light in a vacuum or air because the difference is insignificant.

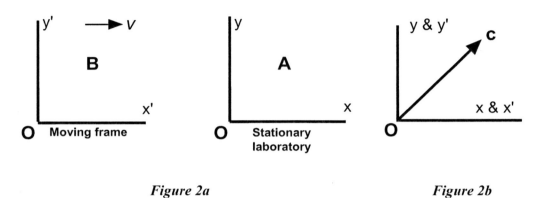

Figure 2a   Figure 2b

Figure 2: Frames of Reference

In figure 2a, two frames of reference are shown. The one on the left, where an observer B is situated, is the moving frame, which is moving with a uniform velocity v with respect to the laboratory in the $+x$ direction. The frame of reference on the right of figure 2a is the stationary laboratory, in which the stationary observer A is situated. At the exact place and time when the two frames have the same origin O and the same x and y axes, let a pulse of light be emitted at this origin. This is the situation depicted in figure 2b. Here, both frames of reference coincide.

SR propounded that a pulse of light emitted at the coincident origin of the two frames spreads out as a sphere as measured in both frames (one stationary and the other moving) and will spread at the speed of light in either frame. While the light spreads out in every direction as a sphere, the line with the thick arrowhead in figure 2b shows it in one direction only.

SR says that the light spreads out as a sphere whose radius is expanding at the speed c, as measured in all frames of reference that are inertial, i.e. that have a uniform velocity relative to each other. In the case of figure 2, because one frame is stationary and the other travels at a constant speed of v in the $+x$ direction, the two frames can be described as inertial, and therefore SR will apply. The observer at A in the laboratory stationary frame of reference will observe that a sphere of light emanates from the origin and travels outwards at a speed c. Also, the observer at B in the moving frame will observe that a sphere (the one emanating from the same flash of light) spreads outwards at a speed of c as measured in the moving frame (from the same instant and from the same origin that was coincident for the moving frame and the laboratory at that instant). This is as stated in Møller (1952) and Katz (1964). It was also described by Einstein in his 1916 book *Relativity (The Special and the General Theory)*. In his paper launching his general theory in 1916, Einstein stated:

> *Thus the special theory does not depart from classical mechanics through the postulate of relativity, but through the postulate of the constancy of the velocity of light in vacuo.*

Einstein made it clear here that it was solely his claim that the speed of light is always measured as a constant by observers in uniform motion with respect to each other that was the revolutionary aspect of his proposals.

The above is a brief description of the usual interpretation of SR. Later in the book, the basic assumptions of that theory will be the subject of closer scrutiny.

To translate the observations of the stationary observer in the laboratory to the observations of the observer in the moving frame of reference, both of whom must get the same value for the speed of light as measured with respect to themselves, SR has to be used. The allowances that have to be made because of the relative motions of the observers give rise to the equations of SR, which will be derived below.

Note: A 'frame of reference' defines the place with reference to which measurements are being taken. For example, imagine yourself on an aeroplane that is flying at a steady speed and altitude. In this case, you could consider yourself to be in a 'stationary' frame of reference and would observe other things as moving relative to that frame. In this book, the qualification 'inertial' is implied whenever reference is made to a frame of reference under SR.

The Einstein Train

Let us now discuss the Einstein 'train' (figure 3), which Einstein used in his 1916 book to give an example of SR in practice. This is what he wrote:

> *People in this train will with advantage use the train as a rigid reference-body (co-ordinate system); they regard all events in reference to the train. Then every event which takes place along the line also takes place at a particular point of the train.*
>
> *Are two events (e.g. the two strokes of lightning A and B) which are simultaneous with reference to the railway embankment also simultaneous relatively to the train? We shall show directly that the answer must be in the negative.*
>
> *When we say that the lightning strokes A and B are simultaneous with respect to the embankment, we mean: the rays of light emitted at the places A and B, where the lightning occurs, meet each other at the mid-point M of the length A—B of the embankment. But the events A and B also correspond to positions A and B on the train. Let M' be the mid point of the distance A—B on the travelling train.*

Just when the flashes (as judged from the embankment) of lightning occur, this point M' naturally coincides with the point M, but it moves towards the right in the diagram with the velocity v of the train. If an observer sitting in the position M' in the train did not possess this velocity, then he would remain permanently at M and the light rays emitted by the flashes of lightning A and B would reach him simultaneously, i.e. they would reach him just where he is situated. Now in reality (considered with reference to the railway embankment) he is hastening towards the beam of light coming from B, whilst he is riding on ahead of the beam of light coming from A. Hence the observer will see the beam of light emitted from B earlier than he will see that emitted from A. Observers who take the railway train as their reference-body must therefore come to the conclusion that the lightning flash B took place earlier than the lightning flash A. We thus arrive at the important result:

Events which are simultaneous with reference to the embankment are not simultaneous with respect to the train, and vice versa (relativity of simultaneity). Every reference-body (co-ordinate system) has its own particular time; unless we are told the reference-body to which the statement of time refers, there is no meaning in the statement of time of an event.

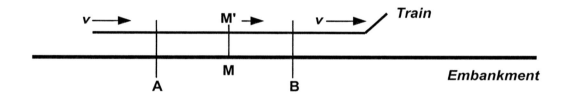

Figure 3: Einstein's Train

Remember that, according to SR, the speed of light *must* be the same to the two observers.

The reader may be surprised at Einstein's deductions. The person travelling on the train is assumed to be an expert in relativity theory! He is not allowed to conclude that the reason for the consecutive arrival of the two light signals is that the light has had a speed, in relation to himself, that is affected by the speed of the train. If he concluded that the light had speeds of $c - v$ and $c + v$ arriving from A and B respectively, this would have explained the matter equally well and in a far simpler manner. However, like Einstein, who wrote this explanation of the events, this person is a firm believer in SR.

The conclusions stipulated by Einstein are a necessary part of SR, which solved the problems thrown up by the Michelson and Morley experiment. No other solution seemed possible to Einstein. We shall revert to this matter later when the Michelson and Morley experiment is shown not to be the final word on this intriguing puzzle.

Having considered the moving train, we now move to the derivation of the main formulae of SR.

Time and Special Relativity

If one accepts the original assumptions on which SR is based, a number of curious consequences follow. One consequence of SR is that if two observers who are moving relative to each other measure an interval of time, they may not get the same result. Events that appear to be simultaneous to one observer may not appear to be so to a second observer who is in steady motion relative to the first observer. To show how this is so, consider figure 4, which depicts the usual SR derivation of the relationship between time as observed by two observers, one of whom is moving relative to the other.

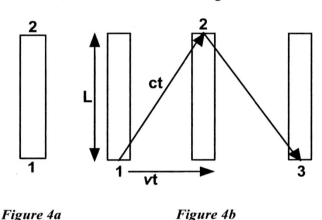

Figure 4a   *Figure 4b*

Figure 4: Stationary and Moving Clocks

Figure 4a depicts a 'rod clock' – an imaginary rod, which is used to measure the time taken for a light signal to traverse the length of the rod. A light flash is emitted at point 1 and travels up a stationary rod to point 2, where there is a reflector that directs the light back down again to point 1. It is assumed that the detector is infinitely fast. An observer who is stationary in relation to that clock will record a total time of $2L/c$ for the light signal to travel up and down the length L of the rod.

Another rod clock is depicted in figure 4b. This clock is moving with uniform velocity v in the $+x$ direction. The clock is oriented at right angles to the direction of motion.

As mentioned before, the basic assumption of SR is that the speed of the light is the very same to the stationary and the moving observer. The automatic consequence of this is that the time measured by the moving observer must alter to match that basic assumption.

The speed of the light signal is assumed to be the same in relation to an observer who stays stationary in the laboratory (at point 1 in figure 4a) and to an observer who travels with a moving clock that is moving to the right at a speed of v (as in figure 4b). The observer who travels with the clock also records the light as travelling up the rod (which is moving to the right at speed v) and back again in a time of $2L/c$.

Let us define t as the time taken for the light to travel up or down the rod clock as observed by the observer who is stationary in the laboratory. Let us define t' as the time taken for the light to travel up and down the rod clock as observed by the observer travelling with the clock. The distance that the clock travels to the right in time t at velocity v is vt. From the right-angled triangle, we see that:

$$v^2t^2 + L^2 = c^2t^2$$
$$t^2(c^2 - v^2) = L^2$$

and remember that $L/c = t'$ (as defined by SR). Therefore, since

$$t^2 = (L^2)/(c^2 - v^2) = (L^2)/(c^2)[c^2/(c^2 - v^2)]$$

From this,

$$t^2 = t'^2[1/(1 - v^2/c^2)]$$

and

$$t = t'[1/(1 - v^2/c^2)]^{0.5}$$

Because it is used so often, it is convenient to shorten this relationship. The usual format is to take γ (gamma) as being equal to $[1/(1 - v^2/c^2)]^{0.5}$.

Therefore, $t = \gamma t'$. If the velocity (v) is very high, i.e. very close to the speed of light, such as 0.999c, then there is a great difference between t and t' (t = 22t'). At such a speed, the laboratory observer observes the travelling clock to be running at a speed that is 1/22 of the clock in the laboratory. In other words, the travelling clock runs slow in relation to the stationary clock. This is the outcome of assuming that the speed of light is the very same to the stationary observer as to the moving observer.

Following from the above discussion, it is deduced that *"all moving clocks run slow, whether they be rod clocks, or atomic clocks, or biological clocks"* (Katz, 1964) because, for example, the intervals of a heart beat of the traveller will be observed by the stationary observer to be slower than his or her own heart beats. This follows from the fact that all clocks that are synchronised maintain that relationship. Such experiments are called 'thought experiments'; they are imagined occurrences. So, if we accept SR, we must believe that it is true that a moving clock runs slow with respect to a stationary observer.

Relative Motion

Figure 5 is a typical diagram used to aid the derivation of SR relationships. It shows times elapsed and distances travelled. It is often termed a 'space-time' diagram. The speeds are taken as uniform and in straight lines. The times are chosen to give round numbers in the results.

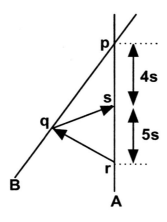

Figure 5: Relative Motion

B moves from B to p. A moves from A to p, where A and B meet. A is the observer in the stationary laboratory (oneself). At r, A sends out a signal to see where B is, and this signal is reflected from q back to meet A at s. A measures the time from when the light signal was emitted until it returned as 5 seconds. As stipulated by SR, A assumes that the signal took the same time to go to B as the return journey took from B back to A; therefore, A calculates that the time to reach B was 2.5 seconds. After s is passed, A measures a further 4 seconds before they both arrive at the same time at p.

The time taken by B to get from q to p (from the point of view of A) is the time taken from a point halfway between r and s to p; this time is 6.5 seconds. This is the time t referred to above.

However, the time taken by B is t = 6.5 = γt'; thus t' = 6.5/γ seconds. To calculate γ, we need the speed of B. The distance travelled by B is 2.5 light-seconds. (One light-second is the distance travelled by light in one second; this is 300,000 km.) A knows that B was that distance away when the signal hit B at q because A reckons that the signal took 2.5 seconds to get there. B travels this 2.5 light-seconds of distance in 6.5 seconds to arrive at p and meet A. The speed of B is distance divided by time, i.e. (2.5c)/(6.5) km/s.

As derived earlier, γ is $[1/(1 - v^2/c^2)]^{0.5}$. We have worked out that v is (2.5c)/(6.5). This gives the value of γ as 13/12. Therefore t' is t/γ = (6.5)/(13/12) = 6 seconds. This means that SR yields a time for B to go from q to p of 6 seconds. A sees that same interval as 6.5 seconds. B's time is running slower by 7.7% compared to A's time. This is the slowing of time as predicted by SR.

Because it is the relative motion of A and B that matters, the reader may be tempted to question whether the clock of A would similarly run slow according to observer B. We shall discuss this conundrum in the next chapter.

13

Distance

Before the launching of SR by Einstein in 1905, measurement of distance was considered to be straightforward. One metre of length was one metre of length, no matter who was doing the measurement. With the introduction of SR, it seemed that the measurement of length depended on the relative speed of the observer. Similar to the moving clock in figure 4, the length of a rod travelling parallel to the x axis is measured by an observer who travels with the rod and by a second observer who stays in the laboratory. One rod stays in the laboratory, and an exactly similar rod of equal length sets out at high speed. The same type of relationship emerges. Consider a rod travelling along the x axis with both ends on the x axis as it travels along (Katz, 1964).

Two ends of a rod are measured to determine the length of the rod. L' is the length as measured in the moving frame. L is the length as measured in the stationary laboratory.

$$L' = X'_2 - X'_1 = \gamma(X_2 - X_1) = \gamma L$$
$$L = L'/\gamma$$

As the value of γ is always greater than one, the length of the rod as measured in the laboratory frame (L) is less than the length measured in the travelling frame (L'). The length of the moving rod appears contracted to the stationary observer. This is called the 'Lorentz contraction'. At a speed of 0.999c, the travelling rod would be measured as 1/22 of the length of the original stationary laboratory rod.

Einstein made clear that such differences were not an illusion. He stated that *"space and time data have a physically real, and not a mere fictitious, significance"* (1922). He also made it clear in his first 1905 paper that the reverse situation applied: *"It is clear that the same results hold good of bodies at rest in the 'stationary' system, viewed from a system in uniform motion."* In other words, both rods are shorter as viewed from the other system; both of these systems are in uniform motion relative to the other. It is solely the relative motion that matters, and it is immaterial which system is considered to be at rest and which is considered to be in motion.

Momentum and Mass

In the same way, momentum is affected by SR. In Newtonian terms, momentum (p) is defined as $p = mv$, where m is the mass and v the velocity. Because of the relative motion, when a particle is travelling at velocity v, SR requires that $p = \gamma mv$. This relativistic equation can be interpreted in two ways: (i) the mass gets greater as the speed increases, or (ii) the momentum gets greater by a factor γ. Both (i) and (ii) amount to the same thing.

In SR, with respect to momentum and similar calculations, it is usually taken that the mass of a moving object increases with velocity. Therefore, to get the speed of an object up to the speed of light would need infinite momentum. As Einstein put it in *The Meaning of Relativity* (1922) (page 44), *"Momentum becomes infinite on approaching c."* Other texts say that mass becomes infinite when a speed of c is approached. Some texts just say that the momentum becomes infinite without specifically deducing that the mass becomes infinite. As Katz puts it (1964), *"the choice of interpretation is a matter of taste"*.

Energy

Einstein published a three-page second paper in 1905 as a quick follow-up to the paper that deduced SR. In this second paper (entitled *Does the inertia of a body depend upon its energy-content*), he stated that *"If a body gives off energy L in the form of radiation its mass diminishes by L/c²."* He recorded here in words the relationship between energy and mass and the square of the speed of light. This later took the familiar form $E = mc^2$ (the energy in an object is equal to its mass multiplied by the square of the speed of light).

Under SR, the energy required to get a particle to attain the speed of light is infinite because, as we know from the previous section, mass (or momentum) increases with velocity and becomes infinite at the speed c.

$E = mc^2$: Who Got There First?

The equation $E = mc^2$ is synonymous with the name Einstein. However, it may come as a surprise to many to find out that Einstein was not in fact the first to derive the famous equation. In 1903, the Italian Olinto De Pretto, who was an engineer/industrialist with experience in materials and their properties, gave the precise formula $E = mc^2$. It was first published in June 1903. De Pretto delivered a second paper on November 29th 1903 in Venice, and this paper was published in the proceedings of the Venetian Royal Institute of Science, Literature and Art in February 1904. This is a translation of what De Pretto concluded in that paper:

> *Given then $E = mc^2$, m = 1 kg and $c = 3 \times 10^6$ km/s. anyone can see that the quantity of calories obtained is represented by 10794 followed by 9 zeros, that is more than ten thousand billions. To what terrible result has our reasoning brought us? Nobody will easily admit that an amount of energy equal to the quantity that can be derived from millions and millions of kilograms of coal is concealed and stored at a latent state in one kilogram of matter of any kind; this idea will be undoubtedly considered foolish. However, even if the result of our calculations be reduced somewhat, it should be nevertheless admitted that inside matter there must be stored so much energy as to strike anyone's imagination. What is in comparison to it, the energy that can be derived from the richest combustible or from the most powerful chemical reaction?*

De Pretto was amazed at his $E = mc^2$ equation.[3] What more proof do we need that this Italian preceded Einstein by two years?

---

[3] In his paper, De Pretto used the symbol *v* for the speed of light.

De Pretto's Reasoning

The reasoning used by De Pretto is very simple. Here is a synopsis of his derivation in a section headed *Energy of the Ether and Potential Energy in Matter*:

- Gravity attracts.

- A nearby mountain attracts a suspended lead wire.

- The force of attraction that unites all particles, molecules and atoms (even chemical cohesion) is the same force.

- To break a steel wire of 1 square millimetre cross section requires a 60 to 120 kg weight. This is small because it is concerned with molecules being separated.

- To break open atoms requires chemical reactions, which require much more energy.

- Not even mechanical force or chemical force is enough to separate the elementary particles that form atoms.

- There are therefore four degrees of attraction: the attraction between bodies, i.e. gravitational; molecular attraction; atomic attraction; and ultra-atomic attraction joining elementary particles.

- Two rough sheets, one of glass and the other of metal, can easily be separated. The rough contact plates have but a few points of contact. The smoother the plates, the greater the effort needed to separate the sheets. The attraction between the sheets varies inversely as the square of the distance between the sheets. Ideally, we could have such a smooth surface that the two sheets act as a single body (a very far-fetched idea).

- If molecules are separated by one ten-millionth of one mm, we take as the base case that of the steel wire of one square mm cross section that requires 120 kg to effect breakage. That is 120 kg/mm^2.

- Assume that the invisible roughness of the smooth faces of sheets in contact is one 10,000[th] of one mm. This is very different from our assumption regarding molecules – a thousand times different.

- If the distance between the two sheets is 1,000 times greater, then the attraction is 1,000 squared smaller than the force that holds molecules together. With this relationship (120 kg/mm^2), the attraction that holds two sheets of 10 cm sides together will be 120/1,000,000; we need 1,200 g to detach the sheets.

- These figures cannot be taken as a precise example but serve to give an idea of the attractive force between molecules.

- Atoms, being nearer to each other, must be much more solidly attracted.

- Particles of matter must be prevented from falling upon each other, and they are kept in continuous vibration around the point of equilibrium. As well as for particles of matter, this applies for ultra-atomic, atomic particles and molecules.

- All the energy in the universe resides in the ether. This is an infinite amount because space is infinite. All other forms (light, electricity, heat) are derivatives, which are by-

16

products caused by the movement of matter. Taking into account the immense speed of vibration of the ether, the formula mv^2 gives us an idea, if not a measure, of the immensity of the force it represents. Particles are prevented from falling one upon the other by the ether vibration, which maintains them in continuous vibration.

- Matter uses and stores energy as inertia, just like a steam engine that uses the energy in steam and stores energy in inertia as potential energy.

- All components of a body are animated by infinitesimal but very rapid movements equal perhaps to the vibration of the ether. It must be concluded that the matter in any body contains the sum of the energy represented by the entire mass of that body if it could move through space with the speed of a single particle.

- Such deductions lead us to an unexpected and incredible consequence. One kg of matter launched at the speed of light would represent an unimaginable and incredible amount of energy.

- The formula mv^2 gives us the potential energy[4] and the formula $mv^2/8338$ gives us such energy in calories.

- Given then $E = mc^2$, m = 1 kg and c = 3 x 10^6 km/s, anyone can see that the quantity of calories obtained is represented by 10,794 followed by 9 zeros, which is more than ten thousand billion.

- To what terrible result has our reasoning brought us? Nobody will easily admit that an amount of energy equal to the quantity that can be derived from millions and millions of kilograms of coal is concealed and stored at a latent state in one kilogram of matter of any kind; undoubtedly, this idea will be considered foolish.

- However, even if the result of our calculations is reduced somewhat, it should nevertheless be admitted that there must be so much energy stored inside matter as to strike anyone's imagination. What is the energy that can be derived from the richest combustible or from the most powerful chemical reaction in comparison to it?

- If it is accepted that all particles of matter are in motion, they may not necessarily vibrate with the same speed as the ether. Also, it is not perhaps rigorously correct to compare the latent energy to the energy represented by the same amount of matter that moves as one unit in space with the same speed. Whatever way you view it, we are forced to admit that there is such energy inside matter as beggars belief.

- De Pretto goes on the discuss uranium and thorium and their radioactive decay. He reasons that the emission of radiation from these substances was another case of energy transformation.

- De Pretto argues that the vibrations in matter must appear as heat. From this he deduces that within a huge mass (like the earth) where the losses are minimised, temperature must be great. He proposes this as a potential alternative explanation or contributor to heat at the centre of the earth.

---

[4] Literally 'forza viva' as used by Liebnitz

- In conclusion, De Pretto says that the energy in the universe is represented by the energy of the ether in motion = mv^2. The term v is the speed of the simple vibrations of the ether, taken as being equal the speed of light, and m is the total mass in the universe.

Because De Pretto used the symbol v for the speed of light, his finding gives the same mc^2 as used nowadays. Therefore, we can conclude that the formula $E = mc^2$ was first discovered in 1903 by De Pretto. It was a 'latent energy' of mv^2 that De Pretto deduced as being present in all matter. The energy had to be released, and he did not know how that could be done.

There was a misprint in De Pretto's paper (kg for g). I wonder what errors of no significance have been made in this book. The famous Michelson made three such errors in his publications. Fortuitously, two of these cancelled each other out and the third was picked up in a later publication, as will be discussed in a later chapter.

De Pretto's reasoning is based on logic. Because it undermines the belief that Einstein was first with the famous equation, this important matter is highlighted at the very beginning of this book. The original Italian paper was obtained to confirm that it really existed in the original Italian form and that the date was right. Some people will be offended by the notion that a mere industrialist/engineer proposed the famous equation first. However, only one person can be first, and the nationality or occupation of the proponent is irrelevant.

De Pretto's analysis was before the discoveries of the details of the makeup of an atom. His reasoning conforms to the concept of 'binding' energy, which was later identified as holding the nucleus of the atom together. To pull apart the constituent parts of a nucleus of an atom requires energy equal to the binding energy that holds it together. The mass of a nucleus is lower than the mass of its constituent parts; the difference is represented by the mass equivalent to the energy that holds it together. In other words, the binding energy concerned is equal to the 'missing' mass multiplied by c^2. De Pretto had reasoned that somehow there had to be a potential energy (binding energy) residing within the atom that held it in its configuration.

Connection Between Einstein and De Pretto

Could Einstein have had access to the work of De Pretto? Was there a family connection? Michael Besso, a colleague of Einstein and a lifelong friend, is mentioned by name at the end of Einstein's first 1905 paper on relativity: *"I wish to say that in working with the problem here dealt with I have had the loyal assistance of my friend and colleague M. Besso, and that I am indebted to him for several valuable suggestions."*

Besso was also a friend of the De Pretto family and could surely have provided the common link and alerted Einstein to the De Pretto publication in Venice. Here are some of the family connections that existed. The young Einstein lodged with a family named Wintelers. A son of that family married Einstein's sister Maja, and a daughter of the family married the aforementioned Michael Besso. Furthermore, Einstein lived for a while in Italy, where his family moved when he was about 15. He had studied Italian at high school and got equal marks in German (his native tongue) and Italian (in which he was fluent). In the same publication in which his first 1905 paper on relativity appeared (*Annalen der Physik*), Einstein had reviewed several Italian articles – one in March 1905. He would have been well able to appreciate the writings of De Pretto.

The brother of Olinto De Pretto, Augusto De Pretto, was a colleague of Beniamino Besso, an uncle of Michael Besso. Augusto De Pretto and Beniamino Besso both worked as managers of the Italian Royal Railways, and it is obvious that Beniamino should have known something of the 'foolish ideas' of Augusto's younger brother. Beniamino Besso was always very close to Michael, who lived in his uncle Bengamino's house during his studies in Rome. Since De Pretto discussed his conjecture with people well before it was published in 1903 (he says that people considered him a fool!), it is certain that all people acquainted with him and his brothers knew of his 'foolish idea'.

De Pretto's amazing paper must have created some controversy when it appeared in 1903. Sadly, De Pretto was shot dead by a woman over a business deal in 1921.

Earlier Mass-Energy Equations

There are many earlier publications that describe particular experiments on the connection between mass, energy and the speed of light. Turner and Hazlett (1979) give a history of several derivations, including those by Hasenöhrl (1905) and Thompson (1881). Papers by Thompson (1885), Heaviside (1889), Poincaré (1900), Kaufann (1901 and 1903), Abraham (1902 and 1903), Lorentz (1904), Soddy (1904) and Hasenöhrl (1904 and 1905) are listed in a paper by Fadner (1988) entitled *Did Einstein really discover $E = mc^2$*. These papers describe experiments on charged particles or electrons. Soddy is quoted as saying that *"radioactivity occurs at the expense of the mass of the system."*

Surprisingly, Fadner did not mention De Pretto or Preston (1875). A paper by Moody (2005) says that Preston, Poincaré and De Pretto pre-date Einstein in deriving the famous equation.

S Tolver Preston is also said by Bjerknes to have been the first to derive the equivalence of mass and energy by the formula $E = mc^2$. Let us consider that claim. Preston assumed that the ether was comprised of particles that were travelling at the speed of light and, from this, worked out the energy that would be contained in the ether. Preston said that a volume of ether *representing the total mass of one grain would be contained in a cubical portion of space with the side of cube equal to forty-five feet*". He continued:

It may be computed that a quantity of matter representing a total mass of only one grain, and possessing the normal velocity of the ether particles (that of a wave of light), encloses a store of energy represented by upwards of one thousand millions of foot-ton, or the mass of one single grain contains an energy not less than that possessed by a mass of forty thousand tons moving at a speed of a cannon ball (1,200 feet per second); or otherwise, a quantity of matter representing a mass of one grain endued with the velocity of the ether particles, encloses an amount of energy which, if entirely utilized, would be competent to project a weight of one hundred thousand tons to a height of nearly two miles (1.9 miles).

In this example, Preston gets a value for E as less than one thousandth of mc^2. He assumed that the energy contained in the ether was immense (mc^2), where m was the mass of the matter contained in the ether. He discussed the transfer of such energy from the ether to ordinary matter as occurring in *"explosives"* or the *"dynamic effect of lightning"*. Preston did not derive the energy in ordinary matter as being equal to mc^2. We will meet this same Preston later in chapter 9 when discussing his experiments on unipolar induction.

The French scientist Poincaré, as described in Ives (1952), had derived an equivalence between energy, mass and the square of the speed of light in 1905. Poincaré also delivered a paper at St Louis, U.S.A. entitled *The Principles of Mathematical Physics* (1904), in which he stated:

> *The principle of relativity according to which the laws of physical phenomena should be the same, whether for an observer fixed, or for an observer carried along in a uniform movement of translation; so that we have not and could not have any means of discerning whether or not we are carried along in such a motion.*

Indeed, in a paper in 1906, Einstein had acknowledged that Poincaré had already derived the equivalence. When commenting on his own 1905 paper, where he originally gave the equivalence, Einstein wrote, *"Even though the simple formal observations which must lead to the proof of this assumption is already contained in the main in a work by H. Poincaré, I, for reasons of clarity, will not refer to that particular work."* It is to be wondered what extra 'clarity' resulted from not mentioning the earlier work.

Another derivation is attributed to Heaviside in 1890; the reference to this is in the book *Voice Across the Sea* by Arthur C. Clarke (1974 edition), where we read, *"By 1890 he had already arrived at a rigorous proof of the famous relationship E=MC², thus anticipating Einstein's more general formulation of this law by some fifteen years."* A search by this author of Heaviside's papers and books failed to find that derivation. That does not mean that it does not exist; it merely indicates that the search by this author was unsuccessful.

From the above discussion it is seen that a connection between mass, energy and the speed of light squared was known before Einstein entered the scene. We have a choice in determining who was the first to publish the equivalence between energy and mass in the famous equation. Depending on one's nationality, one can claim that the originator was one of several people. One thing is certain, **it was not Einstein who first developed the equation E = mc².**

De Pretto was the first to set down a logical reasoning behind his derivation of the famous equation and to set down the direct transformation of the mass of normal matter to the total equivalent amount of energy. Preston is ruled out on the basis that he was out by a factor of over 1,000. In relation to Preston's derivation, Moody noted that *"it is unclear whether the calculations actually fit the equation E = mc²"*. Preston's calculations do not do so, as described above. De Pretto derived the precisely correct factor.

There was no Irish contender in this race. A neutral investigator gives De Pretto clear priority in this important scientific discovery.

Einstein gave no references to other authors in his 1905 paper. We can but wonder why! Was it simply plagiarism? Einstein's 1905 paper was 30 pages long, and the practice even at that time was to refer to earlier work in the particular field. The paper before Einstein's in the journal had 30 references, and the one after it had 12. During the entire year of 1905, *Annalen der Physik* had only Einstein's paper and three very short experimental papers that did not give references. In an earlier paper in 1905 on a different topic and in a paper in 1904, Einstein had given references.

Some authors claim to have uncovered a flaw in SR. We shall not dwell on those claims of a theoretical flaw because this book is concerned with experimental evidence that contradicts SR. An example is Ives (1952), who says that there is a flaw in Einstein's derivation of the equivalence. His short paper concludes that Einstein *"did not derive the mass-energy relation"*. This is a topic debated over the years, but no clear outcome has emerged. Many publications claim to have identified a flaw in Einstein's papers while many other papers refute such claims. Such debates congest the Internet with vituperative controversy, are not fruitful and lead nowhere. Let us give Einstein the benefit of the doubt and proceed to examine in the following chapters how his theories stand up to experimental evidence. In 1905, Einstein said that *"the introduction of a 'luminiferous ether' will prove to be superfluous inasmuch as the view here to be developed will not require an 'absolutely stationary space' provided with special properties"*.

Einstein left the possibility, but not the necessity, of an ether. In 1935, in his book *The World as I See It*, Einstein wrote that:

> *Space without an ether is inconceivable. For in such a space there would not only be no propagation of light, but no possibility of the existence of scales and clocks, and therefore no spatio-temporal distances in the physical sense. But this ether must not be thought of as endowed with the properties characteristic of ponderable media, as composed of particles the motion of which can be followed; nor may the concept of motion be applied to it.*

In 1920, Einstein gave a lecture in Leyden in Holland, where he reinstated the idea of an ether. *"Space without ether is unthinkable,"* he said. So, Einstein was somewhat ambivalent on the ether question.

Einstein gave several derivations of the famous equation. In 1906, he derived the equivalence between energy and mass by a different method. He did this by considering the momentum of photons as they moved from one end of a closed box to the other. In 1922, Einstein derived the equivalence by yet another method.

Einstein's SR was devised after the famous formula was derived by De Pretto. It should be stressed, therefore, that any process that conforms to the famous formula in no way necessarily confirms SR. This is despite the fact that many texts claim that every confirmation of $E = mc^2$ is proof of SR.

The 'universal theory' developed in this book does not propose any amendment to the mass-energy equivalence. $E = mc^2$ is correct, but this has nothing to do with SR, which will be shown to be incorrect in the following chapters.

However, Einstein is generally credited with highlighting the fact that *"with bodies whose energy-content is variable to a high degree (e.g. with radium salts) the theory may be put to the test"* (Einstein 1905, second paper). This is the precursor and forecast of atomic energy, nuclear power and the atom bomb and is a stunning contribution to the development of physics. De Pretto had mentioned the radium salts in passing in his 1903 paper. Was Einstein the first to spot that possibility as a practical possibility? He was the first located by this author.

Summary

On the above evidence, the famous equation $E = mc^2$ was *not* discovered by Einstein but by De Pretto. It was derived before 1905. Italians have tried to get the matter widely known with limited success (Professor R. Monti (1996) and Professor U. Bartocci, who published a book on the topic in 1999). Perhaps an Irish author is in a good position to state the priority of De Pretto.

In a book entitled *Albert Einstein the Incorrigible Plagiarist* (2002), Bjerknes carries the matter to extremes. *"Was Einstein an honest man?"*, *"Was his memory faulty?"*, *"Was he a liar?"* are samples of questions in that book. Bjerknes also makes a plausible argument in favour of Einstein's first wife, Mileva, having submitted the 1905 first paper under her name. Einstein later paid over to Mileva the Nobel Prize that he was awarded years after he had abandoned her for a new life and wife. Why?

Chapter 2

Problems with Special Relativity

The Twin Paradox

Special Relativity (SR) eventually threw up some strange anomalies, or so-called 'paradoxes'. To date, the problems with SR have been explained away as being caused by our limited understanding of the phenomena involved. That defence is wearing thin. When reflecting on the difficulty of believing the consequences of SR, Tolman (1987) said:

> . . . *if the two postulates of relativity are true it is evident that our natural intuitions as to the nature of space and time are not completely correct, presumably because they are based on a too limited ancestral experience – human and animal – with spatial and temporal phenomena.*

In other words, we are not down out of the trees for long enough! Pagels (1984) wrote:

> *If the speed of light as measured by an observer at rest relative to a light source is the same as the speed of light as measured by an observer in motion relative to the source, then it must be that, somehow, the measuring instruments change from one frame of reference to the other in just such a way that the speed of light always appears to be the same.*

Clearly Pagels was not entirely happy with this requirement. As an example of the type of abstruse deductions that result from SR, Bernard Russell (quoted by Geroch, 1978) stated:

> *When physically impossible for a body to travel so as to be present at both events, the two events are called 'space-like'. An event E occurs to me. Anything that happens after the light reaches there (i.e. elsewhere) is after 'E' in any system of reckoning time. Any event anywhere that I would have seen before 'E' is physically before the event 'E' in any system of reckoning. But any event which happened in the intervening period is neither definitely before nor after. Anything that occurs on Sires and which I see before 'E' occurs to me, is before 'E'. Anything Sires does after he has seen 'E' is definitely after 'E'. But anything he does before he sees 'E', but so that I can see it after 'E' has happened is neither definitely before nor after 'E'. Contemporary with 'E' is this in-between period.*

Mysterious! This book sets out to develop a theory that will satisfactorily explain the anomalies described below.

The first enigma that is examined here, and the one that is most quoted, is the so-called 'twin' paradox, otherwise known as the 'clock' or 'twin-clock' paradox. It is much quoted because most people cannot quite believe the result. However, to accept SR, we must accept this paradox.

Let us set down the details. If a twin goes off on a spaceship for a long trip at nearly the speed of light, that twin would be much younger on return to earth than the twin who stayed behind (Fock, 1964; French, 1968; Hawking, 1988; Young, 1992). If the twins were five years of age when they separated and the speed of separation (v) was 0.999999c, then when they meet again after 60 years of time as measured on earth, the twin who remained behind would be 65 years old while the traveller would be five years and one month old.

As detailed in chapter 1, the calculation is as follows: $t = t'\gamma$, where $\gamma = [1/(1 - v^2/c^2)]^{0.5}$ and $t = 60$ years (according to the earth-bound twin). Since $v = 0.999999c$, we can express γ as $(1 - 0.999999^2)^{-0.5} = (0.000002)^{-0.5} = 707$. Thus, $t = 707t'$. So, the 60 years of time to the stationary twin (t) is 707 times the time to the travelling twin (t'). The time to the travelling twin is therefore $60/707 = 0.08$ of a year, which is one month.

It is agreed in a few texts (Møller, 1952; Rindler, 1982; Dingle, 1972, for example) that, strictly in accordance with SR, the twin who stays behind will appear to the traveller to be younger. Let the moving twin consider himself to be stationary; he will observe the other twin going away at high speed relative to himself. In this case, it will seem to the traveller that the one who stays behind is the younger. After all, it is the 'relative' motion that determines the result according to SR. But this is rather puzzling – how could either twin be younger than his sibling?

Note that one twin is assumed to stay on earth (one frame of reference); the other twin accelerates away, eventually decelerates, stops, accelerates in the reverse direction and then returns to earth to slow down and stop beside his twin. This raises a complication because the traveller is not at all times in an 'inertial frame of reference' as defined in SR (i.e. a frame of reference that is travelling at uniform speed relative to another frame of reference).

To begin at the beginning, let us refer to the first 1905 paper on relativity by Einstein. He showed that the x dimension of an object in a moving frame would 'appear' shortened to an observer in a fixed frame. In the next paragraph he stated, *"It is clear that the same results hold good of bodies at rest in the 'stationary' system, viewed from a system in uniform motion."* Einstein is saying here that the x dimension of objects in a fixed and in a moving frame would appear shortened to the observer in the opposite frame. We can use the term vice versa to describe this reciprocity. Einstein then proceeds to discuss 'time' and, as in the case of dimensions, concludes that a travelling clock is perceived to run slow.

Strangely, significantly and amazingly, Einstein does not, at this juncture, refer to the vice versa situation when discussing time, even though he had done so when he discussed dimensions earlier on the same page.

What was left unsaid was that, to an observer travelling with the moving clock, the stationary clock would also appear to run slow. Instead, Einstein went on to lay the foundations for the subsequent twin controversy, as follows (where K is the inertial frame of the laboratory):

From this there ensues the following peculiar consequence. If at points A and B of K there are stationary clocks which, viewed in the stationary system are synchronous; and if the clock at A is moved with the velocity v along the line AB to B, then on its arrival at B the two clocks no longer synchronise, but the clock moved from A to B lags behind the other which has remained at B by 1/2 tv²/c² (up to magnitudes of fourth and higher order), t being the time occupied in the journey from A to B. It is at once apparent that this result holds good if the clock moves from A to B in any polygonal line, and also when the points A and B coincide. If we assume that the result proved for a polygonal line is also valid for a continuously curved line, we arrive at this result: If one of two synchronous clocks at A is moved in a closed curve with constant velocity until it returns to A, the journey lasting t seconds, then by the clock which has remained at rest the travelled clock on its arrival at A will be 1/2 tv²/c² second slow. Thence we conclude that a balance-clock at the equator must go more slowly, by a very small amount, than a precisely similar clock situated at one of the poles under otherwise identical conditions.

In 1919, Einstein again referred to clocks on a rotating disc and said, *"that placed on the circumference runs slower than that placed at the centre"*.

It should be noted that Einstein stated here that SR applies in the case of uniform translational motion and also in the case of movement on a closed circuit. This derivation by Einstein is proof that analysis of motion on a circuit cannot be said to be forbidden under SR. This contentious issue will appear many times in the following pages. It is clear that SR applies to motion on a polygonal path and also on a closed circuit. It is surprising that very few authors who have written about the twin paradox refer to the original Einstein paper, from where the whole puzzle emanated. Even though there is acceleration involved in the orbital path, Einstein did not refer to any acceleration when describing a clock sent on a polygonal or orbital path and coming back to the same spot. Why did Einstein not say that, according to the travelled clock, the stationary clock would have gone slow by the same amount?

Seventeen years later, in 1922, Einstein recorded for the first time (underlining by this author) the reverse situation for both dimensions and time (referring to a stationary system K and a moving one K') as follows: *"the clock goes slower than if it were at rest relatively to K'. These two consequences, which hold, <u>mutatis mutandi,</u> for every system of reference, form the physical content, free from convention, of the Lorentz transformation."*

No reference to this important statement by Einstein has been located in the many papers and treatises on the twin-clock paradox. Maybe the Latin phrase *mutatis mutandi* put readers off the scent. Maybe it did not suit writers to quote this statement. This author must admit to having checked the phrase in the dictionary to find out its precise meaning. In the above statement, Einstein records that the vice versa situation applies for the 'time' recorded by clocks.

The authors of papers on the paradox go to great trouble to get the twins to meet again. To do this, one twin is made to depart in a straight line, turn around and come back. This involves the following stages: an acceleration away, a steady speed stage, a deceleration, a stopping, a reversing, an acceleration back towards home, a second steady speed stage, another deceleration and, finally, a stopping beside the twin who remained stationary.

The acceleration or deceleration is said by many authors to cause the differential ageing of the travelling twin. Very few bring the travelling twin around on an orbital path back to the starting point, as did Einstein in his 1905 paper. Einstein stated that the slowing of the moving clock is apparent *"when the points A and B coincide"*. In other words, the same formula applies to the case where the clock moves away and comes back to the same spot, on any circuit. Not a single reference to this clear statement by Einstein has been uncovered in 100 years of polemic on this topic.

There is an escape argument for adherents of SR. When launching his general relativity theory, Einstein made this statement in his 1916 paper:

The word 'special' is meant to intimate that the principle is restricted to the case where K' has a motion of uniform translation relatively to K, but that the equivalence of K' and K does not extend to the case of non-uniform motion of K' relatively to K.

Einstein does not repeat here what he said in his 1905 paper, where he applied SR to a clock moving in a circuit as well as to one moving in uniform translational motion. However, he never withdrew that 1905 statement that SR also applies to motion *"in any polygonal line"* shape and to motion in a *"continuously curved line"*. He also applied it in the case of a closed curve. If SR applies to straight-line motion, then it makes perfect sense that it must also apply in the case of the other types of motion that he stipulated.

Some say that the 1916 paper supercedes the 1905 statement. To make the problem in accordance with this interpretation of SR, there must be no element of acceleration involved. Let us devise such an experiment. Let the five-year-old twins pass each other by in outer space while moving in a straight line at uniform high speed with respect to each other. Do not arrange that they ever meet again. (This edition of the twin paradox does not seem to have been proposed to date.) Assume that the twins travel at a mutual speed of recession of 0.999999c with respect to each other. If they continue at that speed for 60 years (as understood by either of them), then, according to SR, without ever decelerating or reversing, the age of each person according to the other would be reckoned as five years and a month. It is not necessary for the two to see each other ever again or to return to the starting place to verify this. The calculation according to SR shows this should be so.

Now, we have a problem. The ageing has not occurred during any acceleration or deceleration phase. The different ageing has occurred during uniform movement in a straight line with respect to each other. If the twins had separated from each other in outer space rather than on earth, they would have no way of knowing which one was going away and which one was 'stationary'. Thus, according to either, the other twin is younger.

Remember that Einstein said that the effect is *mutatis mutandi*! Photographs could be taken by either twin after 60 years of their own recorded time and 'posted' to the other twin. What would the photographs show? They would hardly confirm what either twin understood the situation to be because each photograph would record the rather mature (I almost wrote 'aged', but I am older than that!) other person. In either case, 60 years of their own time should equal one month of the time of the other twin. How could this be? The situation is totally symmetrical, and no appeal of 'time being different' for the twins can help to make the situation asymmetrical. Taking the timeframe to be 100 years, either twin could be dead while the other would be supposed to be a child!

We find some authors who point out this dilemma. For example, here Møller (1952) discusses the timekeeping in two systems (S and S') in relative motion:

A clock which is moving with the velocity v relative to S will be slow compared with the clocks in S. When we keep in mind that the systems S and S' are equivalent it is obvious that a clock at rest in S will similarly lag behind the clocks in S'.

To avoid such a nonsensical conclusion, the current explanation in all physics textbooks is that only the travelling twin ages slower.

Who dares to say that the emperor has no clothes? SR has assumed the role of a 'religion' in science; it is not acceptable to say that one disbelieves it.

So, this problem is now more than a paradox. The word paradox is a euphemism. It is just ridiculous. Because the result is so crazy, it is always trotted out to make the audience puzzled (and to appear stupid). Pity the students of theoretical physics today. We shall return to this topic in more detail in chapter 7, which is devoted to the paradox and which includes an article by Einstein (1918) in which he made a vain attempt to wriggle out of the problem. Adherents of SR never mention this article. Why not?

Length Contraction

Another 'paradox' arises as follows. When deductions are drawn from the contraction of the length of a travelling rod running along the x axis, as described in chapter 1, much play is made upon this length contraction. From SR, we have deductions as follows (Rindler, 1982):

A man carrying horizontally a 20 foot pole, and wanting to get it into a ten foot garage – he will have to run at a speed of 0.866 c and make $\gamma = 2$ so that the pole contracts to 10 feet. It will be as well to insist on having a massive block of concrete at the back of the garage so that there is no question of whether the pole finally stops in the Inertial Frame of the garage or vice versa. So the man runs with his (now contracted) pole into the garage, and a friend quickly closes the door. When the pole stops in the rest frame of the garage it is, in fact, being 'rotated in space time', and will tend to assume, if it can, the original length relative to the garage. Thus if it survived the impact, it must now either bend or burst the door.

This story comes to the conclusion that the rod could have fitted into a garage of length 5.4 feet at rest or 2.7 feet in motion (i.e. the garage in motion). The text notes that no such paradox seems to have been encountered before 1960 (when Rindler first published it). However, the Irish scientist J. L. Synge had outlined the same problem some 20 years earlier. The solution to this so-called paradox will also be given later in this book.

Bear in mind that it is solely in the direction of travel that the shortening occurs. A person going headfirst would be shorter from head to toe but would be unaltered in girth (or perhaps 'thickness'!).

The Mass Paradox

If the mass of any object increases with speed and is infinite at the speed of c, how can it be that photons of light that travel at the speed of light have no mass that has ever been measured? According to Katz (1964), *"It is remarkable that the relativistic relationship between Energy and Momentum is valid for all particles, even those with zero mass like neutrinos or photons."*

O'Rahilly (1938) was scathing on this point as he asserted that there is no evidence of any rest mass of a photon. There are authors who suggest that a photon has a non-zero rest mass. Vigier (1990) puts forward the idea and also attributes it to Einstein and Schrödinger. A photon surely is a strange thing. It travels through a vacuum (and through air approximately) at a speed of c, at which all bodies, according to relativity theory, are supposed to have infinite mass.

How can my mass alter depending upon who is observing me and at what speed relative to me they are travelling? It is such concepts that are suspect and are examined in this book. Consider the effects of such deductions. On a large rock on a quiet beach on the north coast of Spain, near Santander, I am sitting minding my own business, reflecting on the possible explanations for the paradoxes of SR. My mass is 70 kilograms (kg). Two other persons pass by at colossal speed – let's say one travelling at 0.9c and the other at 0.9999c relative to me. I do not notice them as I am engrossed in my private world of thought. These observers measure my mass; one gets a mass of 160 kg while the other gets a mass of 7,000 kg.

According to SR, what is measured by these observers is what is real to them. As stated earlier, Einstein said that these changes are real and not illusory. This is plainly not actual to me because I sit calmly without any change in mass. If the two observers ever slowed down and came to speak to me, I would certainly affirm that my mass did not change to suit their observations.

There are others who do not believe this conundrum. Schlegel (1973) says: *"Physical systems undergo relativistic transformations only in their interactions with other physical systems (including observers)"* and *"because the photon is in a single interaction at a given instant, it cannot simultaneously have a set of different values of frequency and wavelength for observers in different coordinate systems"*.

Problem with the Speed of Light

Consider the following statements (Einstein, 1922): *"Every inertial observer measures the same value, in free space, for the speed of light relative to himself"* and *"Light is propagated with a velocity c at least with respect to the defined inertial system."* How does light know how to behave relative to an observer? It is difficult to believe that a photon of light that I record as travelling away at a speed of c will be measured as travelling at a speed of c relative to an observer who is receding from me at a speed of 0.99c. Is light a magician?

Consider the position of a photon of light that emanated from a faraway galaxy 5,000 million years ago at a distance of 5,000 million light-years from the current position of earth. (A light-year is the distance (9.5×10^{12} km) travelled by light in one year. The photon of light has been travelling towards earth for 5,000 million years and has just arrived here. If we had a clock riding piggyback on the photon, this clock would not have recorded any passage of time according to SR. It is difficult to believe that no real 'time' has elapsed for the photon. Have photons no age? The photon has taken 5,000 million years to get here travelling at a finite speed (c), and at the same time, has taken zero time according to itself.

The π Paradox

Consider the conundrum posed by Ehrenfest (1909). It was repeated by Einstein and Infeld (1938), and also by Zukav (1991) in a chapter aptly named *General Nonsense*. When considering two concentric revolving circles, Zukav said, *"the ratio of the radius to the circumference of the small revolving circle is not the same as the ratio of the radius to the circumference of the large revolving circle"*. He goes on to say that when an observer is revolving with the circle, the ruler that is used to measure the distance along the circumference contracts in the direction of motion.

This situation would lead to a changing value of π or to differing measuring standards for measuring the radii from those used to measure the circumferences. This conundrum will be addressed in more detail later.

Basis of Relativity

What did Einstein say concerning the basis of his theories? It is surely best to quote verbatim. In his 1935 book, he records, *"I am anxious to draw attention to the fact that this theory is speculative in origin; it owes its invention entirely to the desire to make physical theory fit observed fact as well as possible."* He also states:

The law of the constancy of light in empty space, which has been confirmed by the development of electro-dynamics and optics, and that of the equal legitimacy of all inertial systems (special principle of relativity), which was proved in a particularly incisive manner by Michelson's famous experiment, between them made it necessary, in the first place, that the concept of time be made relative, each inertial system being given its own special time.

Einstein's SR is based on the single assumption that the speed of light is a constant as measured by observers who are in uniform motion with respect to each other. It was devised to explain away the null result from the Michelson and Morley experiment (1887). Notice that Einstein referred specifically to the Michelson experiment here. Einstein and Infeld (1938) wrote that the result:

> *. . . was a verdict of 'death' to the theory of a calm ether-sea through which all matter moves. No dependence of the speed of light upon direction could be found. Every experiment has given the same negative result as the Michelson-Morley one, and never revealed any dependence upon the direction of motion of the earth.*

That was certainly true in 1938. We shall find later that when performed to far greater accuracy than was possible in Einstein's lifetime, the Michelson and Morley experiment gives a totally different result. This result will be shown to destroy the foundations of SR. However, the reader will have to wait (as did this author) until much later to find the details of this surprising, nay astounding, fact. Einstein also wrote in the same book that:

> *. . . the theory of relativity resembles a building consisting of two separate storeys, the special theory and the general theory. The special theory, on which the general theory rests, applies to all physical phenomena with the exception of gravitation.*

So, if the special theory loses its basis, the general theory is also without foundation. According to Einstein, *"the elements which form their basis and starting-point are not hypothetically constructed but empirically discovered ones,"* which he describes as having *"security of the foundations"*.

On the speed of light, Einstein asserts that *"light in vacuo always has a definite velocity of propagation, independent of the state of motion of the observer or of the source of light"*. He states that this *"is powerfully supported by experience"*. Einstein saw, as a defined law of nature, that the speed of light was a constant. He called it a *"general law of nature"* (1916). Who could blame him? He had found a brilliant way out of the dilemma set by the result of the Michelson and Morley experiment. Einstein said, *"The chief attraction of the theory lies in its logical completeness. If a single one of the conclusions is proven wrong, it must be given up; to modify it without destroying the whole structure appears to be impossible."*

This book concentrates on many experiments meticulously carried out by teams of scientists in various countries over the past 100 years. In his 1922 book, Einstein advocated such an approach *"to cover the greatest possible number of empirical facts by logical deduction from the smallest possible number of hypotheses or axioms"*.

In this book, a theory of universal relativity (UR for short) is developed. Its precepts will contradict certain precepts of SR. The reader is asked to reserve judgement and to await the proof that will unfold.

Chapter 3

Time and Motion

No Time Difference on Earth

Einstein forecast in 1905 that a balance clock at the equator would be found to run slower, by a very small amount, than one at the poles. He said that the faster velocity of the clock at the equator compared to a clock at the pole would cause a difference in their timekeeping. However, tests done by Pound and Rebka (1960) showed no difference in the time of clocks at different places on earth. Clocks at rest at the earth's surface, at average sea level, keep the same time, independent of latitude. However, Einstein was not at fault in this matter because he did not know the cause of Pound and Rebka's result.

An explanation of why clocks run at the same rate anywhere on earth at sea level was given by Cocke (1966). Anyone interested in the details of that amazing discovery had better read that paper.

The earth is in the shape of an 'oblate spheroid' – a sphere flattened at the poles. When the earth was formed some 4,000 million years ago, it was presumably in a somewhat 'fluid' form; the length of the intervening time would have caused it to take up a particular form, which is dictated by the forces upon it. The final shape adopted by the earth is such that clocks happen to run at the same rate at sea level anywhere on its surface.

Hafele and Keating Tests on Moving Clocks

Let us now discuss some key tests of relativity theory. Hafele and Keating (1972) carried out experiments that purported to prove that moving macroscopic clocks run slow. Hafele and Keating's results are examined here in detail because they are quoted in most university physics textbooks as proof that the SR forecast for the slowing of moving clocks is correct.

The evidence provided by Hafele and Keating was derived from the differences between time recorded by atomic clocks transported in aeroplanes eastward and westward around the earth and time recorded by a standard clock station fixed to the earth. The *Science Citation Index* lists some 300 references in published papers up to 2005 to the Hafele and Keating tests. Many university and other texts on physics, such as Arfken et al. (1989), Ohanian (1989), Beiser (1991), Rindler (1991), Blatt (1992), Cutnell and Johnson (1995), Davies (1995), Young and Freedman (1996), Walker (2004), Giancoli (2005) and Halliday et al. (2005), quote the tests as proof that SR is correct. Commenting on these tests, a leader in *Nature* in 1972 said that the agreement between theory and experiment was *"most satisfactory"*.

Hafele and Keating did not publish the actual original 'raw' test results (which would have let the cat out of the bag) but an amended 'massaged' version, which conformed to the result they had forecast. The original raw data was obtained by this author by making a phonecall to the United States Naval Observatory (USNO) following publication of his paper in 1995 that queried the test accuracy. The data was mentioned in a reference in the 1972 Hafele and Keating paper, but that reference gave no clue as to the importance of this data or that it would contradict the published conclusions of those authors. The massaging of the data was obviously a case of 'the end justifying the means' and shows that sometimes the peer review system is not as foolproof (or unbiased) as it seems.

There was some controversy before the actual tests were done, which indicated worldwide interest in the experiment. Schlegel (1971) pointed out that, under the traditional interpretation of relativity, when comparing a clock on the earth's surface with one on an aeroplane, the clock on the aeroplane (moving relative to the ground-fixed clock) should run slow. Schlegel said that this effect should not depend on whether the aeroplane was going eastward or westward. Over short distances that approximate to straight lines, this should have credence. Hafele (1971) replied that *"substantial and subtle aspects of the theory which when ignored or misunderstood often lead to confusion"*. The words 'subtle', 'misunderstood' and 'confusion' appear regularly in papers on the twin paradox (see later). They are useful terms for confusing the timid or putting anyone off the scent.

The hype at the time was such that Hafele and Keating probably felt they had to get the expected result. They had 'burned their boats' by publishing in advance what they intended to do and the result that they forecast. Reputations were at stake. What temptation there must be for researchers to get the expected result to justify the monetary support received for their efforts!

If the evidence put forward by Hafele and Keating had been found to be convincing, the investigation by this author into the veracity of SR would undoubtedly have finished there. Ironically, having shown that those tests were fatally flawed and having proceeded from there to investigate SR further, it was later discovered that atomic clocks did really run slower at higher velocities with respect to a particular spot in our solar system (the centre of the earth). This will be discussed and a reason for it postulated later in the book.

That was a very lucky twist for this author. Had the Hafele and Keating results been believed by this author, the investigation into SR could very well have stopped there, in which case the rest of this book would never have been written.

Appendix 1 gives a blow-by-blow description of how the Hafele and Keating deception was perpetrated. Anyone interested in that saga can read the whole story there. However, for the general reader, here is a flavour of what was done.

Table 1 shows the Hafele and Keating actual raw test results and the radically altered massaged results that were published to the scientific world as the supposed results. The actual test results were never published. A study of table 1 shows that the published results bear no sensible relationship to the actual results.

Table 1: Hafele and Keating actual and published test results

	Eastward		Westward	
Clock no.	Actual test results	Published results	Actual test results	Published results
120	−196	−57	+413	+277
361	−54	−74	−44	+284
408	+166	−55	+101	+266
447	−97	−51	+26	+266
Average		−59		+273
Forecast result	−40		+275	

(All values in nanoseconds: 10^{-9} sec)

The forecast results were −40 going eastward and +275 going westward. You can see that Hafele and Keating did a pretty good job at making the published figures line up with the forecast result! The barefaced effrontery is breathtaking. I wonder if university texts will quietly drop all references to the Hafele and Keating tests, without any stated reason and without further ado? One has already done so.

Some authors quote a later test as vindicating the Hafele and Keating tests and SR. The test was done by Alley in 1979 at Chesapeake Bay, U.S.A. An aeroplane was sent in circuits over the area. However, as stated by Taylor and Wheeler (1992):

The Chesapeake Bay experiment was conducted to verify the results of the General Theory of Relativity; the aeroplane pilot was instructed to fly as slowly as possible to reduce the velocity effects. The plane used would stall below 200 knots and so a speed of 270 was used.

Therefore, the test had nothing to do with confirming SR.[5]

Let us speculate as to why Hafele and Keating did what they did. Here is a guess. Before Hafele and Keating did their test, it was probably known (secretly by classified information) by the USNO authorities that atomic clocks behaved in a certain fashion. Perhaps the USNO had already discovered that the clocks ran slow with respect to the earth's centre. Perhaps they had already sent a clock into orbit? With this knowledge, Hafele and Keating, under the aegis of the USNO, undertook the tests. With the foreknowledge of the result that they expected, they were confident of the outcome. With this certainty, they felt comfortable massaging the actual test readings.

Management of the USNO would also have felt comfortable with this because the tests done by Hafele and Keating were really a foregone conclusion. If any other group did similar tests to a greater accuracy at a later date, there was confidence that Hafele and Keating would be vindicated. Remember that Hafele (1971) proposed in advance of the tests the idea that the clocks should run slow with respect to the geocentre (the earth's centre). Why would he do that unless he already knew that this was so? Furthermore, in response to the query *"what would be the rate of a standard clock that is moving relative*

---

[5] The Hafele and Keating flights had a cruising speed of about 400 knots.

to stationary standard clocks on the geoid?", Hafele responded with *"The standard answer that moving clocks run slow by the well known factor gamma is almost certainly incorrect."* We will show why Hafele and Keating made this strange statement in chapter 5, which deals with the synchronisation of atomic clocks on the earth.

The 'standard answer' to which Hafele referred was the traditional interpretation of SR. He proffered no explanation for this extraordinary claim. In other words, he said that SR was almost certainly wrong and that he would prove it! There was great confidence behind the outcome that Hafele and Keating expected. That is an 'Ockham's razor' guess by this author.

Evidence that the Hafele and Keating tests proved nothing was published by this author in Ireland in 1996 and internationally in 2000. These papers were the subject of a publication in Japanese by Harada in 2002.

Sagnac Effect

While browsing through comments on the Hafele and Keating tests, reference was found to something called the 'Sagnac effect'. What was it? The Sagnac effect turned out to be a very important item, which, as we shall see, contradicts SR. For this reason, it is described below in considerable detail. The reader is encouraged to dwell on this section because the Sagnac effect is critical to the new theory proposed in this book.

It is worth mentioning at the outset that Professor J-P Vigier published a paper in 1997 that agreed with the conclusions to be given here, which were first published by this author in 1995. Much of that 1995 paper was reproduced verbatim (including the diagrams) by Vigier with this author's permission. Vigier was Professor of Gravitational and Cosmological Relativity at the Pierre & Marie Curie University in Paris. The sad news of his death was announced as this book was being edited. International physics conferences have been named after him (Vigier II was held in Canada in 1997, Vigier III was held in the U.S.A. in 1999 and Vigier IV was held in Paris, France in 2003).

The Sagnac effect was discovered by a Frenchman of that name and published in 1913, which was three years before the general theory of relativity was introduced by Einstein. Sagnac showed that light took different times to traverse a path in opposite directions on a spinning disc.

The general reader may skip the mathematics to equation (13) and simply accept that the times taken by the light signals to go around the spinning disc (as measured on the disc) are different by the derived amount.

Figure 6 shows a schematic representation of the test. A source at A sends light to a half-silvered mirror at C. Some of the light goes from C to D, E, F and C and is reflected to an observer at B. Some of the light goes around the other way. The whole apparatus (including A and B) turns with an angular speed of ω.

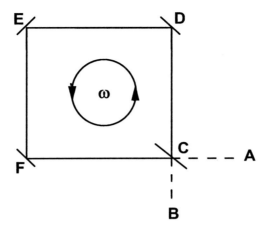

Figure 6: Sagnac Test

The difference in time (d*t*) for the light to traverse the path in opposite directions was derived by Sagnac as:

$$dt = 4A\omega/c^2 \tag{1}$$

where A is the area enclosed by the light path and ω radians per second is the angular velocity of spin. By reversing the direction of the spin of the disc, Sagnac got double the amount, and this made the result more detectable. The inequality shows up as fringe shifts at an interferometer at C.

It is extremely important to realise that the light source (a flashlight) and the measuring device (an interferometer) were both fixed to the rotating disc and rotated with it. A photographic recorder also rotates with the disc and records the fringe shift that occurs at the interferometer.

Sagnac showed that the centre of rotation could be away from the geometric centre of the apparatus without affecting the results. He also showed that the shape of the circuit was immaterial; a proof of this will later be derived. The area concerned was 0.86 m² and the rotational speed was 2 Hz.

Sagnac thought the so-called 'ether' was the cause of the difference, but, as will be shown later, there is another explanation. It seems that the work of Sagnac and of others who later did the same test was ignored because they thought the effect was caused by an ether, which was later said by Einstein to be superfluous. The detailed and meticulous tests done over many years by Sagnac should be taken seriously. He published a dozen articles from 1897 to 1914, all on the same topic of the behaviour of light and interferometry. He devised many novel items of equipment to solve the problems he posed.

To get a simple derivation of the Sagnac equation, consider the theoretical circular model shown in figure 7, as derived by Post (1967). Post is a pioneer in the examination of the Sagnac effect, and his 1967 paper is the seminal publication on this topic.

Two light beams emanate from the light source at S, one travelling clockwise and the other counter-clockwise around a circular disc of radius r. The light source S is fixed on the rotating disc. The disc itself is rotating with an angular velocity ω in a clockwise direction. The counter-clockwise beam is going against the rotation of the equipment and returns to the light source when the source is at S' (distances greatly exaggerated for clarity). The second beam, travelling clockwise with the direction of rotation of the equipment, returns to the light source when the source is at S". As viewed by an observer on the spinning platform, the light signals return to the same point but at different times. Points S, S' and S" are on the fixed laboratory desk as they would be marked beneath the spinning disc by a stationary observer in the laboratory.

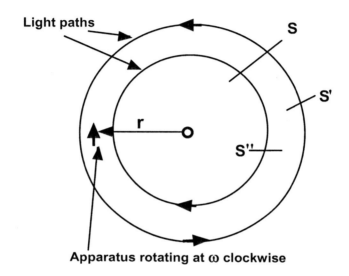

Figure 7: Circular Sagnac Test

Taking t_0 as the time observed when the disc is stationary, i.e. the path length divided by the speed of light, we have:

$$t_0 = 2\pi r/c \qquad (2)$$

When the disc is put in motion, a light signal is emitted from the light source at S; a portion of the signal goes clockwise (denoted by the inner line in figure 7) and a portion goes counter-clockwise. The time t' for the counter-clockwise beam to complete a circuit as observed aboard the spinning disc is:

$$t' = 2\pi r/(c + v) \qquad (3)$$

where v is the speed of a point on the periphery of the disc.

The difference between equations (2) and (3) is:

$$t_0 - t' = \frac{2\pi r}{c} - \frac{2\pi r}{c+v} = \frac{2\pi v}{c(c+v)}$$

36

So the difference in time (dt') between the stationary and the counter-clockwise cases is:

$$dt' = t_0 - t' = t_0 v/(c + v) \qquad (4)$$

For the other direction, where t'' is the time for the clockwise beam to arrive back at point S", the difference (dt'') between the stationary and the clockwise case is similar:

$$dt'' = t'' - t_0 = t_0 v/(c - v) \qquad (5)$$

Equations (3) and (5) may be stated as follows: The moving observer thinks that the light has, relative to oneself, completed one revolution of the disc ($2\pi r$) at velocities of $c \pm v$ in the two opposing directions.

   To get the difference in time (dt) between the time for the light to go clockwise and counter-clockwise, adding equations (4) and (5) gives $dt' + dt'' = dt$, and where $v = r\omega$ for circular motion and $A = \pi r^2$ is the enclosed area.

$$dt = 4A\omega/(c^2 - v^2) \qquad (6)$$

Furthermore, because v^2 is negligible for practical tests, it can be ignored, leaving us with the formula developed by Sagnac (equation (1)).

   In equation (4), for small values of v, dt' is $t_0 v/c$. As v approaches c, dt' becomes $t_0/2$, and the speed relative to the observer now becomes $2c$. In equation (5), as the speed v approaches c, dt'' becomes infinite because the light and point S are travelling in the same direction and the time for the light signal to gain one complete circuit on point S is infinite. At very low velocities, the result is again $t_0 v/c$.

   Other relationships exist. The time differences for the light signals to come back to the place where the light was emitted are also expressible as follows:

$$dt' = t'v/c \text{ and } dt'' = t''v/c \qquad (7)$$

Taking the distance SS' as ds' and SS" as ds'', then, because $ds'/v = t'$ and $ds''/v = t''$, from equations (3) and (4) we see that:

$$dt' = ds'/c \text{ and } dt'' = ds''/c \qquad (8)$$

From (4) and (5), $t'' - t' = dt'' + dt' = (ds' + ds'')/c$. Notice that it is the addition of (not the difference between) the two increments of movement ds' and ds'' divided by the speed of light that gives the difference in the times taken by the two opposing beams of light that traverse the circuit.

   The calculation above is done on the presumption that there is a difference in the time for the signals to get back to the starting point, as is found in practice. The above derivation is used to put a value on the difference. Had no difference been discovered by Sagnac, then no derivation would be attempted!

   Another method of deriving the same formula is to assume that the light travels with respect to the laboratory. If this assumption gives the precise Sagnac result, then this indeed proves that the light behaves in this way. As before, t_0 is the path length ($2\pi r$) divided by the speed of light: $t_0 = 2\pi r/c$.

Both signals are assumed to be independent of the speed of the source at S and are also assumed to travel relative to the laboratory.

Let t' be the time for the light to go from S to S' in the counter-clockwise direction.

$$t' = (2\pi r - ds')/c \tag{9}$$

However, t' is also the time taken for the disc periphery to move the distance ds' in the clockwise direction at speed v. Therefore,

$$t' = ds'/v$$
$$ds' = t'v$$
$$ds' = (2\pi r - ds')v/c$$
$$ds'/v = 2\pi r/(c + v)$$
$$t' = 2\pi r/(c + v) \tag{10}$$

Similar calculations for t'' give the time for the light to go from S to S'' in a clockwise direction:

$$t'' = 2\pi r/(c - v) \tag{11}$$

Subtracting (10) from (11), the difference (dt) between the times for the light to go clockwise (t'') and counter-clockwise (t') is:

$$dt = \frac{2\pi r}{c - v} - \frac{2\pi r}{c + v} = \frac{4\pi r v}{c^2 - v^2} \tag{12}$$

This is the same as already derived above in (6) by the first method.

Equations (9) and (10) are mathematically equivalent – they both give the same time interval. Equation (9) may be stated as follows: The observer in the fixed laboratory observes that the disc periphery moves a distance of ds' while the light completes a distance of $2\pi r - ds'$ around in the other direction from S to S'. The equation describes the time interval as it would be discerned by an observer in the laboratory. Remember that the actual 'observer' (the interferometer) in Sagnac's tests was riding on the spinning disc.

The Sagnac effect shows that the light is not affected by the movement of its source. It also shows that the light travels relative to the laboratory because to assume this gives the correct result in all cases. That the speed of light is independent of the speed of its source (as is sound) is one of the assumptions made by Einstein on the behaviour of light. While it applies in the case of the Sagnac laboratory test, it will later be seen that this is not always the case.

To get a fringe shift of one fringe, the velocity of point S relative to the laboratory in figure 7 has to be about 13 metres per second (m/s) per metre of radius. This is such a low velocity that SR cannot possibly have any measurable effect.

Fringe shift is derived from time difference by multiplying by c/λ. Where the wavelength of light λ is $5,500 \times 10^{-10}$ m and $v = r\omega$, this gives $v = 13.13$ m/s per metre of radius, from:

$$1 = \frac{4A\omega}{c\lambda} = \frac{4\pi v}{3x10^8 x5,500x10^{-10}} \qquad (13)$$

The fringe shifts look like vertical lines that are split horizontally in two. When the disc is stationary, the lines match up; when the disc is put spinning, the two halves move apart. It is from the record of the movement of the lines that the difference in time for the light pulses to traverse the spinning disc can be calculated. (There would be insignificant divergences caused by the tilting of the mirrors as the equipment turns. This was analysed by Sagnac.)

A Favourite Excuse

Let us kill off here a favourite supposed justification for SR that is trotted out whenever the Sagnac effect is mentioned. It is said that in the Sagnac experiment, the light travels different distances going clockwise and counter-clockwise so that light travelling at the constant speed of c takes different times. This is claimed as the reason for the fringe shifts and is said to explain the whole matter in accordance with SR.

However, this is wrong. Sagnac had the light source, the interferometer and the camera all aboard the disc. All measurements are taken aboard the spinning disc. The fringe shifts result from the difference in times taken by the light signals to traverse the circumference of the disc in opposing directions.

Later we shall see that in the case of light signals sent around the earth, the matter is further clarified because we are all aboard the disc (the spinning earth). In this case, there is no doubt that the light signals take different times to go around the earth in an eastward and a westward direction – we cannot step off the earth to view the process and thereby claim that the signals take different times because they traverse different distances.

Dufour and Prunier Tests

Forty years after Sagnac had performed it, the French pair Dufour and Prunier repeated the Sagnac test and got the same result. They then performed important variations on the original Sagnac experiments.

Dufour and Prunier's 1939 test is a practical example of such a variation. In this test, the signal was not solely in the plane of the disc. The path of the light was partly on the spinning disc and partly in the fixed laboratory. Figure 8 is a simplified diagram of the actual arrangements. The light signal was introduced at the axis of rotation at C, sent out to point 1 and then sent from there in opposite directions. No mirror could be placed at the position occupied by the axis of rotation, and extra mirrors were needed to deflect the light around the line of the axis. These details are not shown in figure 8.

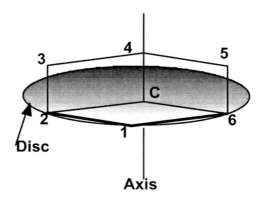

Figure 8: Dufour and Prunier Test

As shown schematically in figure 8, the light first went on a path on the spinning disc (point 1 to point 2) and then went vertically up to a mirror fixed to the laboratory overhead the disc (point 3). It then traversed linear paths 3 to 4 to 5 in the laboratory and came vertically back down to the disc at point 6, whereupon it finished the trajectory on the disc back to the starting point at point 1. The reverse beam went the other way. The plane of the path of the portion that was fixed in the laboratory was parallel to the plane of the disc. The projected area onto the disc of the portion of the path that was fixed in the laboratory was the same as the area enclosed by the light path in the overhead laboratory.

The two short paths 2–3 and 5–6 (10 cm each and exaggerated for clarity in figure 8), which the light followed when going up to the overhead laboratory path and back again, added 3% to the total light path. This would not affect the result because those portions contribute zero to the Sagnac fringe shift. It will later be shown that it is solely movements with and against the direction of rotation that contribute to the result. The mirrors at 1, 2 and 6 rotated with the disc. Because the path 3–4–5 is along radii, this portion would not contribute anything to the time difference.

As stated above, Dufour and Prunier repeated the Sagnac test and got the same result; they used the circuit 1–2–C– 6 all on the spinning disc. The portion 3–4–5 is a path fixed in the laboratory, while 6–1–2 is on the spinning disc. However, the result is the same as for the circuit 1–2–C–6–1, all aboard the disc. We see from these tests that having about half of the circuit fixed in the laboratory makes no alteration in the result.

This Dufour and Prunier test is incontrovertible proof that light travels at a fixed speed of c with respect to the fixed laboratory and is not affected by the speed of the source of the light signal. The Sagnac effect is proof of this simple fact. This conforms to the claim made here that light in a Sagnac test travels in relation to the laboratory. Neither Sagnac nor Dufour and Prunier nor any other author since then has alluded to this fact in their papers. Of course, the mirrors deflect the light beams, and those mirrors are attached to the rotating disc, but the light beams do not adapt to the actual motion of the spinning disc.

Dufour and Prunier did a test with the light source fixed in the laboratory. The result was the same as when the source was fixed to the rotating disc. They also did a test with the photographic plate fixed in the laboratory and the fringes observed from the laboratory. The result was the same as in a traditional Sagnac test, where the photographic plate rotated with the disc.

It should be noted that the fringe shift occurs whether there is an observer present on the disc or in the fixed laboratory. The fringe shift is there to be measured by an observer who is stationary in the laboratory or riding on the spinning disc and who cares to make a measurement.

There is a slight Doppler effect (the change in frequency caused by recession or approach of the object being viewed) in the case where the photographic equipment is in the fixed laboratory because the disc is moving past the viewing lens. Post (1967) discusses the magnitude of the distortion introduced and correctly dismisses the effect as too small (v/c smaller than the basic Sagnac effect) to have any observable effect.

Another interesting paper was published by Dufour and Prunier in 1941. They said they had varied the orientation of part of the path of the light that was overhead in the fixed laboratory and achieved a projected area that was reduced by a factor of 2.5, from 1,346 cm² to 536 cm², from the area used in the earlier test. The alteration had no observable change in fringe shift. It is not clear as to how the result could be achieved. Dufour and Prunier provided no diagram. This particular test remains a mystery.

This author tried to get some information on the Dufour and Prunier tests, but there is no record of them at the laboratory where the tests were carried out (Lycée Louis le Grand, Paris). Perhaps after reading this, someone will place a plaque on the wall where Dufour and Prunier did these pioneering tests.

Why were the tests by Dufour and Prunier not widely known throughout the world? Their work was done between 1939 and 1942 during the Second World War in Paris, which was under German occupation. Their publications would not have been translated or circulated outside France. By the time the war was over and things returned to normal, people were more interested in new work rather than old papers published during the war. Indeed, the 1941 paper was only discovered by this author while searching back for any publication by them, and was not picked up in any reference in later papers, even ones by the two authors themselves, including their 1942 composite paper. Here was a scientific test that was unknown for over 50 years until this author, intent on uncovering some clues on the behaviour of light, searched a dust-laden 1941 volume in University College Dublin. The paper had to have the pages slit open, which shows that nobody had ever read it in the university. Dufour died in May 1942, prior to the publication in September of that year of the composite paper.

Vigier, who has been mentioned earlier in this chapter, told me that he did not know about the work of Dufour and Prunier (even though he was French, as were they) until he came across my 1995 paper.

Einstein and Sagnac

Pogany (1926–28) adapted the extant equipment devised by the young German student

Harress (1911), who had achieved fringe shifts five times larger than those achieved by Sagnac. Pogany had the light emitter and the photographic equipment fixed in the laboratory (as had Harress). He then built new equipment of much stronger construction and used higher turning speeds. The fringe shift achieved was 13 times greater than that achieved by Sagnac (0.9 versus 0.07 fringe).

Einstein did not address the contradiction to his theory in the Sagnac, Dufour and Prunier, Pogany or Michelson and Gale (see later) tests that were published during his lifetime. Sagnac's findings were published two years before and Michelson and Gale's nine years after the publication of the general theory of relativity by Einstein. The work of the French pair Dufour and Prunier could not have been known to Einstein until after the Second World War, by which time he was near the end of his productive life. Perhaps the accuracy of those three tests, at 1:100, was not sufficient to persuade scientists of their veracity. There was also the problem that those tests were advocating that an ether existed and that they did not seem to conform to SR, which was considered to be in accordance with all the known phenomena.

As the years have gone by, the evidence provided by other more accurate tests that do not conform to SR has mounted. The practice of making sophisticated equipment to test physical theory seems to have died away from about that time. It is more popular (and certainly cheaper) to develop theories without doing any tests. It is possible to claim 'proof' of something in a mathematical model by claiming it to be a 'thought experiment'. There is always the danger that the expected result will not be achieved from an actual physical experiment, which takes time and money to develop. It is safer to avoid that danger!

O'Rahilly (1938) makes fun of the mathematical so-called 'proofs' that are prevalent in the area of relativity. It is true that a mathematical set of equations can be derived that give the mathematics of a sphere in two frames of reference that are moving in relation to each other. However, even if we can derive such a mathematical relationship, that is no proof whatever that such a situation exists in nature. O'Rahilly makes this point over and over again. Mathematical models are mighty useful, but only in so far as they represent reality!

T. H. Huxley wrote in 1893–4, *"The great tragedy of Science - the flaying of a beautiful hypothesis by an ugly fact"*. The Sagnac test and the Dufour and Prunier tests yield ugly facts that, as we will see, flay the beautiful hypothesis of SR.

This author has located no reference at all by Einstein to the Sagnac tests, and that can be viewed as very strange because the tests were on the speed of light, which is the basis and core of SR. Einstein visited Miller in the U.S.A. in 1921, where tests on the speed of light were in progress. Lorentz also visited the same site. Sagnac's work was referenced by Silberstein (1921), who worked with Michelson on the latter's 1925 tests (described later). Miller was a co-worker of Michelson. Silberstein (1921) remarked, *"As a matter of fact, Einstein himself never entered into the details of this important problem of rotation"* and *"In fine, the optical circuit experiment may easily become crucial and fatal for Einstein's theory."*

Silberstein was correct, but nobody passed any remarks. Why did Einstein not comment on these tests? Turner (1979) commented that neither the Sagnac nor the Michelson and Gale tests were ever mentioned by Einstein.

Einstein did write concerning the Ehrenfest paradox, which claimed that if SR were correct, the value of π had to be smaller and smaller as a disc got larger and larger when spinning at high speed. Stachel also discusses Einstein's treatment of the rotating disc. In 1912, Einstein wrote, *"on account of the Lorentz contraction, the ratio of the circumference of a circle to its diameter would have to differ from π"*.

When considering a single huge spinning disc, the value of π had to decrease as the radius increased. How could this be? In 1951, Einstein wrote a draft of a letter to be sent to an Australian student who wrote to him querying this matter. He pointed out that to set up a rigidly rotating disc, one would firstly melt the disc at rest, then set the molten disc in motion and solidify it while in motion. He also wrote in 1919:

> *... it is well to remark that a rigid circular disc at rest must break up if it is set in rotation, on account of the Lorentz contraction of the tangential fibres and the noncontraction of the radial ones. Similarly, a rigid disc in rotation (produced by casting) must explode as a consequence of the inverse changes in length, if one attempts to put it at rest. If you fully take this into account, your paradox disappears.*

Such a spinning disc would of course break up under the centrifugal force if the speed of rotation was increased above a certain limit. This is merely because the stress in the material exceeds the amount that can be resisted by the strength of the material. This disintegration has nothing to do with the Ehrenfest paradox.

It is interesting that Einstein states here that the Lorentz contraction is a real observable phenomenon.

Further Tests and Debate

A lengthy debate occurred in France from 1921 to 1942 on the subject of the Sagnac effect. Langevin published an article in 1921, purporting to explain the effect in accordance with SR. He argued that because the effect was of the first order, there could be no distinction between Newtonian or relativistic derivations and therefore the effect was in accordance with relativity theory. That argument could equally have been used to state that the effect was solely in accordance with Newtonian mechanics. Indeed, that whole debate could have equally been used to state that relativity did not come into play at such low velocities (less than 10 m/s in the original Sagnac test) and therefore had no part in trying to explain the Sagnac effect.

In 1935, Prunier published a note discussing the problem. There followed a series of papers by Dufour and Langevin that debated whether or not an apparatus could be constructed to settle the question. Dufour and Prunier then corroborated in a series of practical tests. In 1937, they rigorously repeated the tests originally done by Sagnac. They also carried out important variations on the tests. They repeated the method used by Pogany as described earlier, with the light emitter stationary in the laboratory but with the photographic recorder on board the spinning disc. They also carried out an experiment with both the light emitter and the photographic recorder taken off the spinning apparatus and set up fixed in the laboratory. The maximum deviation from the average of the fringe shifts was 15% for the tests when the light was fixed in the laboratory and 5% to 6% for the tests with the light source fixed to the spinning disc. This difference is to be expected because there was an extra lens required in the former case.

Finally, in 1939, Dufour and Prunier carried out a test (as described above; see figure 8) with the emission of the light and the photographic equipment on the spinning disc but with the beginning and end of the light path on the spinning disc and the middle portion on a path being reflected off mirrors fixed in the laboratory. All the resulting fringe shifts were the same as in the original tests. These results are of critical significance in understanding what is occurring.

Langevin was confounded by these sequential tests. In 1921 he had reasoned that SR had to be correct because it fitted *"the whole of the known experimental facts"* of physics in general and therefore the tests had to be explicable by that theory. Today, this is a favourite 'cop-out' when avoiding an explanation of the Sagnac effect. Langevin had been a believer in the idea of an ether in 1904 but became *"an ardent antiether relativist"* in later years (O'Rahilly, 1938).

In his final essay on this subject in 1937, Langevin proposed that the results published that year by Dufour and Prunier showed one had to assume either (a) the light speed varied to $c + \omega r$ in one direction and to $c - \omega r$ in the other direction or (b) the time aboard the spinning apparatus had to change by a factor of $\pm 2\omega A/c^2$ in either direction. Indeed, Langevin went so far as to say that by assuming (a), *"we find, by a very simple and very general reasoning, the formula for the difference of the times of the path of the two light beams in the Sagnac experiment"*. He also stated that *"the paths are of unequal length because of the inequality of the speed of prorogation"*.

Here, Langevin said that the speed of the light beams varied. Later, in a short note appended to the Dufour and Prunier 1942 paper, he seems to have conveniently overlooked that he had admitted of this possibility. Many references to Langevin refer to his earlier paper in 1921, where he proposed that the Sagnac effect could be explained by relativity theory. His later 1937 analysis is conveniently forgotten.

Dufour and Prunier did not agree with the second option and published a note saying so and giving experimental evidence to back up their argument. Langevin's option (a) agrees with the conclusions in this book.

Dufour and Prunier carried on their experimental work and published the 1939 and 1941 papers described above without any response from Langevin. In 1942, Dufour and Prunier published a composite paper, detailing most of their experimental work to date. At the end of this paper, they state that *"the relativity theory seems to be in complete disagreement with the classical theory and with the result which was thrown up by the experiment"*.

Langevin had been in communication with Dufour and Prunier with regard to another idea. He had suggested that the observation post had to be considered to be at the centre of rotation, even if it were established elsewhere on the disc (as was the case). This was an irrelevant debate because the Sagnac effect is independent of the positioning of the centre of rotation. Dufour and Prunier commented on this incorrect assumption of Langevin and stated that, based on this assumption, relativity could predict an effect that was, at most, about 10% of the actual test results in their particular configuration. It was the supposed positioning of the observation post at the centre of rotation (where it was not) that was calculated to have brought the relativity result to 10% of the Sagnac test result.

Langevin was in a privileged situation during this debate because he was presenting the earlier reports on the proposals and experimental results of Dufour and Prunier. After each Dufour and Prunier publication, Langevin immediately published a refutation in the same journal. His reporting stopped after a while, presumably because Dufour and Prunier objected. Langevin was a member of the Académie des Sciences, which published most of the work. Furthermore, he was on quite a number of the academy's committees. It would seem that to contradict Langevin was not politic.

Langevin was well known to Einstein and had attended the first 'Solway' conference in Brussels in 1911, where Lorentz, Max Planck, Rutherford and Madam Curie were in attendance. Curie was never elected to the Académie des Sciences – was this because she was female? Newspaper reports at that time claimed that Madam Curie was the mistress of Paul Langevin.

This was the end of the French debate. This book takes up the problem that was left unresolved in 1942 (the year Dufour died) and proposes a solution to fit the test results.

Relative to What?

Consider the Sagnac test model shown in figure 7. The light is travelling relative to what? It is popular to avoid, or indeed forbid, any discussion on SR in relation to motion on a spinning disc. This is on the basis that SR applies solely to uniform straight-line motion. In this way the problem is, hopefully, sidestepped.

So, let us simply discuss the problem of the behaviour of light on a spinning disc without reference to SR. In Sagnac's tests, the emission of the light is by a flashlight fixed to the rotating disc; the record of the result is on a photographic plate also fixed to the rotating disc. This is simply a discussion on the speed of the light signal on a spinning disc. Remember that the peripheral velocity of the disc is below 10 m/s in a typical test, and no relativistic effect could possibly be invoked at such a low velocity. There are three possibilities:

A. The light viewed from the spinning disc is observed as travelling at speed c relative to an observer who is aboard the spinning disc.

B. The light viewed from the stationary laboratory is observed as travelling at speed c relative to an observer who is fixed in the laboratory.

C. The light viewed from both the spinning disc and the laboratory is observed as travelling at speed c relative to both an observer who is aboard the spinning disc and one who is in the laboratory.

Let us consider each case in turn:

A: If the light were to be observed by an observer on the spinning disc (where the light is both emitted and observed by equipment spinning on board the disc) as travelling at speed c, then no fringe shift could be seen. This is because the light would have travelled at constant speed relative to the observer who travels with the disc and should be observed as moving at speed c relative to the rotating point S in figure 7, where the light is emitted and observed. However, in the actual test, the times measured for light to travel in the two opposing directions are different and cause fringes, which are recorded on a photographic plate. The observer must therefore conclude that the light is not measured as travelling at a speed of c relative to oneself. The speed is measured as c + v in one direction and c − v in the other direction, where v is the speed of movement of point S relative to the laboratory.

If a photograph were taken from the stationary laboratory and the light were to travel at speed c relative to the spinning disc, as described in some tests, no fringe shift would likewise be seen from the stationary laboratory observation post. This is because there is no shift recorded on a photograph taken aboard the apparatus, and the observer in the laboratory is merely photographing what is happening on board the spinning disc. As discussed earlier, there would also be no significant Doppler shift when the observer is fixed in the laboratory because that effect is v/c times smaller than the Sagnac effect.

B: If the light viewed from the laboratory is actually travelling at a speed of c in relation to the laboratory, the observer (i.e. the photographic equipment) on board the spinning disc would detect a fringe shift. The fact that the fringes are actually observed proves that the light is travelling at speed c in relation to the laboratory.

The fringes are perfectly explicable by the different path lengths (from point S (figure 7) around to where that point is when it meets the light again, i.e. $(2\pi r - ds')/c$ in one direction and $(2\pi r + ds'')/c$ in the other direction). The test results conform exactly with the result calculated under this assumption.

The light is behaving in conformity with the assumption that the rotation of the disc has no effect on the speed of the light. The light is operating independently of the spinning apparatus. The speed of the light is, in this case, also confirmed to be independent of the speed of the source of the light because the source is aboard the spinning disc.

This conclusion is reinforced by the fact that the result is not affected by a change of the centre of rotation to a point other than the geometric centre of the light path.

In the case where the photograph is taken from the fixed laboratory, fringe shifts are also recorded because the photograph is merely recording what is occurring aboard the spinning disc as measured at the interferometer. As discussed above, the fact that the light is found to travel different distances as measured in the fixed laboratory should not be quoted as being in any way a confirmation that SR conforms to the Sagnac effect.

C: The third possibility, where the light would be observed as travelling at a speed of c when viewed from both the spinning disc and the laboratory, is disproved by the fact that the light is not observed as travelling at constant speed relative to the observer on board the spinning disc.

Taking **B** as the correct interpretation lines up accurately with the test results. Options **A** and **B** do not. Notice that in the above analysis of the Sagnac effect, no reference has been made to whether or not the frame is 'inertial' (referring solely to straight-line motion). In the analysis, that is of no significance.

The Sagnac effect is not so much an 'effect' as a confirmation that for tests performed on earth, light travels at a speed of c relative to the fixed laboratory and not to any moving object.

Special Relativity and the Above Analysis

We emphasise that the above analysis of the results of the Sagnac experiment has nothing to do with SR. That analysis is simply discussing how the speed of light that emanates aboard a spinning disc behaves, as seen by an observer fixed to a spinning disc. However, let us see if SR agrees with the experimental results.

SR requires that the speed of light is a constant as measured by all observers in all inertial reference frames (i.e. ones that are moving with constant speed relative to each other). In *The Meaning of Relativity*, Einstein stated that *"the constancy of the velocity of light must hold whatever may be the motion of the source which emits the ray of light"*, and in *The Principle of Relativity*, said that *"any ray of light measured in the moving system, is propagated with the velocity c, if as we have assumed, this is the case in the stationary system"*. Assume for the moment that SR applies to rotational motion – something that will be discussed at length later and shown to be the case.

From the above second statement by Einstein, SR requires that option C be true. It requires that the light be measured as travelling at a speed of c relative to both the observers aboard the moving disc and in the fixed laboratory. The above tests show that this is not so. We shall see shortly that the claim that SR is not applicable to rotational motion is seriously flawed. Indeed, it is simply incorrect.

The Michelson and Gale Experiment

In 1904, Michelson proposed tests to prove whether or not an ether existed. The tests are of direct interest in the current debate because of their relevance to the behaviour of light rather than to a possible ether. Michelson proposed that if two pencils of light were to be sent around the earth in opposite directions and parallel to the equator, then any difference in the time taken by each to traverse the circumference would be discernible. He then had the idea that a short portion of the circumference traversed in either direction would give a measure of the same phenomenon. He said, *"but it is not necessary that the path should encircle the globe, for there would still be a difference in time for any position of the circuit"*. By taking a short part of the circumference, he proposed that by measuring the proportion of this part to the whole circumference, he could compute the effect for the whole circumference.

Michelson calculated that for a circuit of one square kilometre (km), the effect should show a measurable fringe shift. Michelson was ill for a considerable period but in 1925, when he was 73 years of age, he and Gale constructed a large rectangular pipe system laid on the ground (2,010 feet from east to west and 1,113 feet from north to south[6]). The latitude was 41° 46' N. They evacuated the pipes to get a low pressure and measured the light signals going in opposite directions around the circuit.

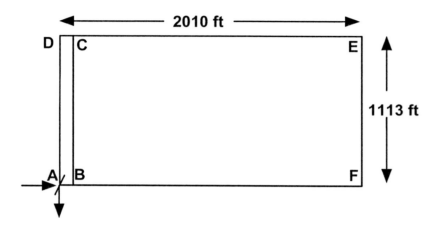

Figure 9: The Michelson and Gale Experiment

There were two circuits, one short (around ABCDA) and the other longer (around AFEDA). The short path was used to provide a reference against which to compare any fringe shifts that would occur. (In the original Sagnac test, the reference fringes could be set when the apparatus was stationary while the light signals were sent around in opposing directions. Michelson and Gale could hardly have stopped the earth's spin to get a record of the stationary fringes!) Light signals were sent in the two directions from a half-silvered mirror at A. The interference on return was also observed at A.

The Michelson and Gale test does not vary ω (the rate of rotation of the earth) but rather varies the area in the Sagnac formula ($dt = 4A\omega/c^2$) by having the two circuits (the smaller and the larger) described above; all of the other factors except the area A are constants. Michelson and Gale derived the formula from a consideration of the times taken by light to traverse the long sides of the rectangle in opposing directions. There would be a zero difference for the time taken to traverse the shorter sides because the direction of the path is towards and away from the centre of rotation.

As will be shown later in this chapter, the Sagnac effect is only evident for motion with or against the direction of spin of the disc. It shows no effect for directions that are towards or away from the centre of rotation.

The spread of the results was very wide. Fringe shifts ranging from +0.55 to –0.05 were recorded. The average was +0.230, which compares with the theoretical forecast of 0.236. This agreed to within 3%, which was a satisfactory result. The fact that the figures went from double the average to below zero may explain why this important test has gone almost unrecorded in textbooks. It could lead to very awkward questions from students, so

---

[6] Michelson freely switched between imperial and metric units in his papers.

why look for trouble?

In his 1904 paper, Michelson debated the possibility that the turning of the earth around the sun might be measured in such a test. The velocity of the earth in orbit around the sun is about 64 times the velocity of the earth's surface speed caused by the earth's turning on its axis at the equator. Michelson estimated that he would need a circuit of 40 km in length to test the effect of the rotation around the sun. Such a test could possibly be done nowadays using laser light.

In the summer of 1923, Michelson performed open-air tests on a circuit of over a mile in length. The fringes could not normally be clearly distinguished. However, for half an hour before and after sundown, the effect of fringes could be somewhat more clearly discerned. In the 1925 paper, Michelson and Gale gave the formula $(4A\omega/c^2)\mathrm{Sin}\Theta$ for the 'both way' difference, where Θ is the latitude. In 1904, Michelson had derived a formula of half that amount and changed this in the 1925 article (when Silberstein pointed out the slip). Michelson was aware of Sagnac's work because Silberstein referred to it in detail in his 1921 paper, where he picked up the slip of a factor of 2 in Michelson's earlier work. This same formula (without the sine of the angle of latitude) was given by Sagnac for his small laboratory tests, where the spin of the earth had an insignificant effect. Sagnac also showed that the centre of rotation could be away from the geometric centre of the enclosed area without affecting the result. In Michelson and Gale's test, the centre of rotation was at the centre of the earth, which is some 4,250 km from the area being used.

The following analysis of the Michelson and Gale experiment is, as far as could be ascertained, novel. It gives a very straightforward explanation of the results; it is simpler than the derivation given by Michelson and Gale in their paper.

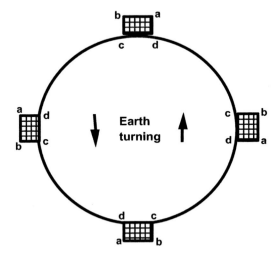

Figure 10: Michelson and Gale Rotating Area

The Michelson and Gale test, which uses the rotational speed of the earth's spin and the area of the rectangular piping system, is really a straightforward Sagnac test. Why is the 'area' that applies not the cross-sectional area of the earth at that latitude? The answer can be seen in the following explanation. In the Michelson and Gale test, the turning of the area at the rotational speed of the earth is seen from considering the area of a quadrilateral as the earth spins. The area abcd in figure 10 is the projection of the Michelson and Gale piping quadrilateral onto the cross section of the earth at the latitude of the test.

This area turns with the rotating earth, as is seen by examining the corners a, b, c and d as the earth turns once per day. After 12 hours, the area has turned upside down and the side d–c is now on top and a–b below. This explains simply why the centre of rotation can be away from the geometric centre of an area in a Sagnac-type test. In one revolution of the earth, the area turns once. Therefore, the angular velocity of the earth is also the angular velocity of the area in the test. The area that turns once per day is the projection of the area of the piping system, which was laid on the ground, onto the cross section of the earth at the relevant latitude. This is why we apply the sine of the angle of latitude. At the equator, there would then be no effect in a Michelson and Gale-type test (where the sine of the angle is zero). At a pole, there would be the full Sagnac effect (where the sine is unity).

The calculations on the Michelson and Gale 1925 tests are as follows. An average fringe difference for the both-way test was found to be 0.230. To get the time difference corresponding to this, we multiply by λ/c, i.e. the wavelength of the light divided by the speed of light.

The wavelength was $5,700 \times 10^{-10}$ m on the test, so the time difference is $(0.23 \times 5,700)/(3 \times 10^{-18}) = 4.37 \times 10^{-16}$ s. This difference is per light circuit of the apparatus. Taking the Sagnac formula and using the angular velocity of the earth (7.292×10^{-5}), the sine of the latitude of $41°\,46'$ (0.666), the area of the piping system in figure 9 (0.207 km^2) and the above wavelength of light ($5,700 \times 10^{-10}$ m) gives a fringe shift of 0.236, which is Michelson and Gale's forecast figure.

Interestingly, it was noticed by this author in these tests that the light going in the counter-clockwise direction was retarded with respect to the light going the other way. From the Sagnac tests (see figure 6), this would indicate that a spin in the counter-clockwise direction was causing the difference. Looking down on the North Pole, we see this is indeed the direction of spin of the earth.

Michelson had conducted another series of tests as described in his 1897 paper. He constructed a large vertical piping system, somewhat like the one described in the later 1925 paper, which was 200 feet long and 50 feet high, in a vertical east-west plane in a laboratory. The piping system was evacuated to *"about half an inch to one inch of mercury"*. He tested to see if the time to send a light signal around the circuit would vary with the time of day. He tried at 6 a.m., noon, 6 p.m. and midnight and concluded from the results that the fringe shift between noon and midnight (the maximum observed) was less than one-twentieth of a fringe. He expected about 7.2 fringes.

The tests confirmed the original 1887 Michelson and Morley tests in so far as the theory of an ether could not be proven. This test was not of sufficient accuracy to have shown the effect later demonstrated by the Michelson and Gale test. It was not feasible to construct a far larger piping system in the vertical position, and that is why the next system was in the horizontal position.

Michelson's experiments and publications are a lesson in clarity and ingenuity. Einstein was well aware of these tests and referred to the ingenuity of Michelson in devising them.

The effect of the spin of the earth is so small that it would not show up in a small Sagnac laboratory test. The fringe shift caused by the earth's rotation on a Sagnac disc test of 1 m diameter would be about 1×10^{-5} fringes at mid-latitudes, and would not be discerned. The Michelson and Gale test was successful in discerning the rotational effect of the earth by having a large enclosed area. There may have been some doubt as to the accuracy of the Michelson and Gale test. However, with the advent of the ring laser (see below), the same type of test has been done to great accuracy.

Yet another test done by Michelson (1913) confirms that light travels in relation to the laboratory. In this test, Michelson bounced light beams off mirrors that were rotating at 1,800 rpm. He proved from the resulting fringe shift that the light:

i.   does not bounce off such a mirror, as a tennis ball would bounce off a moving racquet.

ii. does not take up the movement of the mirror. That is to say that the velocity of the source of the reflected beam coming off the rotating mirror does not have any change in its velocity caused by that moving mirror.

iii. actually ignores the whole rotating apparatus. It moves solely with respect to the laboratory.

This test is a clear confirmation that the conclusions in this book in respect of Sagnac-type tests are correct. The accuracy of the test was 1:50.

Oddly, in this paper (1913), Michelson made an error of a factor of 2, which was cancelled out later by his omission of a similar amount. The error was uncovered by a colleague who has been corresponding with this author on that test. Michelson seemed to specialise in making errors of a factor of 2! However, the experimental results stand up.

The critical Sagnac or Michelson and Gale experiments are very rarely mentioned in university texts. Why?

Ring Laser

The development of the ring laser has led to a far more accurate method of measuring the Sagnac effect. The accuracy in Sagnac's time was about 1:100. In 1963, Macek and Davis carried out a Sagnac test using lasers on a rotating disc of about the same size as that used by Sagnac. Their tests gave an accuracy of 1 in 10^{12}. Bilger et al. (1995) carried out a test using a ring laser that was fixed to the earth, as was the Michelson and Gale piping system. Their aim was to determine the rotational effect of the earth on the behaviour of laser light, which was sent in opposing directions around a small circuit in the laboratory. The circuit was a square of area 0.75 m^2. They used a piping system filled with a helium-neon gas. The test was done in New Zealand at a latitude of 43° 29' S. The apparatus was 30 m underground, fixed in a cubic metre of concrete and tied into basalt.

The ring laser has a property that gives rise to the beating of counter-propagating modes at a frequency df, where $df = (4A\omega)/\lambda P$, ω is the angular rotation – in this that of the earth, λ is the wavelength of the light used and P is the perimeter of the ring laser. Bilger et al. achieved an accuracy of better than 1 part in 10^{12}. The accuracy of this result is a twelve order of magnitude improvement on the Michelson and Gale test, while the area concerned is less by a factor of 277,000 (Anderson et al., 1994).

The performance of the ring laser is somewhat different from that of the traditional Sagnac test. In the ring laser, standing waves of the laser light are set up. These are like the standing waves created by shaking a long rope that is fixed at the far end, or like the resonant vibrations of a violin string. In a circular ring laser, these waves stay stationary in relation to the laboratory (Martin, 1986). If the ring is now rotated, the nodes of the standing waves can be recorded as they pass by an observation post. This is a different phenomenon from the recording of a movement of fringes from their stationary position in a Sagnac test. The speed of the passing nodes in the ring laser test depends on the shape of the 'ring'. In the case of, for example, a square or triangle, the wave rotates at a different rate than in the case of a circular configuration. In all cases, the velocity of the passing nodes is directly proportional to the rotation rate (Anderson, 1986). This phenomenon is further confirmation of the proposal in this book: light, in small-scale experiments, travels relative to the laboratory or room in which the experiment is being held.

It was noticed by this author that in the Bilger et al. test, the rotation that caused the retardation of the laser was clockwise when viewed from over the South Pole. This retardation was in the opposite sense to that in the Michelson and Gale northern hemisphere test. Therefore, this Bilger et al. result also conforms to the Sagnac effect.

There was a considerable element of luck in the original Sagnac experiment. It was later found that the light signals can lock onto the circuit and mirrors unless there is considerable vibration; such vibration was present in the Sagnac experiment. In later designs a dither is introduced to ensure that locking does not occur. History would, no doubt, have taken a different turn had the Sagnac test given a zero result, which would have been the case had the equipment been rock steady. In that case, it would have been taken as proof positive of SR!

Circular Path Versus Straight Line

When considering the question of measurement of distance or time, Einstein (1905) accepted that movement in a circular path led to the same result as movement in a straight line. He derived the relationship between the time being kept by a stationary clock and a moving clock. As quoted earlier, when referring to the moving clock, Einstein said, "*it follows that the time marked by the clock (viewed in the stationary system) is slow by 1 – $\sqrt{(1 - v^2/c^2)}$ seconds per second, or – neglecting magnitudes of fourth and higher order – by $1/2v^2/c^2$*".

Having thus derived his formula for straight-line movements, Einstein said, "*it is at once apparent that this result still holds good if the clock moves from A to B in any polygonal line*". He also said that:

> . . . *if we assume that the result proved for a polygonal line is also valid for a*

continuously curved line, we arrive at this result: If one of two synchronous clocks at A is moved in a closed curve with constant velocity until it returns to A, the journey lasting t seconds, then by the clock which has remained at rest the travelled clock on its arrival at A will be 1/2tv²/c² second slow.

Even though the effect Einstein described is infinitesimally smaller than the Sagnac effect (as will be shown later in this chapter), it is the argument of application from a straight path to a curved path that is of interest here. The conclusion that the curved path is the same as a straight path when considering motion and time might be queried in relation to the centrifugal force effect for uniform circular motion. However, as Young puts it, *"there is no component of acceleration parallel to the path; otherwise the speed would change"*.

In 1919, three years after the publication of the general theory, Einstein repeated the statement when he wrote, *"The rotating observer notes very well that of his two equivalent clocks, that placed on the circumference runs slower than that placed at the centre."*

The path, in Sagnac's original test, was made up of straight lines. Harress (1911) did tests with a series of ten prisms around the circumference of a disc. In this case, short straight lines were also present. One of Pogany's tests (1926) had the light travelling around the four sides of an approximate square. This also confirms that when travelling in a straight line (on a polygonal section), the light emitted on a rotating disc does not travel at the speed c relative to the moving disc. As stated by Einstein (1905), there is no reason to credit that light, which travels in a series of polygonal lines, will behave differently from light travelling off in one straight line. Many references claim that we cannot apply SR to motion in a circle or on a closed circuit or to anything but straight-line motion. However, Einstein applied that theory to those situations in the basic paper on SR (1905). As we know, Einstein (1916) later changed his mind when he launched his general theory. He wrote:

The word 'special' is meant to intimate that the principle is restricted to the case when K' has a motion of uniform translation relatively to K, but that the equivalence of K' to K does not extend to the case of non-uniform motion of K' relatively to K.

The fact that Einstein changed his mind on this matter means that authors can selectively quote his writings to suit their purpose whenever there is a seemingly insurmountable difficulty with SR theory.

Adherents of SR say that no matter how large the disc, it does not approximate to a straight line because there is still some rotation involved. However, the centre of the earth (moving around the sun) is taken as a suitable and perfectly acceptable inertial frame for Global Positioning System (GPS) measurements – the GPS is used to monitor the time recorded by clocks on the surface of the earth or on satellites.

There is no such thing as a perfect inertial frame. Everything in the universe is in motion. The earth and everything on it and all other planets and stars are in some degree of motion. The best we can do is choose a frame that is acceptable for the purpose of our measurements in a particular experiment. Let us see how the 'perfectly acceptable' frame of the centre of the earth compares with that used in the various experiments described earlier.

The sending of a clock around the globe on an aeroplane (as done by Hafele and Keating in 1972) takes about 40 hours' flying time. During that time, the earth turns by 1.6 degrees of its orbital 360-degree path around the sun. The centre of the earth turns 2.9×10^{-6} orbital degrees around the sun during a test involving the sending of an electromagnetic signal around the earth at the equator (in GPS tests). During the Michelson and Gale test, the earth turned through an orbital angle of 2.3×10^{-10} degrees. So, this rotation is less by 10,000,000,000 than the frame acceptable in the Hafele and Keating case!

While the light signal went around the Bilger et al. apparatus described earlier, the earth turned on its axis by 1.66×10^{-13} degrees. Bilger et al. used a square of side 0.866 m on a disc of 8,750,000 m diameter (the cross section of the earth at that latitude). In the small laboratory-type tests, the daily spin of the earth would cause a turn by 365 times the above figures.

The non-rotating centre of the earth is acceptable by adherents of the theory of SR as a suitable place to set up a satisfactory inertial frame of reference. However, the surface of the earth (the laboratory in this case) is not considered to be an inertial frame by adherents of SR. Furthermore, in the Hafele and Keating case, the centre of the earth rotates by an angle greater by 10,000,000,000,000 than occurs during the Bilger et al. test. Also, in the Bilger et al. test, there is a rotation that is less by 5×10^{-6} than in the GPS circumnavigation case. For GPS measurements that involve less than a complete circumnavigation, the ratio is proportionately less.

In the original Sagnac test, the earth would have turned 2.8×10^{-13} orbital degrees during the test. During a GPS test around the globe at the equator, the earth would have turned by 10,000,000 times the amount it turned during a Sagnac test. It is indefensible to pretend that SR does not apply to rotation while at the same time applying it daily to experiments like the GPS, which has a far greater amount of rotation than the Sagnac experiment. We could be forgiven for saying that this is a very biased selection of what is termed an 'inertial frame'. It is simply cheating.

The fact that the Sagnac effect was measured in tests using rotating discs led to the idea that the effect could refer solely to rotating frames of reference. However, no comparison could previously be made (before Wang, 2003; see below) for light emitted aboard an object that was travelling off in a straight line because the two light pulses did not meet again to be compared aboard the moving object. Consequently, the literature refers to the Sagnac effect as arising from the rotation of the spinning disc. What is proven by the Sagnac tests is not peculiar to spinning discs or rotating frames of reference. It could only be measured on rotating discs because the light pulses can be made to come back to the same point to be compared.

The results are the same for spinning discs of any radius. With a disc of radius approaching infinity, the result approximates to a straight line. This effect, therefore, applies to objects moving in a straight line. Post (1967) saw that there was a problem with the straight line versus the rotating disc. He said, *"To be consistent with the principle of relativity one has to demand that the Sagnac interferometer and the ring laser cannot lead to a fringe shift or a beat frequency if the equipment is in uniform translational motion."* This author had the pleasure of meeting Post in 1997. Post also wrote:

> *The special theory of relativity does not apply to Sagnac because Lorentz transformations are restricted to pure translation. While this saved the situation from formal contradictions, it did leave a disturbing conceptual discontinuity. Why did galilean kinematics suffice for rotational motion and then fail for pure translation?*

In other words, why was it that SR theory was useless for any motion other than uniform straight-line relative motion, while the old Newtonian theory could explain rotational motion but was claimed to be insufficient for the simplest motion of all – uniform straight-line motion!

Indeed, the Sagnac disc need not approach infinite radius to give us the straight-line effect. If the disc is so large that we cannot distinguish, with the most accurate instrumentation, any deviation from a straight line, then the result is applicable to straight-line motion. As the earth is moving in space with all sorts of movements, from the movement of our universe to the orbital movement around the sun, we cannot ever have an ideal inertial frame on earth. The deviation from a straight line caused by such movements on a distance such as that used in the Michelson and Gale (600 m) or Saburi (0.9 m) test will not be distinguishable.

What have we measured by the fringe shifts recorded in the Sagnac tests? We have indirectly measured the time taken by the two opposing beams of light to traverse the spinning disc in opposing directions. We have therefore proved that the light travels at different speeds in relation to an observer on the spinning disc. This directly contradicts SR.

A recent ingenious test by Wang et al. (2003) shows that the Sagnac result is also achieved by sending out and back again light in a straight-line portion of the light path. This is what this author claimed above, but it is so much more convincing when an actual experiment has shown the same thing. I wonder what excuse will be trotted out now! Wang et al. achieved the seemingly impossible by reversing a light beam sent out on a straight line on a moving platform and measuring the difference in time for it to return. This author had the pleasure of meeting Wang in 1997 and corresponded with him during the tests he performed and since then.

In another paper (2005), Wang gives further details of the experiment; appended to this paper are comments on the experiment by Hatch and Van Flandern, confirming that Wang has succeeded in proving that the Sagnac effect applies to straight-line motion. They both also say that the GPS system uses an adjustment to allow for the fact that the receiver moves with respect to the source of the electromagnetic signal, but the GPS does not put a name on that fact. This adjustment is, of course, caused by a varying speed of the electromagnetic signal with respect to the receiver; to define that would be an anathema to SR because it would prove that the speed of light is not a constant as measured in the GPS systems.

The reader should dwell on the above analysis of the Sagnac test and SR. It is at the core of the claims in this book that SR is not correct. Any claims that the Sagnac experiment upsets that theory were heretofore brushed aside by a statement that Sagnac is a rotational experiment and SR does not apply to rotational experiments. That defence is now shown to be groundless.

SR Versus the Sagnac Effect

Claiming that SR explains the Sagnac effect caused by the slow rotation of a small disc is like saying that it explains the bouncing of a rubber ball against a wall or the fall of a snowflake. The analysis of such experiments does not contradict SR, but the latter has no part in any explanation of the phenomenon.

Some publications that try to use SR to explain the Sagnac effect apply the 'gamma' factor to the denominator of the Sagnac equation ($4A\omega/c^2$) and later in the calculation to the numerator, thereby cancelling out. They then declare victoriously that the answer conforms to the Sagnac results! One has to be vigilant to spot this trick.

Many authors state that SR is not relevant to rotating frames of reference and therefore not relevant to the Sagnac effect, as if that explains the whole matter! Well, if that is so, what on earth (excuse the pun) is the explanation? Some say that general relativity (GR) is needed to explain the matter, which is equally unsuccessful because the incremental effect forecast under that theory is even less than that calculated under SR, as derived later in this section.

It will now be shown that the Sagnac effect and the effect calculated by SR are of very different orders of magnitude (which Post (1967) accepts) and that SR has no role in trying to explain the Sagnac effect. Post says that the dilation factor to be applied under SR is *"indistinguishable with presently available equipment"* and *"is still one order smaller than the Doppler correction, which occurs when observing fringe shifts"* in the Sagnac tests. He also points out that the Doppler effect *"is v/c times smaller than the effect one wants to observe"*. Here Post states that the effect forecast by SR for the time dilation aboard a moving object is far smaller than the effect to be observed in a Sagnac test. Post then ignores the relativity dilation as if it were really there but of insignificant import.

Malykin (2000) does the same but still claims that SR alone can explain the Sagnac effect. The dilation factor is introduced and then ignored as too small to be considered in the result. *"In neglect of small relativistic corrections which are of no practical value"* is how he describes it.

The theory of SR stipulates that the time of the traveller (t') is slower than that of the stationary observer (t_0). It gives the comparison as (see chapter 1)[7]:

$$t_0 = t'\gamma \tag{14}$$

---

[7] The general reader may skip the mathematics and just look at the result after equation (17).

where t_0 is the time for the light to travel a certain distance as measured in the stationary laboratory, t' is the time for the light to complete the same distance as measured aboard the travelling object and γ is the abbreviation used for $(1 - v^2/c^2)^{-0.5}$. Using the binomial theorem to expand γ, we get $(1 - v^2/c^2)^{-0.5} = 1 + (v^2/2c^2) +$ small terms. From equation (14),

$$t_0 = t'[1 + (v^2/2c^2)]$$

$$t_0 - t' = t'(v^2/2c^2)$$

and

$$\frac{t_0 - t'}{t_0} = \frac{v^2}{v^2 + 2c^2} \tag{15}$$

which we will call dt_R – the SR time ratio.

The derivation of the similar Sagnac ratio is as follows: t_0 is the time for a light signal to traverse the circumference of a stationary disc and t' is the time for a light signal to traverse the circumference of a spinning disc according to the observer on the disc. To get the comparison from equation (4):

$$\frac{t_0 - t'}{t_0} = \frac{v}{c + v} \tag{16}$$

which we will call dt_S – the Sagnac ratio.

In both cases, t_0 is the same $(2\pi r/c)$ for a circular path – see earlier in this chapter for a justification for using the SR ratio for the circular path.

From equations (14) and (15), the ratio of dt_S to dt_R is:

$$\frac{v}{v+c} \times \frac{v^2 + 2c^2}{v^2} = \frac{v^2 + 2c^2}{v(v+c)} \tag{17}$$

For small values of v as compared to the value of c, as is the case in all normal experiments, this is equal to $2c/v$. The Sagnac effect is therefore far larger than the effect forecast by relativity theory. For example, in the Pogany test (1926), where the light path was moving with a velocity of about 20 m/s, this ratio is about 30,000,000.

The Sagnac effect is not to be confused with the effect calculated under SR, which has no possible function in explaining the Sagnac effect. The two cannot be said to be manifestations of the same thing, as is often claimed in error (e.g. Allan, 1985; Dieks and Nienhuis, 1990; Hehl and Ni, 1990; CCIR report, 1997; CCDS report, 1980).

It is not the time that changes, as has been proposed by SR, but the speed of the light that changes relative to the observer. The speed of light is no longer sacrosanct.

General Discussion on the Sagnac Effect

The young German student Harress, who unfortunately was killed in the First World War (what a loss to humanity), conducted tests in 1911 on the refraction of light in a moving medium. He used a spinning disc with light sent in opposing directions, as had been done by Sagnac. Harress's tests had both the photographic equipment and the light source fixed in the laboratory, whereas Sagnac had both on the spinning disc.

Harress's results were subsequently examined by Harzer in 1914. Some references claim that Harzer showed that the Harress tests gave the same effect as the Sagnac tests. The publications by Harzer (1914) concentrated on deriving the refractive index of glass in a moving state because Harress had used glass prisms arranged around the disc to deflect the light around in a circle. The derivation of the Sagnac equation from the work of Harress does not appear to have been done by Harzer – at least this author could not identify where it was implied by Harzer. Later, Von Laue (1920) and Pogany (1926) did show that Harress had actually got the same effect as Sagnac but that Harress had not recognised it for what it was. Therefore, while many references attribute the discovery to Harress (e.g. Post, 1967), this author believes that it is correct to give Sagnac the credit for actually achieving the experimental result.

There have been misunderstandings of the Sagnac effect. As an example, Dieks and Nienhuis (1990) said that *"seen from the rotating system, the two signals have equal speeds; measured from the laboratory system, the speeds are v + or − ωr"*. That is incorrect. As was shown by Sagnac, the speed of the light as viewed from aboard the spinning apparatus changed.

Interestingly, Abolghasem et al. (1989) conclude, as mentioned earlier in this book, that the rotation *"causes the velocity of light to be locally different in opposite directions"*. They go on to say:

> . . . one should redefine time or rather 'correct' the local time interval of two adjacent events by an amount, so that the speed of light becomes the same in both directions. This corrected, or 'natural time' interval guarantees the clocks on the rotating disc to be Einstein-synchronised.

This suggestion is the same as Langevin's (1937) second option described earlier (i.e. the time aboard the spinning apparatus had to change by a factor of $\pm 2\omega A/c^2$ in either direction) and shown here to be unnecessary. The same idea was put forward by Trocheris in 1949.

The proposal that the speed of light is altered 'locally' appears in several publications. It is to be wondered if such a statement was inserted at the behest of the referees of such papers who are vigilant of any criticism of SR. The idea seems to imply that the alteration is just a very local affair and that the speed of light in general is constant. Local currents in a battery are those on the plates of the battery as distinct from the current in the outer circuit to which the battery is connected. A local pain in one's toe is not a pain all over the foot. This 'localisation' of the alteration in the speed of light seems like an unsuccessful attempt to pretend that the phenomenon does not really exist or that, at least, it is not a very serious matter!

General Derivation of Sagnac's Equation

As far as could be ascertained, this is the first general derivation of the Sagnac effect based on the fact that the light travels with respect to the laboratory.

Sagnac developed the mathematics of his equation based on the assumption that an ether existed. Fortunately, the result is the same as if the light were measured as travelling at a constant speed with respect to the stationary laboratory, as has been shown to be the case in this book. Because the effect of an ether would be to slow down the light when travelling with the rotation of the equipment and to speed it up when travelling the other way, this gives the same mathematics as those we need. In our case, the rotating equipment tends to leave the light behind when rotating in one direction and tends to catch up with it when going in the reverse direction. This has the same effect as if there were in fact an ether. It is probably because of his insistence on an ether that Sagnac's results have not been recognised for their full pioneering worth. Researchers are too busy to bother reading old papers on ether theory!

Let us set down here the general mathematics of the Sagnac effect on a quadrilateral shape as used by Sagnac in his tests and on the assumption that the light is travelling in relation to the fixed laboratory (as per the conclusions of this book). This is the general case to be compared with the simpler derivation on a circular path done earlier (see figure 7). Again, the general reader can skip to the end of this section without losing the thread of the debate. The derivation shows that the Sagnac equation applies for any shape of circuit.

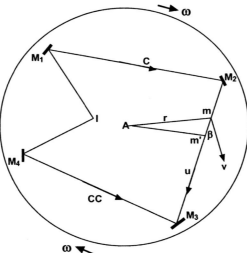

Figure 11: General Derivation of the Sagnac Equation

Figure 11 is a sketch of the original Sagnac layout. There are four mirrors: M1, M2, M3 and M4. The light beams go in opposing directions, having been sent out from the point I. One beam goes clockwise (C) and the other counter-clockwise (CC). The rotation of the disc is clockwise at an angular velocity ω. The axis of spin is at A. The final interference occurs at I, and a photographic record is made by a camera that is fixed to the disc and rotates with it. The disc is 50 cm in diameter, and the enclosed area of the light path is 666 cm².

Let Δl be the length of an element mm' of the perimeter of the rotating circuit (figure 11). Let v be the linear speed of the rotating turntable at the point m (in the tangential direction as shown). Let u, or $v\text{Cos}\beta$, be the component of v following the path of Δl, and let β be the angle between the path of the light and the linear speed of the point m. Let r be the radius to the point m from the axis of rotation A.

If the turntable is not turning, the light beam will propagate from m to m' in the time $\Delta l/c$. Let us assume that the turntable is rotating and that the light travels at the fixed speed of c in relation to the stationary laboratory; that is what is postulated in this book. From this, let us see if we can derive the correct Sagnac equation for the general case of a polygon.

With respect to the element mm' of the circuit, which travels in the same direction as the light path, the light beam C travels at a speed of $(c - u)$. The time ($\Delta t'$) for the propagation of the light beam along the element mm', which is fixed to the rotating table, varies from the stationary condition of the disc under the influence of the movement by $\Delta t' = \Delta l/(c - u) - (\Delta l/c) = [\Delta l/c][(c)/(c - u) - 1]$. Expanding $c/(c - u)$ by the binomial theorem, which in general is $(1 + x)^n = 1 + (n)(x) + [n(n - 1)/2!](x^2) +$ etc, we get $[(c - u)/c]^{-1} = (1 - u/c)^{-1} = 1 + (-1)(-u/c) + \{[(-1)(-2)]/(2)][(-u/c)^2]\} +$ smaller terms $= 1 + u/c + (u/c)^2 +$ smaller terms. Substituting this back above, we get $\Delta t' = (\Delta l/c)(u/c) + (\Delta l/c)(u/c)^2 +$ smaller terms. For the beam that goes in the other direction (CC), we similarly get $\Delta t'' = -(\Delta l/c)(u/c) + (\Delta l/c)(u/c)^2 +$ smaller terms.

When we calculate the difference in the times to go clockwise ($\Delta t'$) and counter-clockwise ($\Delta t''$), the second order terms cancel. Subtracting, we get $2\Delta t = 2(\Delta l/c)(u/c)$, without neglecting terms of the second order but neglecting only terms of the third and higher orders.

So, the delay over the distance mm' of the light C in relation to the light CC is $2\Delta t = 2u\Delta l/c^2$. By putting the integral of $u\Delta l = D$, we find the total delay for the whole circuit to be $\Delta t = 2D/c^2$.

We have $u = \omega r\text{Cos}\beta$ and $dl = rd\theta/\text{Cos}\beta$, where $d\theta$ is the angle at which an element mm' is infinitely small as seen from the axis of rotation (A) in the plane of the circuit. Let $d\alpha$ be the area of the triangle Amm', with the element mm' rendered infinitely small. The element of delay of the light beam has a value $udl = \omega r^2 d\theta = 2\omega d\alpha$. This follows from, for example, a quadrant of a circle giving an angle of $\pi/2$ and an area of $\pi r^2/4$; this area $= r^2\theta/2$. The total delay over the complete circuit is $D = 2\omega A = 4\pi nA$, where n is the number of rotations per second and A is the total area enclosed by the path of the light beams. The total difference in time for the two beams C and CC to complete a circuit in opposing directions is $2\Delta t = 2D/c^2 = (8\pi nA)(c^2)$, which is the Sagnac formula $\Delta t = 4A\omega/c^2$.

We have proved that for a general configuration of the Sagnac experiment, the difference in time for two beams going in opposing directions to traverse the light path is the Sagnac formula. This derivation has been on the assumption that the light travels with respect to the fixed laboratory. The result conforms to the experimental outcome, thus proving the veracity of that assumption.

Proposed Explanations of the Sagnac Effect

In the years since Sagnac published his results in 1914, there have been many attempts to explain the Sagnac phenomenon. Hasselbach and Nicklaus (1993) termed these attempts *"conceptual difficulties"*. Indeed, these authors refer to a paper by Sir Oliver Lodge (1893), who suggested that a test on the lines of that eventually done by Sagnac could be useful. In private correspondence with colleagues (reproduced in Anderson et al.), Lodge said that a fringe shift could be found in a test such as those done later by Michelson & Gale and Sagnac, and gave the first known derivation of the Sagnac formula. Sometimes the attribution of a discovery to a particular scientist seems to depend on taste, or perhaps nationality!

A list of explanations for the Sagnac effect as explained by previous authors is recorded in their 1993 paper by Hasselbach and Nicklaus:

> . . . *optical analogy, general relativity considerations, special relativity analysis, the WKB approximation, the Doppler effect of moving media in an inertial frame, a classical kinematic derivation, dynamical analysis of a non-inertial frame, by analogy with the Aharonov-Bohm effect, by extension of the hypothesis of locality, by adiabatic invariance, using ether concepts, and in other ways. This great variety (if not disparity) in the derivation of the Sagnac phase shift constitutes one of the several controversies that have been surrounding the Sagnac phase shift since the earliest days of studying interference in rotating frames of reference.*

Hasselbach and Nicklaus conclude that:

> *The question whether the Sagnac effect can only be treated adequately in the framework of general relativity (as opposed to a special relativistic treatment being sufficient) has perhaps generated the most extensive controversial discussion in this field.*

The 21 references to these various attempted explanations are given in the text of that paper. Even in such a comprehensive review, there is no reference to the experiments of Dufour and Prunier or Pogany, nor is the paper by Ives (1938) mentioned.

Ives refers to the Sagnac experiment and says, *"the measured velocity of light is a function of the measuring instruments, and can have other values than the constant c"*. In an article entitled *Light Signals Around a Closed Path*, Ives said that the laboratory or the platform on which the equipment was stationed could be rotated without any resultant

Sagnac effect. As we have shown earlier, the light in the Sagnac experiment is travelling with respect to the earth (in this case, the house or building in which the test is being done); any spinning of the laboratory or the platform will not affect the result. Ives was writing during the French controversy described earlier. He referenced the papers by Langevin (1937) and Dufour and Prunier. He misquoted Langevin in relation to the latter's statement on correcting the 'local' time on the disc. Ives does so by a correction factor of γ, whereas Langevin had stated that the choice lay between assuming a correction of $2A\omega/c^2$ to the 'time' or assuming that the speed of light varied and was $c \pm v$ depending on the direction of propagation. To either of these explanations, Ives has mistakenly additionally applied a correction of γ.

Chappell (1979) credits Sagnac as the discoverer of the ether and concludes that *"whatever controls the velocity of light seems to be influenced by Coriolis Force, just as air, water or any other fluid near the earth's surface"*. On the earth, the Coriolis force is at right angles to the direction of travel of the object being analysed here (light beams sent around the globe with and against the spin of the earth) and, in this case, it is the light path that is under consideration. The Coriolis force is also at right angles to the axis of spin. It is the force calculated to allow for the normal equations of motion to be applied to an object in a rotating frame. Being at right angles to the direction of motion and axis of rotation, the Coriolis effect is zero for a circumnavigating route at the equator of the earth. The Sagnac effect on such a circumnavigation by light signals travelling eastward and westward gives its full effect. Notice that this is different from the Michelson and Gale test discussed earlier. In that case, it is the projection of the area used onto the cross section of the earth that contributes to the effect. The Coriolis force has therefore no relevance to the Sagnac effect.

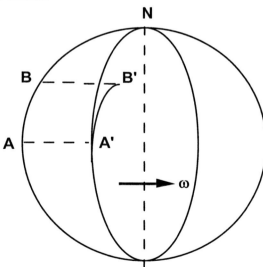

Figure 12: Coriolis Effect

Figure 12 will help to show that the Coriolis effect operates on various components of movements on the earth, whereas the Sagnac effect operates solely on the east-west components of any electromagnetic signals sent around the earth. There is no Sagnac effect caused by sending electromagnetic signals in a north-south direction around the earth.

If a projectile is launched from point A at the equator towards the North Pole, the path will not follow the line of longitude. As the earth turns eastward with angular velocity ω, the line of the projectile, aimed from A towards B, will be A' to B' (A has by now moved to A'), such that the distance A–A' is equal to B–B' (exaggerated for clarity). Similarly, for a projectile launched from the North Pole towards the equator, the line will diverge to the right of the direction of projection. In the southern hemisphere, the deviation is to the left.

The Coriolis effect is similarly detected when walking on a merry-go-round. The Sagnac effect, on the other hand, shows up on electromagnetic signals sent eastward and westward around the equator of the earth. For such signals, the Coriolis effect is zero. In the case of the Sagnac effect, a light signal sent from A to A' will travel slower relative to the surface of the earth than a signal sent from A' to A. This has nothing to do with the Coriolis effect. The only common factor between the Coriolis and Sagnac effects is that both are caused by the rotation of the earth.

The Coriolis effect describes the motion of a projectile that is affected by its radial motion on a spinning disc. The Sagnac effect describes the difference in times for counter-propagating light signals to complete a path on such a disc – it is not affected by any radial motion but solely by the component of the motion with or against the spin of the disc.

A light signal sent from the equator towards the North Pole probably has a deviation due to the Coriolis effect, just like any other projectile. That this might occur will be seen later when discussing in more detail the behaviour of light on the earth. The deviation would be so small that it would be very difficult to detect.

Anderson et al. describe the *"complicated and in places obscure, history and interpretation of the Sagnac effect"*. As we have seen, the Sagnac effect does not prove the existence of an ether but rather shows that light behaves in a certain way, i.e. that it ignores the movement of the spinning apparatus and travels instead solely in relation to the fixed laboratory. The Sagnac tests demonstrate that light does not travel at a constant speed relative to all observers in inertial frames.

The explanation of universal relativity (UR) put forward in this book does not need any convoluted explanation. It is simple, and explains the Sagnac effect totally. It does not agree with SR. To synopsise, the facts of the Sagnac tests are as follows:

1. The light beams are in synchronism when released.
2. The light beams are not in synchronism when they have completed one turn of the apparatus.
3. Any observer on board the rotating apparatus or stationary in the laboratory will observe identical fringe shifts. If the observer is in the laboratory, there would be a

very small Doppler effect when observing the moving apparatus. However, this is insignificant and will not make any observable difference to the result. There was no Doppler effect whatever in the original Sagnac test because the observations were made aboard the spinning disc and the observation point was at a constant distance from the point of interference.

4. The light is behaving as if it were travelling at constant speed relative to the laboratory. It ignores the spinning of the apparatus. The light does not travel at a constant speed relative to the observer aboard that spinning apparatus. As seen from the mathematical derivation from figure 7, the light does not go at a speed of c with respect to the observer on the spinning apparatus. Going in one direction, it measures as going slower than c, and going in the other direction, it measures as going faster than c.

5. Time and distance aboard a spinning disc are identical with time and distance in the stationary laboratory. They are also identical aboard an object that is moving at uniform velocity in a straight line.

These conclusions are in accordance with UR theory, which claims there is no difference in time or distance caused by any motion relative to any observer. They contradict SR.

Because the matter is very important, let us review the question of the Sagnac effect and SR. Adherents of SR come at the Sagnac effect from two angles:

1. One group says that the Sagnac effect and SR have no common ground and have nothing to do with each other. This is based on the claim that, because the Sagnac effect involves rotation, SR is not applicable because SR is applied solely in cases of uniform straight-line motion.

   To this group we address this question: how then do you explain the difference in time for the light signals to circumnavigate the spinning disc (or the spinning earth)? The explanation will have to take into account an experimental result that is tens of millions of times greater than the SR predictions of dilation of time and is of the same order as predicted by Newtonian kinematics. This question cannot be avoided by simply saying that SR is not applicable and that therefore the question is not going to be answered! The light is travelling around the disc at different speeds in the opposing directions. Explain that phenomenon please.

   We have already seen in this chapter that the claim that rotation invalidates any application of SR to the problem is spurious. SR is freely applied to many situations where the rotation is millions of times greater than in the case of the Sagnac experiment.

2. A second group says that SR is involved in analysis of the Sagnac effect but that the effect is so small as to be undetectable. To this group we address this question: how then do you explain the time difference found experimentally? The result is millions of times greater than the effect you have claimed is there but too small to be detected. Explain the experimental result please.

Some even trot out both of the above excuses for not analysing the experimental results under SR, while not appreciating that the two excuses are mutually incompatible.

Fizeau Experiment

What evidence is there that light is affected by the flow of the medium (like water) that it enters? The famous Fizeau experiment (1851) showed that the speed of light in water is affected by the direction of flow of the water.

Fizeau sent a beam of light through a pipe in which water was flowing parallel to and in the same direction as the light beam. He also reflected the same light beam and sent it back in the opposite direction against the water flow. Figure 13 shows the setup of the experiment in diagrammatical form.

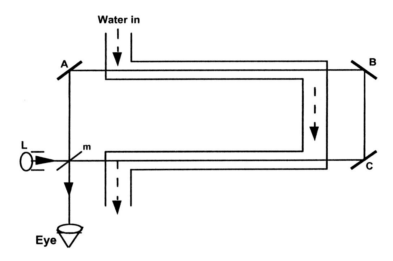

Figure 13: Fizeau Experiment

The water flows as shown by the dashed lines. Light is sent from L to a lightly silvered mirror m. The mirror allows some of the light to go through in the direction m to C to B to A to m and then to the observer's eye. Some of the light is reflected off the mirror and goes around in the opposite direction, i.e. m to A to B to C and back to m to be reflected to the eye of the observer. If the apparatus is turned on with the pipe full of water but the water not moving, no difference is observed in the time taken by the light to traverse the path in the opposite directions. However, when the water is put in motion, the change in the speed of the light on the two journeys is compatible with the light having adapted to the medium of the water flowing in the pipe.

Commenting on this experiment, Katz (1964) says, *"The speed of light in a medium must clearly be with respect to a coordinate frame fixed in the medium, for the very structure of the medium, the position of its atoms and molecules, provides a preferred reference frame."*

In the apparatus, one light beam goes with while the other goes against the water flow. The portions of the light path in air are ignored in the analysis because it is known that the light travelling in the stationary air will not be affected in any way by the water flow. In a hypothetical example in Katz where the path of travel in water for the light was 15 m and the speed of water flow was 3 m/s, the difference in the time for the light to go around with the water flow compared with the time for the light to go around against the water flow was found to be 10^{-15} s. This is about the time for a half oscillation of yellow light. Katz assumed the speed of light to be 0.7c (i.e. 70% of the speed c) in water. To the laboratory observer, the light had adapted to the water pipe with its flow of water. This is all said to be in accordance with SR in so far as observations made in the laboratory confirm the application of the mathematics of SR when applied to measurements made in another inertial frame (e.g. in the water flowing in a pipe).

It is as well to record here that the Fizeau experiment and the derivation of the results quoted above are not as clear-cut as they seem. The speed of light in water is given by Young in his textbook as 0.75c, while Katz uses 0.7c. This 7% difference (0.05/0.7) is significant in relation to the conclusions being drawn by these two authors concerning the Fizeau experiment. It is interesting to compute the results of the Fizeau tests with respect to two different assumptions:

1. The light is travelling in the water as observed by a laboratory observer in accordance with SR.
2. The light merely takes on the velocity of the water in addition to its own velocity. This means that the velocity of the light would be $c/n + v$ or $c/n - v$ depending on the direction of flow of the water, where n is the index of refraction in water and v the speed of flow of the water.

In the Michelson and Morley 1886 repeat of the Fizeau test, experiments were done using (a) pipes of length 3.022 m and flow of 8.72 m/s and (b) pipes of length 6.151 m and flow of 7.65 m/s. In test (b), the classical theory (assumption 2) gives an answer of 1.96 fringes while relativity theory (assumption 1) gives 0.86 of one fringe. The actual test result gave an average of 0.86 of one fringe for test (b); this conforms with relativity theory.

There is some ambiguity concerning the actual length of the pipes used in that Michelson and Morley test. It is not clear whether the tubes were half the above lengths or the full length. The doubt was not removed following this author's correspondence in 1996 with the university where those tests were performed – all records of the actual experiment appear to have been lost.

Smith (1960) misquotes these tests as giving a fringe shift of two fringes and using a velocity of 10 m/s. Such approximate reproduction of the actual test data and results makes it impossible for the reader to check the actual experimental results. This highlights the necessity of always using the original source rather than a quoted reference – several serious misquotations were uncovered in this investigation. Later, a different explanation of the Fizeau results will be proposed, which conforms to the alternative theory being put forward in this book.

Medium in the Sagnac Test

This section is for those particularly interested in the effect of having a medium in the light path in a Sagnac experiment. It can be skipped by the general reader.

How does light behave in a Sagnac experiment when a medium such as glass or water is introduced into the circuit being traversed by the light? Such a refracting medium changes the speed of light as it passes through the material. The following discussion will prove that in a Sagnac test, the introduction of a medium into the path of the light has an effect only if the medium is stationary in the laboratory. If the medium rotates with the disc, there is a zero effect on the Sagnac result. This can be satisfactorily explained by SR and also by a classical calculation.

As calculated by Fresnel in about the year 1800, the required sideways 'drag' that would bring the light from a star straight down the barrel of a telescope, even when that barrel was filled with water, is $1 - (1/n^2)$, where n is the index of refraction of the light in the medium (air or water). This phenomenon is discussed later in a section dealing with the aberration of light.

The theory of the drag of light also applies to light travelling in flowing water or other media on earth. This theory states that the speed of light travelling with (and against) the direction of the flow of a medium is not simply $(c/n) \pm v$, where v is the speed of the medium. An extra drag factor is applied to the velocity v to yield $(c/n) \pm v(1 - 1/n)^2$, just as in the case of the starlight.

The prescriptive tests were those done by Fizeau (1851), Michelson and Morley (1886) and Zeeman (1915). It is agreed in the literature that the Sagnac fringe shift increased as the light traversed the stationary refractive material in the laboratory while the disc was spinning. There is disagreement as to whether there was any change by introducing a co-moving refracting material aboard the spinning apparatus. Post (1967) quotes Dufour and Prunier (1942) as follows: *"Their experiment indicated that the observed fringe shift increases with the presence of a stationary medium in the beam."* Post also commented that *"The effect of the medium vanishes only if the medium rotates with the interferometer,"* although he does not necessarily ascribe this statement to Dufour and Prunier.

The original tests done by Pogany in 1926 gave a slight change when a co-moving medium was introduced aboard the apparatus. The change was slight, from 0.920 of one fringe shift without the interposed material to 0.904 with it interposed. Pogany is accurately quoted in Zernike (1947). Post (1965) suggests that the small difference is due to *"a very slight diamagnetic susceptibility of his glass medium in the optical range"*. Arditty and Lefèvre (1981) reported that Post, Vali et al. and Leeb et al. give *"conflicting results about the involvement of the dispersion of the medium"*.

Many tests have been done where a medium was introduced into the circuit in a Sagnac test. Dufour and Prunier had done such tests by 1942 (reported in Metz and Prunier in a paper in 1952 and in two other papers by Metz in the same year). Their tests were solely with the medium fixed in the laboratory. The second Metz paper (1952) could be interpreted as referring to a test where the medium moves with the turning disc, but the

Metz and Prunier paper makes it clear that this was not the case.

Post (1967) debates the value to be given to the drag coefficient. He says that the coefficient is *"similar to but not necessarily identical with the Fresnel-Fizeau coefficient of drag for translational movement"*. He comments that the traditional value is only pertinent to straight-line uniform motion and that the correct Sagnac test result is got by assuming that the drag coefficient is not equal to the Fresnel-Fizeau coefficient, and omits the final dispersion term of that equation. Post agrees that a co-moving medium does not affect the Sagnac test result, but that the use of a medium that is fixed in the laboratory increases the fringe shift by a factor of n (index of refraction).

Furthermore, Post says:

> *. . . the search for a physically meaningful transformation for rotation is not aided in any way whatever by the principle of general space-time covariance, nor is it true that the space-time theory of gravitation plays any direct role in establishing physically correct transformations.*

In other words, Post says that the result of the Sagnac test is a phenomenon that cannot be explained by general relativity (GR) theory. He also states that the time dilation factor of SR must be put equal to unity to give the correct result. This statement is tantamount to saying that SR or GR has nothing to contribute to an explanation of the Sagnac effect. This book agrees with that statement. Post was the pioneer of the explanation of the Sagnac effect.

Arditty and Lefèvre (1981) gave a review of the papers by earlier authors and discuss the fact that conflicting results are quoted in various papers (including Post) over the years. They first carry out an analysis of a simple Sagnac effect based on a straightforward kinematic method. This shows that using that method, the correct result is achieved. Again, SR is not invoked.

It is worth reproducing Arditty and Lefèvre's analysis, which shows that the introduction of a co-moving medium into the circuit in a Sagnac test does not affect the result. Consider the simple case of a circular circuit. In a vacuum, the Sagnac effect time difference is $4A\omega/c^2$, as derived earlier in equation (1); c is the speed of light in a vacuum. If the vacuum is replaced by a medium of refractive index n, then, when the interferometer is stationary, the light travels at a speed of c/n in that medium in both directions.

When the interferometer is set spinning with the Sagnac disc, the light goes at speeds of $c/n \pm \alpha v$ in the opposing directions, where α is the drag coefficient discussed earlier in relation to the Fizeau test and v is the speed of movement of the periphery of the circuit. Substituting $c/n \pm \alpha v$ for the $c \pm v$ in the derivation of equation (1) gives (to first order in v/c) $[4A\omega/c^2][(n^2)(1 - \alpha)]$.

Arditty and Lefèvre discuss the value to be assigned to the drag coefficient α. They show the proper use of the two different formulae for that coefficient. These are $\alpha = 1 - 1/n^2$ (derived by Fresnel in 1818) and $\alpha = 1 - 1/n^2 - (\lambda/n)(dn/d\lambda)$ (derived by Lorentz in 1895), where λ is the wavelength of the light. The third term, $(\lambda/n)(dn/d\lambda)$, is a

Doppler effect term and is also called the 'dispersion' term.

The Michelson & Morley and Zeeman tests are substantially challenged by Lerche (1977) as not having the required accuracy to decide between the conflicting theories of Fresnel and Lorentz. A detailed analysis of the earlier tests, and in particular of the Zeeman tests, is given by Lerche. The accuracy of the equipment used, the need to have laminar flow in the water pipes (flow was 1,000 times too great for laminar flow) and other inaccuracies in the equipment and the test are discussed. Lerche concludes that an experiment with an improved accuracy of one order of magnitude is required to decide between the conflicting theories. Tests by Macek et al. (1964) using a ring laser and the liquid CCl4 did not show conformity with the drag theory for light in liquids. A later analysis of their results, carried out by Kantor (1971), shows that the results of the test are not reliable and that the formulae used are not correct.

In 1972, Bilger and Zavodny (1972) did a test that seemed to confirm the existence of the dispersion term, but the accuracy of the experiment was also not sufficient to give a dogmatic result. Later Bilger and Stowell (1977) did a test using a small ring (half-inch thick) of fused silica. This test confirmed, to acceptable accuracy, that the dispersion term was needed in the drag coefficient. Bilger and Stowell commented that Post had used the coefficient without the dispersion term. A test done by Leeb et al. (1979) showed that using the second definition for α (which has the additional dispersion term added to the first definition) would not give the correct result where the medium was moving with the rotating disc. The difference predicted by the second definition was 15% greater than that forecast by the first definition. This test is probably the first one done to an accuracy that could differentiate properly between the two formulae. Arditty and Lefèvre explain why Post had the reason incorrect but got the correct answer. They also explain why the earlier authors had conflicting analyses.

Arditty and Lefèvre show that the first formula is to be used where the measurements are being made in the frame of the moving medium, as in the case of the original Sagnac test. The second formula is to be used where the measurements are being made in the stationary laboratory while the medium is moving with the spinning disc.

A Doppler shift will be detected when the measurement is made in the laboratory while the light is travelling in the medium and while the medium is moving with respect to the laboratory. Arditty and Lefèvre then show that application of the Doppler correction to the first equation above yields the second equation. They discuss the correct application of the two formulae. In the original Fizeau test, the second equation should be used because the measurements were in the stationary laboratory. In the case of the original Sagnac test, however, the measurement is of the difference in time for the light to traverse the circuit as recorded on board the moving disc. In that case, the first formula is the one that is applicable. Arditty and Lefèvre commented on the fact that Post correctly used the first formula. Indeed, Post also concluded that the kinematic approach in analysing a Sagnac test gives the correct result. Post also remarked that the Sagnac test detects absolute rotation.

Arditty and Lefèvre showed that using the first formula above ($\alpha = 1 - 1/n^2$) and applying it to the formula derived above, $[4A\omega/c^2][(n^2)(1 - \alpha)]$ gives the original Sagnac

69

formula $4A\omega/c^2$ because the n^2 is cancelled out. This conforms to the test results that show that the Sagnac result is not affected by the insertion of a medium in the circuit. It makes sense that there is no Doppler effect (dispersion term) where there is no relative motion between the observation place and the object being observed, as was the case in the original Sagnac test.

Arditty and Lefèvre also did an analysis based on relativity theory of the case where the medium is stationary in the laboratory, and they got an answer that conformed with experimental results. At this point, we are just remarking that either a kinematic analysis or a relativity analysis conforms to the test results for this example. It should be noted that to get the correct result, the drag coefficient had to be applied in all cases where the medium is stationary in the laboratory. Any reader interested in studying the matter in greater depth is advised to read the Arditty and Lefèvre paper. There appeared to be no physical explanation as to why such a strange coefficient needed to be applied. SR theory gave one explanation. In this book, a straightforward explanation is derived without calling on relativity theory.

On the question of whether or not the drag coefficient is the same in the case of uniform motion in a straight line and for motion on a spinning disc, a test by Vali et al. (1977) gives the answer. The tests on a fibre ring interferometer showed, to moderate accuracy, that the result is the same in either case. This Vali et al. result conforms to the proposals put forward in this book.

Electrons, Neutrons and Atomic Beams

Hasselbach and Nicklaus (1993) carried out a Sagnac test on electrons in a vacuum. The results agreed with the Sagnac formula to an accuracy of 1 in 3. The tests indicate that electrons travel relative to the laboratory in which these small-scale tests were done. Earlier it was shown that light also travels relative to the laboratory in such small-scale tests.

Tests done in 1975 by Colella, Overhauser and Werner (known as the COW tests) and in 1979 by Werner et al. showed that a Sagnac effect occurred with neutrons. Although the apparatus was small-scale and laboratory-based, this was not a typical small-scale laboratory test because the spin that was causing the Sagnac effect was the rotation of the earth. Later developments of their ideas are detailed in a 1980 paper. In these tests, they showed that there was a Sagnac effect acting on neutrons in agreement with the Sagnac basic equation (1). They could swivel the apparatus to have the plane in which the neutrons travelled facing in different directions. The effect was zero when the plane of movement of the neutrons was in the north-south direction, whereas the effect was at a maximum when the plane was east-west. The tests were done using a very small area (8.864 cm^2). Following much development of the apparatus, the results were produced to great accuracy.

These findings confirm that the Sagnac effect is caused in this experiment by the rotation of the earth. It is solely the movement of the neutrons in the plane of rotation of the earth that contributes to the Sagnac effect. Movement in a north-south plane contributes nothing. The projection of the actual path onto the east-west direction is what gives the effect. This test proves that, just as in the case of the Michelson and Gale test using light, neutrons do not take up the spin motion of the earth.

In a Sagnac test, Riehle et al. (1992) showed that a calcium atomic beam also behaved in a similar manner to neutrons and electrons.

These tests on light, neutrons, electrons and calcium atomic beams are all simply explicable by the assumption that they all travel (a) with respect to the fixed laboratory in the small-scale laboratory tests or (b) with respect to the earth's centre in the case where the effect is caused by the rotation of the earth.

Given then $E = mc^2$, m = 1 kg and c = 3 x 10^6 km/s. anyone can see that the quantity of calories obtained is represented by 10794 followed by 9 zeros, that is more than ten thousand billions. To what terrible result has our reasoning brought us? Nobody will easily admit that an amount of energy equal to the quantity that can be derived from millions and millions of kilograms of coal is concealed and stored at a latent state in one kilogram of matter of any kind; this idea will be undoubtedly considered foolish. However, even if the result of our calculations be reduced somewhat, it should be nevertheless admitted that inside matter there must be stored so much energy as to strike anyone's imagination. What is in comparison to it, the energy that can be derived from the richest combustible or from the most powerful chemical reaction?

Olinto De Pretto (1903)

Chapter 4

Light

Let us introduce a mixture of some old and some new ideas to dispel the paradoxes of Special Relativity (SR). To overcome the difficulties with SR as outlined earlier, let us consider using a simple definition of time. Let 'time' be taken as independent of the speed of light or the relative speeds of different observers or their relative positioning. This means that time is absolute and not relative, as claimed in SR. This is a reversion to the understanding in pre-Einstein times. The ideas will seem initially to be a reversion to Newtonian physics but this is not the case, as will be seen.

The time when an event occurs should be taken as defined as the instant it occurs when considered by someone who gets the information concerning that event at infinite speed, i.e. immediately. While nobody can, in practice, receive information with infinite speed, the only person who can come close to that ideal is the person right there on the spot. No matter how small the distance from the event to the person, an interval of time must elapse before that information is transferred. Even if you look at a picture on a wall, you cannot get information from the picture at anything other than the speed of light. Admittedly, the delay is so infinitesimal that it does not matter. To all intents, it appears to us to be a transfer of infinite speed.

We are not able to distinguish between information that arrives to us quickly and information that takes a long time to arrive. For example, when we look at an aeroplane against the sky at night, we also see light from stars in the background and perhaps from a street lamp nearby. We 'see' all these as simultaneous events, but we know they are not. We see these objects because light travels from them to our eyes. The further away the object, the longer the light takes to travel to our eyes and the further back in time the event occurred. The aeroplane will have moved a tiny amount by the time the light from it comes to us so that we are seeing its position a tiny while ago (about 10 millionths of a second). A distant star will have moved a greater distance than the aeroplane because the light from it takes longer to arrive to us.

We are primarily interested in the distribution of light through space (for observations of what is happening in outer space) and air (for observations on earth).

If some event occurs at this moment on a galaxy that lies at a distance from the earth of 1,000 million light-years (one light-year being 9.5×10^{12} km), that event will not be known to anyone on earth until 1,000 million years from now. Likewise, whatever happens here today would not be known at the place that is currently occupied by that galaxy until the elapse of a period of 1,000 million years of time as recorded on earth. Where will that galaxy be by then? There is no known way that the information can be transferred any faster than at the speed of light or other electromagnetic radiations (all of which travel at the same speed, namely 'c').

73

Behaviour of Light

It is usual to refer to the speed of light and not to the speed of the other electromagnetic radiations because the speed of light is such an important phenomenon to us. We do not see microwaves or radio waves. Maybe it is just as well because there are so many of these travelling around us in the atmosphere.

Let us apply Russell's explanation of 'contemporary' (from chapter 2) to the above example of a galaxy that is 1,000 million light-years' distance away. If we did something today (event 'E' as described by Russell), then, as stated above, this could not be noticed in that galaxy until 1,000 million years had elapsed. A further 1,000 million years must elapse before we can confirm that an observer on the galaxy has seen our event. We would therefore have a period of 2,000 million years that is 'contemporaneous' with the event 'E'. This is stretching the credulity of the reader, to say the least. 'Contemporary' had better have a more sensible meaning. Physicists can discern objects that sent out light 1,000 million years ago (and much earlier in the history of the universe), so this example is a practical one.

In the book *The Einstein Myth and the Ives Papers*, the editor Dean Turner points out that the proponents of SR claim that no time elapses for the passage of light from one place to another. He quotes several authors on this point, including Eddington (1929):

> . . . *it takes no time for light to travel from one point to another, that if one could travel at the speed of light, one could move along the orbit of the Earth from 1 January of this year to 1 January of next year in no time at all.*

The assumption that light travels in 'no time' leads to the result that the light emanating from a faraway galaxy takes no time to arrive to earth. This means that light from a galaxy that is 15,000 million l-y distance from earth arrives here and is supposed to depict the position and behaviour of that galaxy as of today. This is despite the fact that the galaxy may not still exist and certainly would not be at the same position in space after the 15,000 million years taken by the light signal to arrive to earth.

Bondi (1964) said that *"there is no passage of time for light"*. Turner is caustic on this claim: *"No one can meaningfully say that light travels at a rate of 186,283 miles per second and in the same breath insist that it takes no time for light to travel."*

It is proposed in this book that ageing, as well as the time of occurrence of any event, has nothing to do with the speed of light or other electromagnetic phenomena or the relative speed of an observer. It is to be hoped that bats do not think that their ageing is tied to the speed of sonic messages. Admittedly, the case of bats is quite different from the twin paradox because the speed of light is said (under relativity theory) to be measured as the same to all observers, no matter what their steady relative speeds, whereas the speed of sound has never been said to have such a property.

It does not matter where in the universe an event is happening or at what speed an observer is travelling relative to any other event or place or person. In the universal relativity (UR) introduced in this book, 'time' does not depend on relative motion of any kind.

So far, UR seems to be identical to Newtonian physics, but to explain the new theory, it will later be seen that some concepts other than those of Newtonian physics are necessary.

To recapitulate: Einstein (1905) stated that *"The laws of electrodynamics and optics will be valid for all frames of reference for which the equations of mechanics hold good."* This law, which he named the principle of relativity, was restated in his 1922 book as the principle of special relativity: *"The laws of nature are in concordance for all inertial systems."* Einstein also stated (1905) that *"Light is always propagated in empty space with a definite velocity c which is independent of the state of motion of the emitting body"* and *"any ray of light measured in the moving system, is propagated with the velocity c, if, as we have assumed, this is the case in the stationary system"*. In 1922, he stated this as *"In a vacuum light is propagated with the velocity c, at least with respect to a definite inertial system."*

It is proposed at this stage of the debate that the speed of light in free space moves relative to absolute space (or the fixed stars, as is often stated). It is not affected by what generated the light or whether the source was stationary, accelerating or moving in a straight line. It is not possible to stop light going off in all directions once generated unless it is blocked off from going in a particular direction by something opaque.

Light coming from a distant body behaves in accordance with Einstein's first postulate, which is that light is not affected by the movement of its source. A body may at times be receding from or approaching the earth when light is emitted, but the light takes the same time to travel to earth. There is nothing extraordinary about this idea. Sound behaves in the same manner when emitted in still air on earth. Sound does not take up the velocity of its source.

It is not possible with current technology to measure the speed of light relative to earth as that light traverses outer space coming from a distant star.

Consider a source that emitted an instantaneous light flash (see figure 14).

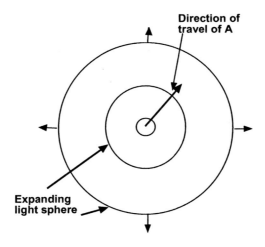

Figure 14: Light Spheres

The light spreads out in all directions in an ever-expanding sphere. An observer A was at the origin when the light began to emanate and is travelling in the direction of the thick arrow. The speed of light relative to the origin is 300,000 km/s. This must be so because the light is spreading out at that speed from the origin.

The speed of the light relative to the observer A, who is moving with respect to the origin, is not, however, 300,000 km/s. It is $c \pm v$, where v is the speed of the observer A with respect to the origin. Because the light flash expands in all directions, the direction of motion of the observer must coincide with a radius of the expanding sphere.

Bouncing Ball

Consider two persons, one a passenger on a train and the other on the platform at a railway station. The person on the train bounces a ball on the floor of the carriage as the train travels at a constant speed in a straight line along the track. The person on the platform does likewise. Both balls bounce up and down in the same manner. This is in accordance with the laws developed by Newton 300 years ago.

In this discussion, we assume that both balls are identical in elasticity and give exactly the same rebound. Gravity and friction are ignored. In fact, the bouncing of a ball is a complex operation to reproduce exactly. The shape, size, elasticity and momentum of the ball, the angle at which it is thrown, the density, pressure, humidity, temperature and motion of the air, the shape, hardness and position of the floor or wall, the spin imparted to the ball and other features all affect the result. However, let us assume these factors are all ideally equalised.

The bounce rate of a ball on board the moving train is exactly the same as that on the stationary platform or on board a fast-moving aeroplane. The ball can be bounced horizontally against the end wall of the moving train (ignoring the above effects), and again the same bounce rate will be achieved. We all have experience of this phenomenon. While it is now well accepted, it was not generally appreciated until Newton set down his laws of motion 300 years ago.

To go back to Einstein's train (figure 3, chapter 1), it is stated by Einstein that the lightning bolts hit the train at the back and front *"at the same instant"*. If the transfer of information from the back and front of the train was instantaneous to the observers (one on the platform and the other aboard the train), both would appreciate that the bolts struck simultaneously. Einstein argues that because the observer aboard the train meets the light wave that emanated from the front of the train before the light wave from the back of the train, and because that observer knows that the speed of light is constant as measured in the inertial frame of the train, he concludes that the two events are not simultaneous. Einstein assumes that a measurement of the speed of light must give the same result as viewed by both observers. This is not an 'experiment'; it is just a statement of what must be believed if SR is to be accepted.

In figure 15, an observer in a carriage is moving to the right at a speed of u in the $+x$ direction. Another person is on the ground bouncing a ball horizontally to and from a wall that is down the railway track and directly ahead (the train turns around a bend before it hits the wall!). Because the speed of bounce (*v*) is exactly the same for the ball aboard the train as seen by the observer on the train and for the ball being bounced against the wall as seen by the observer on the ground, this does *not* mean that the speed of the ball at the wall relative to the observer travelling on board the train is that same constant speed *v*. The speed of bounce of the ball at the wall relative to the observer travelling in the carriage is *u* + *v* or *u* − *v*, depending on the direction of the bounce. Being the same when measured aboard the train by one observer and on the platform by another does not imply that the speed of both balls relative to both observers is constant. This is so obvious that it hardly needs saying.

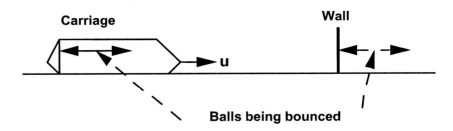

Figure 15: Bouncing Balls

Let us do a similar experiment with the same two observers, one aboard the train and the other at a wall down the track ahead of the train. This time we will let them experiment with light flashes. Both of them will let off a light flash towards a wall – the observer on board the train letting it off towards the end wall of the moving train and the observer on the ground letting it off towards the stationary wall that is situated further along the track. In both cases the light is reflected back to the observer off a mirror on the wall. The method of measurement is assumed to be sufficiently accurate to get the speed of the light flash as 300,000 km/s.

We know from the Michelson and Morley test that the observer situated on the ground and who is testing the light flash speed will get the result 'c' for the speed of the light flash in all directions. In this case, can we assume that the light on the ground travels at a speed of c relative to the passenger/observer aboard the train? Relativity theory says that we can and must. However, as we know from the experiments described earlier (Sagnac, Dufour and Prunier, Bilger et al.), this claim is not sustainable.

Michelson, Morley and Miller Tests

We should reflect again on the famous 1887 Michelson and Morley experiment. That experiment showed no difference in the speed of light in any direction as measured on earth. Even today, an experiment carried out to the accuracy of that original experiment will get the very same result. However, as we shall see, when the experiment is carried out to a far greater accuracy, a different result is obtained. SR was founded on the assumption that the Michelson and Morley experiment was the final answer to measuring the speed of light in different directions. Alas for SR, that was not to be the case. Progress did not cease with the 1887 Michelson and Morley experiment.

Clues to this were the fact that light did not circumnavigate the earth eastward and westward in equal times, as shown by the Michelson and Gale experiment. Also, in the Michelson and Morley experiment, there was a tiny consistent inexplicable resultant difference, which was ignored by the experimenters. Every experiment has tiny inaccuracies in the results; these are randomly scattered and are ignored.

Various experiments testing the speed of light as generated aboard spinning discs also showed the speed of light to vary in opposing directions with and against the direction of spin. The Michelson and Morley experiment does not really contradict the Michelson and Gale experiment or the Sagnac experiment because it was just not of sufficient accuracy to show what those later tests showed.

We are not too sure of all the motions of the earth in space. It moves in our galaxy, but the total galaxy moves in motions in a wider cosmos, which in turn moves in some unknown way. A recent test shows a residual movement of our galaxy in one direction; this is shown by the anisotropic background radiation coming from outer space.

The background radiation coming from all parts of the universe was thought to be exactly the same from any direction. However, recent research has shown that this is not so. A bias of about 400 km/s relative to the earth has been identified in a particular direction. This is described in Smoot et al. (1977). Furthermore, recent research has shown that the universe seems to have an axis and that light velocities coming from the furthest objects vary (Nodland and Ralston, 1997).

Einstein wrote in 1921 (see Clarke, 1984), *"I believe that I have really found the relationship between gravitation and electricity, assuming that the Miller experiments are based on a fundamental error; otherwise the whole relativity theory collapses like a house of cards."* So if Miller was right, Einstein tells us to abandon his relativity theories! Remember this as we discuss the test results of Miller.

In 1926, a very detailed series of tests was carried out in the U.S.A. Many of the tests were done high up on Mount Wilson near Pasadena in California, at an elevation of about 1,830 m. These tests are described in a paper by Miller in *Science* (1926). It is worthy of comment that the tests done were of a very arduous nature, involving observers walking a total of 100 miles around in a small circle in total darkness, while looking through, without being able to touch, an eyepiece that was recording 100,000 results.

Miller discusses the earlier Michelson and Morley tests. Indeed, Miller worked with both of these researchers and later took over with Michelson when Morley retired from the fray. The Michelson and Morley tests were solely to try to see if the movement of the earth on its orbit could be measured. Subsequent tests by Michelson, Morley and Miller had the same aim. Miller discusses the fact that no positive results were obtained in relation to the spinning of the earth or the movement of the earth around the sun or a presumed motion of about 19 km/s of the solar system towards the constellation Hercules.

In other tests done in 1905 by Morley and Miller, dates were chosen so that the motions sought would be in the plane of the interferometer used. A null result was obtained from these tests, just as in the Michelson and Morley tests in 1887. No tests were undertaken to check other directions. It is interesting to note what Miller said in relation to the arrival of Einstein on the scene: *"It was at this time that Einstein became interested largely on the assumption that the ether-drift experiments by Michelson, Morley and Miller had given a definite and exact null result."*

Miller noticed that while the Michelson and Morley tests and subsequent tests by Morley and himself (1905) showed a 'null' result when compared to the expected magnitude of the fringe shift, there was a consistent small inexplicable resultant non-null effect. It was this small and apparently haphazard resultant that Miller subsequently set out to trace. He and his co-workers were all immersed in ether theory, and their paper discussed the manner in which the earth could pass through this so-called ether. All their conclusions are therefore aimed at trying to explain that phenomenon. However, it is in their experimental results that we are interested.

Miller noticed that the small non-null resultant effect at its maximum value corresponded to about 10 km/s, which was a considerable velocity. Miller, however, thought that the result should be at least a velocity of 200 km/s to satisfactorily explain the Michelson and Morley null result, when the orbital velocity of the earth around the sun, its daily spin upon its axis and the then assumed movement of the solar system towards the constellation Hercules were taken into account.

According to Miller, the effect *"did not point successively to all points of the compass, that is, it did not point in directions 90° apart at intervals of six hours, nor point in opposite directions at intervals of twelve hours"*. This seemed to indicate that the effect had nothing to do with the rotation of the earth. When sidereal time was used instead of local time, the results were compatible in showing the same result for the different dates on which tests were done during the year. This showed that the orbital motion of the earth around the sun was not the determining factor. The effect showed that the motion of the earth was in one direction. (As a matter of interest, this was towards a point of a declination of 65° and a right ascension of 262° – whatever that is!) Therefore, the earth and the solar system were shown to be moving in one direction in fixed space.

Miller had difficulty with all of this and stated that *"for some unexplained reason the relative motion of the earth and the ether in the interferometer at Mount Wilson is reduced to ten kilometres per second"*. In other words, he could not explain the result.

Independently in France, the scientist Escangon (1927) did tests similar to those of Miller and got somewhat similar results. This confirmation is important in relation to the following discussion where there were attempts to discredit Miller's findings. Nobody attacked the findings of Escangon, apparently overlooking the fact that his experimental findings were a justification of Miller's work. Subsequently, Shankland (1955) claimed that the Miller results were caused by daily temperature changes. Shankland had worked for Miller. Unfortunately, all the original Miller test results were 'lost' when in the keeping of Shankland.

More recently, other authors discount Shankland's conclusions and propose that there is a consistent movement of the earth in relation to outer space. One is Múnera (1998). Another is the Nobel Laureate Allais (1998), whose conclusions were very firm. They show that the temperature changes were not a factor. Indeed, Miller took great pains to ensure that this possibility was investigated and prevented. Michelson specifically describes this problem in his 1881 paper, where he tested using electric heaters and showed how to avoid any temperature distortions. It seems that the Shankland team set out to confirm relativity theory and that their conclusions are biased. It is also said that Shankland blamed Miller for the fact that Einstein did not receive the Nobel Prize specifically for his relativity theories.

Various resultant directions and magnitudes are proposed for the motion of the earth through space. In 1969, Conklin gave the result as 160 km/s. In 1992, Silvertooth and Whitney published experimental results that purport to give an alteration in the speed of light of 348 km/s in a unique direction in relation to the fixed stars. They say that this figure conforms to the variation in the background radiation. It certainly does not conform to relativity theory, where no change in the speed of light is possible. However, some authors claim that Silvertooth and Whitney's work, which used laser light, is not conclusive.

In 2003, Consoli and Costanzo, in an article entitled *The Motion of the Solar System and the Michelson-Morley Experiment,* conclude from a detailed analysis of the original test results that the velocity of the earth in the plane of the interferometer in the original Michelson and Morley experiment was 201 ± 12 km/s, which is in excellent agreement with the 203 ± 8 km/s got by Miller. They conclude that the fringe shifts are a measure of the velocity of the solar system within our galaxy and not with respect to what is called the Local Group of galaxies that contains 30 or so galaxies including our own. This paper also demolishes Shankland's claims that Miller's results were flawed because of temperature changes.

There is another puzzle concerning the Michelson and Morley experiment. The test was done to see if there was any difference between the times for a split light beam to go with and at right angles to the direction of the orbital movement of the earth around the sun. According to the Maxwell-Lorentz electromagnetic theory, the velocity of the light signal is independent of the source of that light. Doing this test at intervals of six months should have shown the resulting fringes in different positions. There was no such difference (Dingle, 1972). The unchanged position of the fringes conforms to the theory proposed in this book. UR gives a satisfactory explanation of this phenomenon, as will be described later.

What Is Light?

The characteristics of light are puzzling. Let us discuss some examples.

1. Light has the characteristics of waves or particles, which is shown by the two-slit experiment. In this experiment, light is firstly allowed to pass through one thin slit in a screen onto a second screen placed behind the first one. The light depicts a bright image of the slit on the second screen. If that slit is closed off and another slit opened near the first slit, the light again shows a bright slit image on the second screen. So far there is no puzzle. However, when the two slits are opened simultaneously, the image on the second screen is not that of two slits but entirely different. The light behaves as

if it were composed of particles when a single slit is opened, but seems to change to behaving as a wave phenomenon when a second slit is opened. Waves on water give the same effect on the other side of a screen with two slots as does the light in the second case described above. As is often asked, how does the light going through a single slit know how to change its behaviour as soon as the second slit is opened?

2. Using three polarising sheets (figure 16), one that polarises light in the horizontal direction (sheet H), one that does so in the vertical direction (sheet V), and one that does so at 45° (diagonal) to the horizontal and vertical (sheet D), we can carry out a puzzling test.

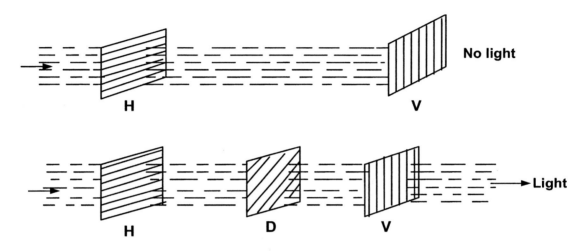

Figure 16: Polarising Sheet Experiment

The light passes through any one of these sheets on its own but does not pass through sheet H followed by sheet V, or vice versa:

$$H + V = 0$$
$$V + H = 0$$

This is as would be expected. Neither does the light (as would be expected) pass through the diagonal sheet followed by the other two in any order nor through the diagonal sheet after the other two in any order:

$$D + H + V = 0$$
$$D + V + H = 0$$
$$H + V + D = 0$$
$$V + H + D = 0$$

So far there is no puzzle. However, putting the diagonal sheet between the other two produces an amazing result – the light comes through the three sheets!

81

H + D + V and V + D + H let light through. If the diagonal polarising sheet is removed from between the other two, the light is again blocked. How can this be? The reader can try this by using three lenses from polarising sunglasses.

When we polarise in the horizontal direction, we block off (typically) all but 1% of the 'vertical' light leaving the first sheet. Some authors claim that the light coming from the first sheet can be split into 'components' at an angle to the horizontal. This is mathematically sensible because any directional entity can be said to be made up of two components at 90° to each other. In the current case this could be, for example, one component at 30° to the original direction of polarisation coming out of the first sheet and the second component at 90° to that. Mathematically or theoretically, you can resolve any vector into two components at 90°, but how can this occur physically?

After the first polarising sheet, the light is said to be vibrating (99% of it) in one direction only. At most, there would remain some 1% vibrating in random directions. Surely the *random* light is the only part that can, at this stage, be polarised in the 45° direction. Random light can be polarised in any direction. If a significant amount of the horizontally polarised light can still be resolved to a direction at 45°, then has it been polarised horizontally at all?

What is mysterious is that the introduction of the 45° filter causes the effect that it does. Does it 'twist' the incoming light? It would need to be possible to twist light by any filter that is not at 90° to the direction of polarisation of the incoming light, and it is mysterious how this can be. A formula known as Malus's formula gives the correct answer for the intensity of the light coming from the various filters in this problem, but what is the mechanism?

This is how Zukav (1979) describes it:

According to quantum mechanics, diagonally polarised light is not a mixture of horizontally polarised light and vertically polarised light. We cannot simply say that the horizontal components of the diagonally polarised light passed through the horizontal polariser and the vertical components of the diagonally polarised light passed through the vertical polariser. According to quantum mechanics, diagonally polarised light is a separate thing-in-itself. How can a separate thing-in-itself get through all three filters but not through two?

Zukav continues, *"Our eyes are ignorant of the fact that what they are seeing is 'impossible'. That is because experience does not follow the rules of classical logic. It follows the rules of quantum logic."*

Sachs (1998), in a supposed discussion between three persons, has one person say that *"one photon passing at a time would not know which way to go, that is to transmit through the crystal or to reflect from it! - or to rotate its direction of polarization"*. Graneau and Graneau (1993) also discuss this peculiar experiment and say that a filter at 45° does not turn the light through that angle.

3. An Irish scientist named Bell carried out an experiment at the CERN centre in Switzerland in 1965. It is known as the Bell Experiment and has led to much speculation. Bell set up an experiment in which he had two detecting slits on the left

and right of an emitter that was situated halfway between the two slits and that shot out identical pairs of photons. The slits were cut in two discs that were lined up with their centre lines coincident with the centre line of the emitter of the photons. When the photons are let off, they have a random, but similar, polarisation.

If one photon of a pair goes through the slit on one of the discs, its twin always goes through the slit on the other disc. This occurs because the photons have the same polarisation and the two slits have been set up to have exactly the same orientation.

In the starting position for the experiment, the slits are lined up and a certain number of photons pass through the two slits. However, Bell found that by rotating one of the discs containing one of the slits through different angles, a strange result emerged. If one of the slits is rotated through 25% of the slit width, a certain number of the photons now miss one slit but go through the other slit. A certain number still go through both slits as 75% of the slit width is still in line with the other slit. So far, so good.

The problem occurs when the angle is increased to say 50% of the slit width. The number of photons that now go through one slit but not through the other is not according to expectations. The number of pairs of photons that behave in this fashion is far greater than statistically expected. It seems as if the second detector knows when the other one has been rotated through the extra 25%. How can this be? One might ask why the phenomenon occurs only when the second increment of rotation of the slit is made and not the first 25%. This is a mystery.

Carrying the deduction from this phenomenon to its logical (or perhaps illogical) conclusion results in speculation that if the two slit detectors were separated by a very large distance anywhere in the universe, the same effect would occur. This is known as 'action at a distance' and leads to the mystery as to how this can happen instantaneously. It seems as if by altering the slit orientation on one disc, the number of photons that will pass through the slit on the other disc is also altered.

The above is a simplified explanation of the Bell experiment. Interested readers can read more in Pagels (1983).

4. If light is polarised in a particular direction and then reflected off a surface, some peculiar effects occur. If the reflection is off a mirror, no change in the direction of polarisation occurs. If the reflection is off polished metal, no change occurs. However, when the polished metal is the end of a strong electromagnet that is turned on, the light has its plane of polarisation changed (Bondi, 1964). This effect was seen by Faraday as proof that there was a link between light and magnetic effects.

In Test No. 2159, Faraday (1846) showed that polarised light behaved in a peculiar manner when sent across the end of a magnet. This test is described in more detail in a later chapter dealing with Faraday's tests. If light is sent through 'heavy glass' as it approaches the end of the magnet, it is turned through an angle. If the glass is placed after the light has already passed by the end of the magnet, the light is turned the other way. If the light is made to pass by the end of the magnet and through the glass, not in line with the centre of the magnet pole but just above or below the magnet, no effect results. It is clear that whatever effect is applied to the light, it is reversed after it has passed the magnet. The heavy glass was one substance that encouraged this effect; there were others. From this test it appears that the magnetic effect of a magnet on polarised light is equal and opposite on the other side of the magnet. As well as a north and a south pole, the magnet appears to have an 'east and west' effect as well. What is that effect?

5. Another property of light has recently been discovered that could shed some light (no pun intended) on this subject (Musser, 2003). This is that light can possess orbital angular movement. If you think of light as composed of particles, the photons are pictured as zipping along a corkscrew path. This discovery is about a decade old. What next?

6. What is the nature of the light that is spontaneously emitted by various bodies? This puzzle is described in an article by Nathaniel Holme (1800) entitled *Experiments and Observations on the Light which is spontaneously emitted with some degree of permanency from various bodies.* The paper describes meticulous experiments on the light that emanates from rotten wood, peat matter, some marine animals when alive and most of them after they die, animal flesh after death, and the glow-worm and firefly. Holme showed how the light could be transferred from one object to another and how its lifetime thereafter varied according to the treatment given to the object containing the light. These phenomena may be explicable today and are mentioned here as a curiosity from over 200 years ago. This paper was discovered by looking at the earliest volume on a shelf in the library of University College Dublin, where almost all of the research papers quoted in this book were located.

7. Light that passes through a natural sugar has a different polarisation from light going through manufactured sugar.

There is a common puzzle in all of the above. What is the nature of light? A reasonable conclusion could be that the nature of light is not understood, even to a slight degree.

Postulates that say light is of a particle-cum-wave nature are no more correct than postulates that say it is one or the other. A proper explanation of the nature of light that can explain the above experimental results has yet to be produced. The third puzzle is very like the first one – both are showing the peculiar behaviour of light when thin slits are involved. The second puzzle is also of the same ilk. The polarisation of light is, in effect, a batch of slits oriented in one direction.

The deduction of Bell (in 3 above) on action at a distance can be ignored until someone solves the problem of the behaviour of light in relation to slits. There may then be no necessity for such a far-fetched idea as action at a distance. Indeed, action at a distance at infinite speed is such a preposterous solution that there must be some explanation as to why light does these tricks.

It is clear that light is neither a wave nor a particle phenomenon. It is not fully explained by quantum theory. It seems a pity that quantum mechanics does not explain light fully. In the book *QED* by Feynman, quantum theory is seen as fitting everything except the polarisation problem concerning light, and has the reader almost persuaded that light is just 'particles'. Quantum theory has a plausible explanation for the two-slit

84

experiment.

It is appropriate to quote Scott Murray here. He published an interesting lucid series of articles in *Wireless World* in 1972–3. He took various aspects of physics and examined the basis for the extant theories. He says:

Modern physics, as now taught accepts the doctrine of duality, which says that light radiation (sun light, radio waves and x-rays) consist of both waves and particles at the same time. Whether its wave-like properties or particle-like properties predominate will depend on the details of the particular experimental set-up. If I use a diffraction grating I shall see waves; if I use a photo-cell I shall see photons; if I follow a diffraction grating by a photo-cell I shall see both forms of light within the confines of the same experiment. It matters not that waves (as in electromagnetic theory) and photons (quantum theory) are mutually-exclusive concepts, each of which specifically denies the validity of the other. I must learn to ignore the logical conflict and get on with the remainder of my job as though the conflict did not exist.

Murray highlighted all sorts of anomalies concerning light. The above is just a taste of what he penned.

Light has an extraordinary talent for spreading out and out in the universe without much diminution of its ability to spread further and further. It seems to have no problem going off for 15,000 million years without losing its visibility.

Consider what happens to light that is arriving to us now from a galaxy at a distance from earth of, say, 7,000 million light-years. This light was created at a spot in the cosmos all that time ago. It then went on its merry way in ever-increasing spheres, spreading out in all directions. Just consider how large the sphere is now – it must have a diameter of 14,000 million light-years. To where is this great sphere expanding? All the light spheres from all the light sources cross each other as they expand, without apparently blocking or deflecting each other. We can but wonder why.

Just think about this. The blink of light that emanated 7,000 million years ago would by now be a sphere with a radius of 7,000 million light-years. At what speed is the surface of that sphere expanding? The expansion is related to $2\pi rc$, where r is 7,000 million light-years. However, the speed of expansion (and the light is expanding to cover the whole surface of the sphere) is billions of billions times the speed of light. The light itself is moving transversely at that immense speed. It is supposed that no information can be transferred at a speed greater than c, yet here we have a practical example of where information on a faraway galaxy is being transferred laterally at a far, far greater speed.

The above discussion on the spreading spheres of light does not, however, bring information directly to us at a speed faster than c. It is merely a lateral spreading of a light signal at those immense speeds, while the direct line of the signal still travels at that constant speed of c. If light consists of photons, how do these divide and multiply to keep the surface of such expanding spheres supplied with the capacity to illuminate?

The transfer of information is limited to the speed of light, but this does not mean that an event only occurs when we see it. As a simple example, if some event occurs now on a galaxy at a distance of 100 million light-years from here, then that event has actually occurred now (in universal time). We cannot know about it on earth at this time; if anyone is where the earth currently resides in 100 million years' time, they will then observe the event.

Einstein remarked in *The Meaning of Relativity*, *"That material velocities exceeding that of light are not possible, follows from the appearance of the radical $(v^2/c^2)^{0.5}$ in the special Lorentz transformation."* However, by definition, having set the speed of light as a constant as measured in all inertial frames and having used that rule to get the Lorentz transformation, it is hardly surprising to find out later from the mathematical equations that the speed of light now comes out as the maximum possible and equal to the constant value assumed. That is like saying that all persons are 2 metres tall by definition and then seeming surprised to find from the ubiquitous 'thought experiment' that all persons are in fact 2 metres tall! Einstein recognised this 'circular' argument when he wrote (in his 1916 book), *"Of course this is not surprising, since the equations of the Lorentz transformation were derived conformably to this point of view."* Quite!

All light travelling transversely across our eyes is travelling at a speed faster than c. The light from the sun travels transversely across our eyes at about a billion times the speed of light. All such fast-travelling transverse light is not noticed. Our eyes do not detect it. This is just as well because we would be blinded by all that light. Similarly, all the other electromagnetic radiations have transverse spreading of the spheres of their expansion.

Let us give the last word on this subject to Professor Garret Scaife, Professor of Engineering at Trinity College Dublin, who said in 1995, when proposing a vote of thanks at my first lecture on this subject, *"Light is a particle on Mondays, Tuesdays and Wednesdays and a wave on the other days of the week."*

Aberration of Light

Stellar aberration was discovered in 1725 by the British astronomer James Bradley. His tests showed that light coming from a star as viewed from earth has an apparent position that allows for the orbital speed of the earth around the sun.

Figure 17 shows a telescope aimed at an angle A to the horizontal at the actual position of the star. Because the earth is moving at a velocity *v* in the +*x* direction, the telescope has to be aimed at a different angle, A', to correct for this movement. Consider the viewing of a star that is near the North Pole star in the northern hemisphere. When the earth is going to the left of the direction of the starlight, the telescope has to be tilted to the right, and when the earth is travelling to the right of the starlight, the telescope has to be pointed the other way. In the in-between positions the tilt is less; it is zero when the earth is at the points in its orbit around the sun where there is no motion of the earth to the right or left of the direction of the starlight. The time of year determines the direction in which the earth is moving relative to the light coming from that star.

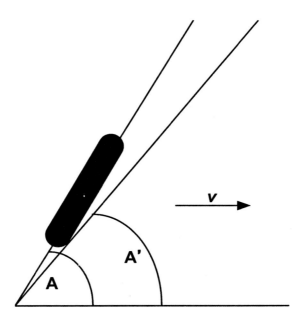

Figure 17: Aberration of Light

A further important discovery was made by Arago in 1810. Arago discovered that starlight was reflected and refracted on glass in exactly the same way as was light that emanated in the laboratory.

These two requirements (Bradley and Arago) were apparently contradictory because the direction of the light showed that the earth was orbiting around the sun while the refraction and reflection of the light seemed to prove that the earth was stationary. This was a great mystery to the scientist of the day. That question will be discussed later.

Bradley's aberration could be explained as being like the behaviour of falling rain when viewed from a moving vehicle, assuming that light was composed of particles. On the other hand, a wave theory of light would fit the aberration phenomenon provided that the light travelled through an 'ether' that was unaffected by the motion of the earth. The ether would have to pass freely through the earth without the earth having any effect on it. How could the reflection and refraction phenomena be explained? In 1842, the Irish scientist Stokes proposed a 'jelly ether' theory as an explanation, and this persisted into the last century.

In 1871, Airy carried out an experiment in which he filled a telescope barrel with water and found that the position of a star did not alter from the position as viewed when the barrel was filled with air. Because light travels slower in water, one would expect that the telescope would need to be tilted further to keep the starlight in the field of vision. The 'Fresnel drag coefficient' was used to explain this effect. The light was assumed to be 'dragged' sideways by the water by precisely the required amount. It would be an amazing coincidence if the drag were precisely the amount that would explain the aberration phenomenon. This requirement was partly instrumental in the later development by Einstein of SR. In physics, it is generally found that coefficients that have to be invented to explain phenomena are later shown to be unnecessary.

Einstein (1905) explained aberration as being due to the relative motion of the star and the earth. Hayden (1993) shows that by this, SR equates aberration angle with the orbital velocity of the earth minus the velocity of the star divided by c. He then asserts that the aberration is not due to the relative velocities of star and earth, but is caused by just the earth's orbital velocity. He also asserts that binary stars clearly do not exhibit an aberration that depends on the relative velocity of source and observer. Hayden's analysis would cause a problem for SR. In an earlier paper, Eisner (1967) had provided a different explanation that seemed to answer Hayden's analysis; that paper stated that the cause of aberration was indeed as Hayden said, but that it could be explicable by a different interpretation of SR. Eisner's explanation is accepted in Taylor and Wheeler (1992). However, Eisner's paper contradicts SR, which states that the relative motion of source and observer is all that matters. So Eisner's explanation is itself in contradiction of SR. It is hardly acceptable that in trying to salvage SR, we contradict that theory in the effort!

Phipps (1989) agrees with Hayden's analysis and refers to Synge (1964) as having earlier provided the correct analysis. A similar idea is in a book by Wesley (1991). This topic is the subject of ongoing debate.

We develop below an alternative explanation that does not need SR.

Extinction Theory of Light

In 1968, Ockert analysed the Fizeau experiment based on the extinction theory of light. This theory is based on the fact that the history of a beam of light is extinguished when the beam passes through a very small thickness of material. For air at ground level, that effect takes place in about 1 mm of distance. Ockert describes the process as follows:

The photon penetrates a very short distance 's' moving at its normal velocity 'c'. After passing a certain number of water molecules, the photon is extinguished by transferring its energy to an electron. After a period of time, the electron re-emits the photon which proceeds down the tube at a velocity 'c' until it is again extinguished, and so on.

Ockert continues: *"When the photon exists the energy travels at the full velocity c as if it were a vacuum. When it is extinguished, the energy is at rest in the fluid."* and

If the water moves at velocity v, the energy also moves at velocity v during the time the light is extinguished. When the light is not extinguished, the photon moves at velocity c. Then the old question reappears. It moves at a velocity of c relative to what? Relative to the water? Relative to the brass tube? Relative to both?

Ockert then goes on to prove that the light moves relative to the tube and thus to the laboratory in which the experiment is being conducted. Ockert showed that, using the convected ether theory of light, if the light is taken as travelling at a speed of c relative to the tube (but not relative to the flowing medium), the experimental results conform to the Fresnel drag of $1 - 1/n^2$.

Ockert summarised his conclusions as follows:

. . . the incorporation of the detailed mechanism by which light traverses a moving medium leads to analytical results which vary from observed and verified experimental results, unless the analysis includes a $c \pm v$ effect for slowing or speeding the light relative to the physical medium moving at velocity v relative to the laboratory.

Ockert commented that this was not consistent with Einstein's theory and thought it might conform to a convected ether theory. Ockert's analysis conforms to the theory put forward in this book, which requires that the light travels relative to the laboratory (or as Ockert stated, the tube) and not relative to the flowing water.

We saw above that the Fresnel drag coefficient was assumed (or invented) because, as shown by Airy, it was needed to explain the fact that light coming from a star was not affected by water in the barrel of a telescope. French says:

Thus for example, with visible light. A thickness of about 10 - 5cm of glass or 0.1 mm of air at atmospheric pressure is almost enough to erase any possible memory, as it were, of the motion of the original source. This phenomenon, known as extinction (even though it may or may not involve any appreciable loss of intensity of the light beam), has invalidated some of the observations (e.g. the apparent motions of binary stars, that were at first believed to provide confirmation of Einstein's second postulate – the invariance of c.

SR has an explanation that yields the Fresnel drag directly without any 'ad-hoc' invention. The derivation of this is seen in French. For our purposes, it is sufficient to accept that SR has a good explanation of the Fresnel drag coefficient. This derivation has been understood to be a strong confirmation of SR. Ockert's extinction theory derivation provides an alternative explanation under UR, as will now be derived.

When the interferometer is set spinning in a Sagnac test, in which the light passes through a medium, the light goes at speeds of $c/n \pm \alpha v$ in the opposing directions, where α is the drag coefficient discussed earlier under the Fizeau test and v is the speed of movement of the periphery of the circuit. Substituting $c/n \pm \alpha v$ for the $c \pm v$ in the derivation of equation (1) (see chapter 3) gives, to first order in v/c, $(4A\omega n^2/c^2)(1 - \alpha)$.

Earlier we discussed the paper by Arditty and Lefèvre where the value to be assigned to the coefficient α is discussed. They show that $\alpha = 1 - 1/n^2$ is correct for the Fizeau experiment.

Ockert, in another paper (1969), raises the thorny question of what the speed of light is relative to a moving medium. He says, *"If Einstein is correct, it has to be c/n regardless of the velocity of the moving medium. However, the value that would be predicted from the experimental results of Fizeau and Michelson is c/n - v/n²."*

That this is so is seen from the above speed $c/n \pm \alpha v$, where $\alpha = 1 - 1/n$, which gives $c/n \pm v - v/n^2$. This shows that the speed as measured in the medium is, as Ockert states, $c/n - v/n^2$. How can that be so? The velocity of light under SR, as measured in any inertial frame, is supposed to be identical, and here we have two different values for the two inertial frames – one frame is the laboratory and the other is the frame of the flowing water that is moving at uniform velocity in a straight line. SR predicts that the value is c/n, where n is the index of refraction of the medium. Ockert says that the velocity measured in the medium is $c/n - v/n^2$. This is because the result of measurement (taken in the fixed laboratory) is $c/n \pm v(1 - 1/n^2)$ when the medium is moving at a velocity of v. The velocity of the light as measured in the medium would then be $c/n \pm v/n^2$ because the medium is travelling at a velocity of v and the v term is eliminated.

What test was ever done to measure the velocity of light as recorded in a moving medium? The Sagnac test discussed earlier, with an interposed medium in the circuit, is such a test. Arditty and Lefèvre showed that the velocity of the light in the medium as measured in that medium was $c/n \pm v/n^2$, as did Ockert. They also derived that the light went at different velocities with and against the movement of the medium as measured in the frame of that medium. They showed that, otherwise, the result of the Sagnac test using water as the medium would not have been the same as in the case of using air (or a vacuum) as the medium; the result in both cases was the very same.

Here we have some further confirmation that the velocity of light in a medium in a moving frame is not the same as in that same medium in the fixed laboratory. Otherwise, the velocity of the light in the moving medium as measured in that moving medium would be c/n, just as it is in the fixed laboratory with a stationary medium.

If Ockert's theory of extinction of light is applied to the Fresnel drag of starlight, the same result is achieved. Ockert's analysis shows that, in the Fizeau test, the change due to the velocity v of the fluid is $v(1 - 1/n^2)$. This can be plus or minus depending on whether the fluid is flowing in the same or opposite direction to the light signal. In the same way, if the fluid is flowing sideways or in any other direction, the amount of the alteration will also be $v(1 - 1/n^2)$, where v is the component of the velocity in the direction concerned. The light coming from a star would, in this theory, arrive at the earth at a speed of c relative to outer fixed space. Ockert assumes that the light always continues in the same direction while passing through the fluid. This includes continuing in the same direction after the light has been extinguished and re-emitted.

After the above had been penned, some later papers were discovered that came to the same conclusion but did not refer to Ockert. One is Marinov (1977) and another Kosowski (1978). Even later, an earlier paper by Antoni (1953) was uncovered (in Italian), which gave exactly the same idea, with all the mathematics and reasoning, long before Ockert! Where does any trail end? One wonders whether the former two authors never came across Ockert's work or whether Ockert knew of Antoni. So perhaps any idea that explains some conundrum is ripe for plucking, and it is not surprising that many people spot the ripe fruit. A thorough search of literature should uncover such earlier publications on the same topic, but how many have the patience and determination to carry out such an arduous task? The 4,000+ publications perused by this author are but a selective sample that was uncovered relevant to the topics discussed here. Many are not referenced in this book because they are purely theoretical treatises of a speculative nature, with no discussion of experimental evidence to back up the opinions and therefore of no significant impact.

A refinement of the above Lorentz formulae was derived by Einstein (1914) in a short concise paper. He differentiated between the formulae to be used when the medium used was a liquid such as water and when it was a solid like glass. He showed that the correct formula is $\alpha = 1 - (1/n^2) - (\lambda/n)(dn/d\lambda)$ when the moving medium is a liquid but is $\alpha = 1 - (1/n^2) - (\lambda/n^2)(dn/d\lambda)$ when the moving medium is a solid. He showed that both formulae simply contain a straightforward Doppler effect. He also explained that Harress had not got a dispersion effect because of the fact that the light was introduced to the solid glass sector at right angles to the direction of the motion of the spin of the disc.

The way to do research is to attack the facts at the point of greatest astonishment.

Celia Green

Chapter 5

Synchronisation of Clocks

This chapter investigates the procedure used to synchronise clocks at different sites on the earth.

We will begin by discussing the publications of the international organisations charged with the task of setting rules for the synchronisation of clocks. It will be shown that these standards are at variance with sound experimental facts. Next, we will set down the method of clock synchronisation that should apply. We will then discuss some correspondence on the topic between this author and the committees that set the rules. The chapter closes with a description of some interesting experiments that are relevant to timekeeping.

There is some repetition in this chapter of facets discussed earlier in the book to emphasise the importance of the points being developed.

Einstein Synchronisation

The Einstein synchronisation of clocks is done as described in his 1905 paper. He defines the time at a spot A and at another spot B of space. He says:

We have not defined a common 'time' for A and B, for the latter cannot be defined at all unless we establish by definition that the 'time' required by light to travel from A to B equals the 'time' for it to travel from B to A.

This definition by Einstein is not borne out in practice; the time for light to travel from one point to another is not always measured as the same as the time for the reverse journey. This has been proven in the Sagnac experiments and in numerous other experiments described earlier. It is also disproven in the daily Global Positioning System (GPS) signalling system, where the time for the light to go around the earth in one direction is not the same as the reverse journey. Einstein continued:

Let a ray of light start at the 'A time' t_A from A towards B, let it at the 'B time' t_B be reflected at B in the direction of A, and arrive again at A at the 'A time' t'_A.

In accordance with definition the two clocks synchronise if $t_B - t_A = t'_A - t_B$.

We assume that this definition of synchronism is free from contradictions, and possible for any number of points; and that the following relations are universally valid:-

1. *If the clock at B synchronises with a clock at A, the clock at A synchronises with the clock at B.*
2. *If the clock at A synchronises with the clock at B and also with the clock at C, the clocks B and C also synchronise with each other.*

Thus with the help of certain imaginary physical experiments we have settled what is to be understood by synchronous stationary clocks located at different places, and have evidently obtained a definition of 'simultaneous' or 'synchronous' and of 'time'. The 'time' of an event is that which is given simultaneously with the event by a stationary clock located at the place of the event, this clock being synchronous, and indeed synchronous for all time determinations, with a specified stationary clock.

In agreement with experience we further assume the quantity

$$\frac{2AB}{t^{l}{}_{A} - t_{A}}$$

to be a universal constant - the velocity of light in empty space.

It is possible to synchronise clocks on the earth, as defined by Einstein, by sending signals in the north-south direction but not in the east-west direction. This is because light signals go at speeds of $c \pm v$ in relation to the surface of the earth in the west and east directions respectively. Indeed, because we have identified a difference in the speed of light, clocks cannot be Einstein-synchronised on the earth in general. However, Einstein avoided this problem by then defining the speed of light as the average of the out and back speeds and always equal to 'c'.

Many claim that Einstein's scheme of synchronisation cannot be applied to other than straight-line motion. In his 1905 paper, as discussed earlier, he applied the scheme to clocks moving in a polygonal or curved motion. Later, in 1916, he seemed to limit the application to uniform translational motion; at least he did not repeat his extension of the application to a polygonal shaped path or to a closed circuit. However, the organisations setting the rules for synchronising clocks have no compunction about applying their rules to the rotating earth. We can be forgiven for taking that as vindication of the following criticism.

Grøn (1975) discusses the problem of synchronising clocks on a rotating disc. He states that *"it implies that Einstein's synchronisation convention cannot be used by mutual synchronisation of the clocks on the disc"*. Grøn also concludes that *"even locally the velocity of light on the rotating disc is different from c"*. He agrees that an observer on the disc observes *"a variable velocity of light"*.

If a clock A is synchronised with a clock B and B is in turn synchronised with a clock C, this does not mean that clocks A and C are synchronised with each other, as Einstein had stipulated above. The reader should bear in mind that the whole scheme of Einstein synchronisation does not work in practice. The international standards for synchronising atomic clocks on the earth will now be seen to be based on a fallacy.

International Standards and Their Flaws

There are many committees and sub-committees involved in the setting of rules for the synchronisation of clocks. To indicate the multiplicity of committees, some are listed here. The reader is not expected to memorise the list!

The International Telecommunications Union (ITU) in Geneva, Switzerland, which is operating since 1948, has a committee (CCIR) that, amazingly, is older (having started in 1934) than the parent ITU. The ITU is a UN organisation that issues reports on the synchronisation of clocks. It might claim to be descended from the International Telegraph Union, founded in 1876, but the 1939/45 war disrupted the genealogy.

The International Bureau of Weights and Measures (BIPM) in Paris, France, which was set up in 1879, also has committees that report on the same matters. The BIPM operates under the supervision of the International Committee for Weights and Measures (CIPM), which itself comes under the authority of the General Conference on Weights and Measures (CGPM) and reports to it on the work accomplished by the BIPM. The CIPM set up a sub-committee in 1956 called the Consultative Committee for the Definition of the Second (CCDS), which changed its name in 1997 to the Consultative Committee for Time and Frequency (CCTF). There were 48 persons present at a meeting of that committee in 2001. The reader is supposed to be utterly confused by now.

The standards for the synchronisation of clock stations are as published in 1990 and 1997 by the CCIR. Similar rules are in the 1980 publication of the CCDS. These various bodies publish documents that sometimes contradict publications by other committees. It will be shown that the standards are in rather a mess and in urgent need of revision.

Interestingly, yet another committee, the Joint Committee on General Relativity for Space-Time Reference Systems and Metrology, was jointly set up in 1997 with the International Astronomical Union but was abandoned in 2001. It would be amusing to have been a fly on the wall at the meetings held by that committee.

This author is not a fan of committees, as can be gathered from an earlier publication, *How to Make Your Life Easier at Work* (McGraw Hill: USA, 1988), which was published in seven languages. These particular committees have excelled themselves in concocting rules that are inconsistent and incorrect. But then, there has to be international agreement on the scheme to be used!

Clocks Run Slow with Respect to What?

We shall see further evidence in this chapter that atomic clocks run slow in proportion to their speeds with respect to the centre of the earth. This surprising physical fact was not suspected until about 1970. We saw in chapter 3 that the Hafele and Keating tests showed this to be the case. This is just a fact of nature. Atomic clocks all run slow in direct proportion to their speed with respect to that spot (the earth's centre). The slowing can be said to be with respect to a pole of the earth (because that is equivalent). It can also be said to be with respect to 'nearby space', which is stationary with respect to the earth as it orbits the sun.

Consider the case of two clocks, one fixed to the surface of the earth at the equator and the other travelling around the globe on an aeroplane at a ground speed of x eastward. The movement of the second clock with respect to the first (their relative motion) is x. However, these two clocks do *not* have a slowing with respect to each other that can be calculated simply from their relative motion of x, as is supposed to happen under Special Relativity (SR). We saw earlier that the analysis of motion around the earth is allowable under SR, even though most adherents of that theory disagree vehemently because of the element of rotation involved. Earlier we discussed the matter of what constitutes 'rotation' and what might be an acceptable amount of rotation under SR.

The first clock, which is stationary on the earth's surface at the equator, slows by an amount that depends on the speed of the surface of the earth v with respect to the earth's centre. At 103×10^{-9} s (103 nanoseconds (ns)) per day, this is considerable. The second clock, which is moving eastward at a speed of x with respect to the earth's surface, is slowing by an amount proportional to $v + x$. Therefore, the ratio of the slowing of the two clocks is $x/(v + x)$. The slowing is *not* by an amount that is in proportion to their relative speed of x. This surprising fact was discovered when such clocks were first launched riding on satellites. In this chapter, we shall give the evidence for this fact when discussing the Global Positioning System (GPS). However, it has been glossed over as if it were in accordance with SR.

Three Corrections

The international rules concerning the corrections used for synchronising clocks at different sites on the earth state that the corrections are 'relativistic'. We shall see that one of the three corrections has nothing whatever to do with SR or, indeed, with GR.

Synchronisation of clocks at different sites on the earth is easily performed using the GPS with its orbiting satellites above the earth. It is a pity that the organisations setting the rules did not just stick to the experimental facts and avoid trying to force-fit the facts to pretend that they conformed to relativity theory.

Consider the rules they have set. Three corrections to be applied, as listed in the above publications, are as follows:

A. A correction to take account of the special relativistic effect caused by carrying a portable clock at speed aboard an aeroplane from one site to another

B. A correction to allow for the height above sea level

C. A correction described as being for the *"rotation of the earth"*

Correction A is quantified as $v^2/2c^2$ (a good approximation of gamma). This is the slowing as calculated under SR (see Index under 'gamma'). A clock transported from one site to another will have this correction applied, which is computed from the velocity of the aeroplane on its journey. In this case, v is often computed from the speed of the aeroplane relative to the ground. This is incorrect because it will be decisively proven later in this chapter that the slowing of the clock caused by velocity should not be calculated from its velocity with respect to the ground; it should be calculated from its velocity with respect to the centre of the earth. As discussed above, it is not the ground speed of the aeroplane that determines the difference in time that will be recorded on the two clocks being compared. The difference is determined by their respective speeds in relation to the earth's centre. We shall see that the calculations in a practical example in one of the above publications are flawed.

Correction **B** is quantified as $g(\phi)h/c^2$. This is the speeding up of time, where g is *"the total acceleration due to gravity (including the rotational acceleration of the earth) evaluated at the geoid"* at a latitude of ϕ, and h is the height over sea level. The CCIR and CCDS publications state that this correction is calculated under GR theory. It will later be shown that this factor is also deduced without invoking GR. However, let that be for now.

Correction **C** is quantified as $(2A_E\omega)/c^2$, where A_E is the equatorial projection of the area enclosed by the path of travel of the clock being transported from one site to another (or of the area circumscribed by the equatorial projection of the triangle whose vertices are the earth's centre and the two sites, in the case of the sending of an electromagnetic signal between the two sites) and the lines connecting the two clock sites to the centre of the earth and ω is the angular velocity of the earth. As the area A_E is swept, it is taken as positive when the projection of the path of the clock (or signal) onto the equatorial plane is eastward.

Both reports (CCDS and CCIR) include all three corrections under the umbrella description of being *"of the first order of general relativity"*. The first two corrections can be claimed under the theory of relativity. What is the third?

Readers who have already studied the earlier section on the Sagnac effect will recognise the factor for what it is. It is precisely a Sagnac correction. This correction is properly applied in the case of electromagnetic signals under the rules, even though its description of being 'relativistic' is a misnomer. However, as we shall see, it should not be applied in the case of the physical transportation of a clock from one site to another.

The CCIR report assumes that when a clock is physically transported around the globe at the equator, a Sagnac-type correction has to be applied to the time recorded by that clock. Because the area is taken as *"positive if the path is traversed in a clockwise sense as viewed from the South Pole,"* a clock transported around the earth in a eastward direction would gain time by +207.4 ns relative to the supposed clock at the centre. The 1997 report also has the same derivation.

Consider two such clocks that are sent from the same starting point at the equator in opposite directions around the earth. When they have completed one revolution each, there would be a supposed time difference of 414.8 ns between them. We would then have the strange situation where we have three clocks at the same spot (the two that circumnavigated the earth in opposing directions and another that remained stationary), all recording different times. A paper by Weber (1997) discusses this same anomaly but passes it off as another paradox. That paper discusses the peculiar situation where a signal is sent right around the rotating disc (or earth) in order to synchronise a clock with itself. Different answers are derived when the signal is sent in opposing directions. So, we have a clock that is not synchronised with itself by either signal.

There are some changes in the latest edition (1997) of the CCIR rules. The main heading still refers to relativistic effects as *"Relativistic effects in a coordinate time system in the vicinity of the earth"*. The Sagnac term is still referred to as the *"effect of the earth's rotation"*. The CCIR appears to be struggling to get a sensible system.

False Correction to the 'Time'

Consider the reason for the corrections stipulated by the CCIR. The whole basis of SR is that the 'time' on a moving object is slowed in proportion to its speed in relation to an observer at rest. The CCIR has no compunction about the use of SR theory on the earth's rotating surface.

If we assume that the speed of light as measured on the rotating earth must be the constant value c, then perforce we must vary the 'time' on the earth by the Sagnac formula as compared with 'time' measured from that geocentric reference frame. As we have already seen, SR is designed specifically to alter the 'time' on the moving object in direct accordance with the requirement that the speed of light is assumed to be the constant value c aboard that object.

Changing the time aboard the rotating earth by this large amount has no justification other than to make a false correction to compensate for the fact that the velocity of light is not a constant in the eastward and westward directions on the rotating earth.

The CCIR Calculations

Here is how to apply the incorrect SR correction to the 'time'. Though incorrect, it looks very scientific and is mathematically consistent. Applying a correction of the form $v^2/2c^2$ to the time taken for two clocks that move at speeds of v relative to the ground to circumnavigate the earth in opposing directions gives the following result.

The moving clocks have speeds of $\omega r + v$ and $\omega r - v$ in the opposing directions relative to the geocentric time frame; r is the radius of the earth and ω its angular velocity. Substituting these two speeds for v, the time dilations of the two clocks are

$$\int \frac{1}{2}\left[\frac{\omega r + v}{c}\right]^2 dt \quad \text{and} \quad \int \frac{1}{2}\left[\frac{\omega r - v}{c}\right]^2 dt$$

respectively. The difference between these two time dilations is therefore

$$\int \frac{2\omega r v}{c^2} dt$$

When the two clocks have gone right around the equator (a distance of $2\pi r$), the $\int v dt = 2\pi r$ and the difference between the time dilations is $(4\pi r^2 \omega)/(c^2)$, which is the same as equation (1), which we derived earlier in chapter 3 (Burt, 1973). The result is independent of v, so the speed of transportation of the clocks will not affect this result.

This analysis gives the Sagnac formula as a supposed correction for the difference in the time taken by two electromagnetic signals sent in opposing directions around the globe or for the time correction to be applied to clocks that are transported physically around the globe in an east-west direction. This is the correction published in the CCIR and CCDS reports.

We should not be surprised at this result. The analysis is done on the assumption that the speed of light is the very same in all directions, ignoring any evidence to the contrary as provided by the Sagnac tests or the Michelson and Gale experiment or, as we shall see below, the GPS monitoring system. Had the answer not been equal to the Sagnac formula, the calculation would have been in error. As already pointed out, the calculation is designed falsely to alter the 'time' to conform to the pretence that the speed of light is equal travelling around the earth in opposing directions.

The same type of derivation was instituted by Hafele and Keating (1972) when they considered the clocks being transported around the earth on aeroplanes. They took 'nearby space' as the viewing position and also assumed that the speed of light on the earth had to be the constant value c. As already quoted, Hafele (1970), in answer to the query *"what would be the rate of a standard clock that is moving relative to stationary standard clocks on the geoid?"*, responded with this extraordinary statement: *"The standard answer that moving clocks run slow by the well known factor gamma is almost certainly incorrect."* The 'standard answer' to which Hafele referred was SR! He was not referring to flying this clock at a height but just moving it on the earth's surface. He then proceeded to derive a similar formula to that derived above on the assumption that the speed of light was a constant c on the spinning earth.

This is quite a significant admission. Hafele actually says here that SR is incorrect! We now know that he had 'let the cat out of the bag' back in 1970, but the significance of what he said was overlooked or was not appreciated.

There is one big nasty problem with all of the above. The Sagnac tests, done with ever-increased accuracy down through the years, show a difference in the time taken by electromagnetic signals to circumnavigate any spinning disc (including the huge disc comprising a cross section of the earth). This proves that there is a difference in the speed of the signal in the opposing directions (eastward and westward). This difference contradicts a basic assumption of the scheme of synchronisation that is used.

In the analysis of the Sagnac effect, as shown earlier, time in the laboratory is the very same as time upon the spinning disc. However, the SR analysis above is based upon the SR assumption that the 'time' is different in the laboratory from that upon the spinning disc.

Synchronising by Electromagnetic Signals

Two methods are used to synchronise clocks at clock stations. The most common method, which is in daily use, is to send an electromagnetic signal via a satellite from one site to another. A second method is physically to transport a clock from one site to another and compare the times recorded at the two stations. This method is expensive, difficult to effect and rarely used.

Consider the first method. In all cases of synchronising clocks by electromagnetic signal comparison, the Sagnac correction is properly quantified in the CCIR report. The timekeeping authorities are therefore applying it correctly, even if they are under the illusion that it is derived from the theory of GR. The Sagnac correction is nowadays automatically applied to all electromagnetic signals sent around the earth for clock synchronisation.

If signals could be sent from the centre of a rotating disc out to clocks on the periphery of that rotating disc, these clocks could be synchronised with the one at the centre. However, as Weber (1997) points out, the clocks on the periphery cannot be synchronised with each other by sending a signal directly between them. It is a pity that we cannot send signals to the centre of the earth and out to the periphery to synchronise our clocks! It is a puzzle why clocks are not taken by those who are supposed to set the rules (ITU, CCDS, CCTF) as slowing with respect to the non-rotating centre of the earth (as they really are).

The slowing with respect to the centre of the earth tends asymptotically to zero as the speed of light is approached. It has been shown by Ives and Stilwell (1938 and 1941) that the frequency of a moving atomic clock reduces asymptotically to zero at the speed of light. This is consistent with the proposition in this book that clocks run slow on the earth in proportion to their speed v with respect to the earth's centre, and asymptotically to c. It does not show that the 'time' runs slow, but that the recorder on the atomic clock shows a lesser reading.

For the clock to run slow asymptotically as the speed approaches the speed of light, $t = [1 + (v + \omega r)^2/2c^2]t'$ by the binomial theorem (see Index), where t' is the time on the travelling clock, t is that on the stationary clock at the geocentre, r is the earth's radius at the relevant latitude and ω is the angular velocity of the earth. Thus, $t = t' + [t'(v^2 + 2v\omega r + \omega^2 r^2)]/2c^2$. When v is small (as defined in the CCIR report), $t = t' + (\omega^2 r^2 t')/2c^2$.

Considering the time t' for one complete revolution of the earth, $t' = 2\pi r/\omega r = 2\pi/\omega$. The enclosed area of the path of the clock is $A = \pi r^2$. $1 = A/(\pi r^2) = t'/(2\pi/\omega) = \omega t'/2\pi$, giving $A = r^2\omega t'/2$. So, $t = t' + \omega A/c^2$ per day or per revolution of the earth. A stationary clock on the earth's surface will slow by that amount in relation to the fixed centre of the earth in one day.

In fact, the behaviour of clocks on the earth is a simple matter. As shown in detail in this book, all clocks on the earth run slow with respect (relative) to the non-rotating centre of the earth. Therefore, a clock that is stationary at the equator will run slow all the time by a certain amount with respect to that spot. At the equator, $v = R\omega$, where R is the radius of the earth (6.378×10^6 m) and ω is the angular velocity of the earth (7.272×10^{-5} radians per second), which results in 1.195×10^{-12} s/s, which is 103.2 ns, or 103×10^{-9} s per day. That slowing of the clocks is very significant – bear in mind that accuracies of 10^{-15} s are being sought nowadays. The daily slowing is 100,000,000 times that accuracy aim.

Synchronising by using electromagnetic signals must allow for the fact that the speed of those signals differs in the easterly and westerly directions. Correct treatment should calculate the difference in time and allow for that in the calculations. However, the CCIR gets the right answer by changing the 'time' by the Sagnac effect. Electromagnetic signals circumnavigating the earth eastward or westward are performing a Sagnac test on a huge disc of diameter equal to the cross section of the earth at the latitude concerned. The centre of the earth corresponds with the laboratory in the small Sagnac test. By taking as the starting point the non-rotating centre of the earth as it moves on its orbit around the sun, the CCIR takes a place where the velocity of light may be considered, for the purposes of the experiment, to be a constant. The non-rotating centre is therefore a good place from which to begin any calculation.

So far, so good, but the problem arises when trying to get from that basis to measuring time on the spinning earth. As we proved earlier when discussing the Sagnac effect and the Michelson and Gale test and other Sagnac-type tests, the time on the spinning earth is the very same as the time at the centre of a spinning disc. The CCIR report, on the other hand, while tacitly agreeing that all measurements of time must be referred to the non-rotating centre of the earth, alters the 'time' on the spinning earth by the huge Sagnac correction in order to compensate for the fact that the speed of electromagnetic signals eastward and westward on the earth is not the same as at the centre. This is done despite the many tests that prove that the speed of the signal is not constant in the east-west directions. This fact is repeated here ad nauseam to stress the vital importance of the statement.

Allan et al. (1985) did a Sagnac-type test between standard timekeeping stations in the U.S.A., Germany and Japan. These tests also confirm the Sagnac effect, as applied to electromagnetic signals sent around the earth in opposing directions, to an accuracy of 2% over a period of three months. The work of Allan et al. is referenced in the CCIR report. They conclude that *"the light synchronisation error due to the earth's rotation was clearly observed"*. In other words, they confirm that the Sagnac effect is clearly measured without admitting that this proves that the speed of light is shown to vary with and against the spin of the earth.

Some publications try to show that the Sagnac effect is part of the GR theory. Winkler (1991), a member of the CCIR committee, in a paper on the subject of the synchronisation of clocks around the world, ascribed the Sagnac effect to the general theory of relativity. He attempted to explain the effect by saying that *"accelerations have an effect on timekeeping and on the propagation of light"*. As the reader who has studied the Sagnac effect will appreciate, this statement in incorrect; acceleration does not account for any of the correction. Winkler also stated that *"on a rotating system, the velocity of light must be added to (or subtracted from) the speed due to rotation, an effect that produces a time difference for two rays that travel in opposite directions around a closed path"*. Here Winkler states correctly that the velocity of the light is not the same in opposing directions.

Another example is the paper by Petit and Wolf (1994), employees of the CCIR, which begins by assuming that the light travels at a constant speed c relative to the stationary frame (in their case, the geocentric 'non-rotating frame'). Petit and Wolf specifically state that the light velocity relative to the spinning earth is not c. They take it as corresponding to c + s, *"where s represents the time taken for the signal to travel the extra path due to the motion of b in the non-rotating frame during transmission"*. Here b is a clock moving on a rotating disc. This is exactly the same as the analysis of the Sagnac effect given earlier in this book, where the extra distance travelled by the point S (figure 7, chapter 3) while the signal is travelling around the circuit yields a speed of the light of c + v in one direction. This assumption by Petit and Wolf introduces the Sagnac correction when they calculate time on board the spinning earth because the speed of the electromagnetic signal is c ± v against and with the direction of spin respectively. By introducing the Sagnac correction 'by the back door', such papers then say that the Sagnac effect is under the general theory of relativity. Such derivations claim that the correction 'appears automatically'. It does not; it is introduced by assuming that the velocity of the electromagnetic signal is (correctly) c in relation to the stationary frame of reference (in Petit and Wolf's case, the non-rotating centre), and also (incorrectly) c in relation to the rotating frame of reference.

It is interesting that in a practical example worked out in the CCIR report, for the physical transportation of a clock from one site to another, the largest of the three effects used is from the supposed Sagnac effect (moving a clock at 270 m/s east at 40° latitude at an altitude of 9 km). As will be shown below, it is not correct to apply the Sagnac correction to the time being displayed by the moving portable clock.

A basic difference between the relativistic and Sagnac effects as calculated for movements measured on the spinning earth is that the SR effect is supposed to be non-directional, whereas the Sagnac effect is plus or minus depending on sending the signal westward or eastward respectively and zero in a north-south direction.

The 1990 CCIR report gave an incorrect value for the angular velocity of the earth (7.992 R/s instead of 7.292 R/s). This error was not carried forward into the calculations given in examples in the report. Upon my alerting them to this error, it was quietly corrected in the 1997 edition (without replying, naturally, to the letter notifying them of the error).

Two clocks on the earth at the same latitude have no relative motion with respect to each other. Put more simply, as considered by a person in either city, Washington D.C. does not move with respect to Chicago. It is only when we attempt to compare the time being kept by two clocks in those cities that we have to employ either an electromagnetic signal or a physical transportation of a comparison clock.

The Sagnac correction has to be applied to the time taken by the electromagnetic signal to get from one clock site to another. No corrections should apply to the time being kept by the clocks in relation to each other. The timekeeping of the two clocks does not alter because of the measuring process.

Synchronising by Physical Transportation

Consider now the second method of synchronising clocks – that of the physical transportation of the comparison timepiece. As we saw, synchronising by using electromagnetic signals requires the Sagnac correction. However, we shall now see that synchronising by employing a clock transported on an aeroplane from one site to another is quite different. Consider, for example, where the surface velocity of the earth at the equator is $v = 463.8$ m/s and a portable clock is transported at, say, a speed of $x = 10$ m/s around the earth at the equator. In this case, the difference between the $v^2/2c^2$ and $(v + x)^2/2c^2$ gives a difference of 4×10^{-14} s/s.

An important practical test was carried out by Saburi et al. in 1976. They transported a clock by aeroplane from Washington D.C. (U.S.A.) to Tokyo (Japan) and compared the time displayed by the two clocks on the arrival of the transported clock with the time relayed from one station, via an electromagnetic signal, to the other station.

The two sites were almost at the same latitude. From the Sagnac effect, Saburi et al. calculated that there should be a difference of +0.333 µs (microseconds) – Japan being ahead of Washington D.C. because of the direction of rotation of the earth. The Sagnac correction, on its own, applied to the electromagnetic signal sent between the two sites, bridged the gap to very close agreement with the test results (to –0.02 µs).

Relativistic corrections were then applied to the time recorded by the portable clock. These corrections amounted to 0.08 µs, giving a final result of +0.06 µs. Saburi et al. did not specify how they arrived at what they described as a rough estimate of 0.08 µs. Saburi alone published another article in 1976, where he said that the assumption of a height of flight of 10 km and a ground speed of 900 km/h yielded 0.08 µs. The uncertainty of the readings on the portable clock was ±0.2 µs. This accuracy would possibly not differentiate between the slowing calculated from the ground speed of the aeroplane and the slowing calculated from the respective speeds of the two clock stations with respect to the centre of the earth.

The Saburi et al. experiment proved that a clock that was brought around the earth in an aeroplane at normal speed did not slow by the Sagnac amount. The correction for the flight height over sea level is not separated out in the results by Saburi et al.

A clock at the equator riding on a low-flying aeroplane that is skimming the sea surface while travelling westward at a ground speed of 463.8 m/s will have zero slowing with respect to the earth's centre. This is because the earth's surface at the equator is moving eastward at a speed of 463.8 m/s. Such a clock would keep time with a clock at the centre of the earth.

The correct application of a correction to a clock that is physically transported from one site to another is as follows. The ground speed of the aeroplane should be ascertained and added to the surface speed of the earth at the relevant latitude. This is the $v + x$ discussed above, where x is the ground speed of the aeroplane on which the clock was transported. This slowing should be compared with the slowing that will have occurred to the clock that remained fixed to the earth.

An example will make the method clear. Take the case where one clock remains stationary on the surface of the earth at the equator and a second clock is sent around the earth at a ground speed of 300 m/s at sea level at the equator. What will be the difference in the readings on those two clocks when the second clock completes a circuit? SR predicts that the difference would be $300^2/2c^2$ multiplied by the time to circumnavigate the earth: $(1.3358)(10^5)$ seconds. This applies the relative motion of the two clocks, which in the above case is 300 m/s and gives a slowing of 66.8 ns.

The correct result is derived by finding the ratio of the slowing of the earth-fixed clock to the slowing of the flying clock at sea level as follows:

- The surface speed of the earth at the equator is 463.8 m/s.
- The ground speed of the flying clock is 300 m/s.

- The slowing of the two clocks is proportional to the speeds of 763.8 and 463.8 respectively.
- $(763.8^2 - 463.8^2)/2c^2$ multiplied by the transit time of $(1.3358)(10^5)$ gives a result of 273.3 ns.

Therefore, the relativistic calculation gives a result of 66.8 ns, which is only 0.244 of the correct answer. This explains why, as quoted earlier, Hafele stated that *"The standard answer that moving clocks run slow by the well known factor gamma is almost certainly incorrect."* The 'standard answer' to which he referred was the traditional interpretation of SR. The result for an infinitely slow transportation is 206.5 ns, and for a speed approaching c, it is 66.8 million ns. Practical cases lie between these two extremes.

There is an error in the CCIR (1997 and 1990 reports) calculations as follows. When calculating the slowing of the clocks for the speed at which they are transported, the CCIR simply takes the speed (v) of the clock with respect to the ground and uses that to calculate an SR slowing of $v^2/2c^2$. In the 1990 report No. 439-5, the correction applied for a clock flying in an aeroplane (at a height of 9 km eastward, a speed of 270 m/s and a latitude of 40°) as compared with a clock on the surface of the earth at sea level at the same latitude is given as -4.06×10^{-13} s/s. This correction should read -14.78×10^{-13} s/s. The result is out by a factor of 3.6! The error is caused by assuming that it is solely the relative speed of the clock on the aeroplane with respect to the ground that matters. Such a belief is caused by assuming that SR must be correct. The CCIR should have done the calculation as outlined above.

The reader can try this calculation to confirm that the matter is understood. (The velocity of the surface of the earth at that latitude is 356.26 m/s; the angular speed of rotation of the earth is 7.292×10^{-5} Rad/s; the radius at that latitude is 4885.65 km; 'c' can be taken as 3×10^8 m/s.)

Having made the miscalculation, the CCIR then adds an unjustified correction equal to the Sagnac effect. As we have seen earlier, this so-called 'correction' is merely a practice whereby the 'time' element of the experiment is adjusted to pretend that the speed of light is measured as a constant (c) in such circumstances. There should be no such 'correction' in practice, as shown by Saburi et al. The worldwide GPS, which is independent of the organisations setting the rules (CCIR and CCDS), applies the calculations correctly because they found out long ago that this is what occurs in practice; this should have alerted the CCIR to the correct method.

As we know, the Sagnac adjustment to the 'time' is the precise amount that sustains the illusion that the speed of light is a constant in such an experiment (clock on aeroplane flying at 270 m/s eastward). The CCIR and CCDS are so entrenched in the position that they have long adopted that it would be virtually impossible for them to correct the rules, what with the committee system that rules these organisations. The false correction is introduced to bridge the gap between the incorrect result (-4.06×10^{-13} s/s) and the result that should have been achieved (-14.78×10^{-13} s/s). The Sagnac effect, as we know from the earlier discussion, is precisely equal to that difference (-10.72×10^{-13} s/s). It is a correction to the time involved in the experiment, necessitated by the fact that the speed of light is assumed to be a constant, which it is not.

It is worth noting again that the examples calculated by the CCIR involve rotation around the earth, to which they gaily apply SR; most would say that SR applies solely to uniform translational movement. As shown earlier, we know that claim is not sustainable; if SR applies to uniform translational movement, it should also apply to motion on a circuit. But as we now realise, it applies to neither!

The above debate does not conclude that 'time' runs slow but that, with increased speed with respect to the geocentre, the indication shown on the recording device of atomic clocks displays a lesser reading. Indeed, time remains the very same, as shown in any Sagnac-type test. Such is the confusion among those setting the rules for time on the earth!

Please forgive the considerable element of repetition in the above debate. This matter is so important that is must be properly understood if the kernel of the theory proposed in this book is to be grasped.

Timescales

The International Atomic Time (TAI) timescale was initiated in 1958 and has been maintained ever since. It is never adjusted. Another timescale is the Coordinated Universal Time (UTC), which is the same as the TAI except that it is adjusted from time to time to keep in line with the irregular rotation of the earth. This is achieved by introducing a 'leap second' about once every year to a year and a half on average.

UTC can only be determined to the highest precision after the fact because atomic time is determined by the reconciliation of the observed differences between many atomic clocks that are maintained by a number of national time stations. UTC is the successor of Greenwich Mean Time (GMT) and is sometimes still called GMT. UTC presents problems for computer systems, which store time as the number of seconds from a reference time. It is impossible to determine precisely a future date because the number of leap seconds that will be applied by that date is unknown. This is because the rotation rate of the earth is slowing. This braking is caused by tidal friction. The secular change in the rotation rate increases the length of day by some 2.3 milliseconds per day per century.

In 1980, the CCDS queried the TAI time standard used at that time. The president of the CCDS asked, *"Should the TAI be a coordinated time? In which system of reference? With which theory?"* The president was clearly unhappy about the situation.

The question as to what timescale should be used seems to be still in a state of confusion. Guinot, a member of the CCDS committee, wrote in 1997 that there are problems with the TAI and UTC definitions. In relation to the difference in the readings in the two timescales on a particular date (September 4th 1994 at 0 hrs UTC time), he says that the result comes out as *"quite illogical"*. According to the International Organisation for Standardisation (ISO), the difference between the two timescales comes out as a 'duration' in seconds, whereas it is not a duration. Anyone interested in this minefield should read Guinot's paper.

The CGPM (if you can recall what that is) wrote in 1999 that *"nowadays the continuation of the UTC and especially the leap second is in question".* In 2001, the CIPM recorded that:

> ... *the question of the leap second was a very difficult decision and that opinions were divided, even amongst the experts of the CCTF. Dr Quinn commented that, in his view, it was not a technical decision, but rather a question of whether the time scale is such that the Sun is overhead on the Greenwich meridian at noon. Since this is no longer required for navigation purposes, the reason for the leap second no longer exists. The decision, however, rests with the ITU, within which the CCTF is represented.*

One delegate remarked that *"complications can arise when more than one institute in a country shares responsibility for time and such circumstances called for great diplomacy".*

In 2004, the BIPM reported that another timescale, Terrestrial Time (TT), was introduced and that the latest amendment to it is called TT (BIPM2003); the introduction of yet another timescale will do little to clarify matters.

The CCIR (1990) gives a choice for the standard place to be used as the basis of timekeeping between the non-rotating and the rotating centre of the earth (which has a daily and an annual rotation rate). It defines the TAI as *"a coordinate timescale defined at a geocentric datum line."* The TAI does not differentiate between a rotating and a non-rotating frame of reference.

The 'unit of time' is defined as *"one SI second as obtained on the geoid in rotation".* The TAI timescale and unit of time are therefore not measured at the same place. The unit of time is based on the spinning earth, which has a motion, and therefore a slowing, in relation to the geocentre (rotating or fixed), where the timescale is based. This is clearly an unsatisfactory situation.

The CCIR report recommends that *"for terrestrial use a topocentric frame be chosen".* Indeed, being on a rotating earth, this is the only practicable frame we can use. It has now at least defined a timescale on the rotating earth (where the second is defined). The rules continue: *"when a clock B is synchronised with a clock A (both clocks being stationary on the earth) by a radio signal travelling from A to B, these two clocks differ in coordinate time by..."* a given formula that is the Sagnac effect.

These statements make it clear that 'time' on the rotating earth is viewed as differing from 'time' at the non-rotating centre. This statement does not agree with Post, as discussed earlier; nor does it agree with the analysis of the Sagnac effect. As already shown, it is not the *time* that runs slow but the *timekeeping of the actual clock being used.*

In 1982, the ITU unanimously recommended that the UTC should be used in all of their official documentation. Yet, this was not done in their 1997 publication TF-1010-1.

The question of timescales will be left in limbo as it is of little consequence to the conclusions in this book. For the organisations defining 'time', however, it is more than a little crazy.

How Slow Is 'Slow'?

The stipulation that the transported clock should be moved 'slowly' is significant. This statement is sometimes phrased as 'infinitely slowly'. The CCIR 1990 report states that *"the time of a clock carried eastward around the earth at infinitely low speed at h = 0 at the equator will differ from a clock remaining at rest by -207.4 ns"*. The significance of the height over sea level $h = 0$ is that there is no effect for height over sea level, and the 207.4 ns is all due to a Sagnac correction.

Allan et al. compare the Sagnac correction as applied to slowly moving portable clocks on the earth and to electromagnetic signals used for clock synchronisation. They state that *"the Sagnac effect has the same form and magnitude whether slowly moving portable clocks or electromagnetic signals are used to complete the circuit."* They say that the Sagnac correction applies in both cases and that it has the same magnitude. In the case of the portable clock, they define the Sagnac effect as *"being due to a difference between the second-order Doppler shift (time dilation) of the portable clock and that of the master clock whose motion is due to the earth's motion"* as *"viewed from a local nonrotating geocentric frame"*. However, it is nothing of the sort; it is not a time dilation but a difference in the time taken by signals to circumnavigate the earth in the eastward and westward directions.

Petit and Wolf (1994), who were officers of the CCDS, state that the correction $2A\omega/c^2$ is applied equally *"if the two clocks are compared by using portable clocks or electromagnetic signals in the rotating frame of the earth"*. Whereas Allan et al. specify that the portable clock must be moved 'slowly' and the CCIR 1990 report specifies 'infinitely low' speed, Petit and Wolf do not say that the portable clock is moved at any specified speed.

The statements by Allan et al. and Petit and Wolf are not correct in relation to the speed of the transportation of clocks. Clocks cannot be synchronised by a slow transport scheme. At any speed greater than 'infinitely slow', the so-called Sagnac correction does not apply. We are unable to have an infinite time at our disposal to synchronise clocks! Calling the correction a 'Sagnac' correction is a misnomer. The formula is the same but the two effects are not at all the same.

Because a circle has a perimeter of $2\pi R$ and the peripheral velocity at the rim of a rotating circle is $R\omega$, where ω is the angular velocity, any multiplication of these two gives an answer that contains $\pi R^2\omega$, which is $A\omega$. If the velocity has a limit of c, this will yield some multiple of $A\omega/c^2$ in the answer.

A clock fixed to the earth at the equator slows by $A\omega/c^2$ seconds per day relative to a supposed clock at the geocentre. Note that this $A\omega/c^2$ slowing has nothing to do with the Sagnac effect; the formula looks like that for the Sagnac effect, but we know that this effect is per day while the Sagnac formula is over a fraction of a second for the circumnavigation of the earth. A clock transported eastward at a ground speed of 463.8 m/s slows by $3A\omega/c^2$ per day more than a clock fixed at the equator and by $4A\omega/c^2$ seconds per day with respect to a supposed clock at the geocentre.

A clock transported westward at a ground speed of 463.8 m/s would have speeded up by $A\omega/c^2$ per day compared to a clock fixed at the equator. However, that same clock would have no slowing with respect to a clock at the geocentre because it is stationary with respect to the geocentre; it sits over the non-rotating geocentre because its westward speed cancels out the eastward speed of the earth's surface at the equator. These are practical cases because an aeroplane can travel at the speeds mentioned.

We must remember that it is not the 'time' but rather the display upon the dial of the timekeeping devices that is altering in all of these cases.

Correspondence with Committee

In correspondence between this author and members of the CCDS committee, the following interesting comments were received (quoted verbatim):

1. The president of the CCDS wrote:

> *You are right stating that the Sagnac effect is not relativistic. But it comes out naturally if one writes the equations of time transfer for laser gyroscopes in the context of general relativity, with some very small additional terms that are genuinely relativistic. But this is normal and one can similarly argue that Newtonian Celestial Mechanics are not relativistic, but however, general relativity includes all terms of Newtonian theories of motion plus additional corrections. So it is not wrong to say that Sagnac effect is also relativistic in the sense that it also appears in the solution in a general relativity theory.*

This statement is contradictory. It begins by saying that the Sagnac effect is not relativistic. The surface velocity of the earth at mid-latitudes is about 300 m/s, which is a very moderate velocity. Indeed, the original Sagnac tests had a disc rim velocity of below 10 m/s. There is no question of such low velocities causing other than a first order effect; relativity theory does not and cannot enter into the explanation of the effect. To invoke relativity theory to explain the Sagnac effect is like invoking it to explain the sliding of a hockey puck on ice. The letter is from the president of the organisation that publishes the international regulations in which the Sagnac effect is defined as a 'relativistic' effect!

Let us discuss the statement *"But it comes out naturally"* from the letter. It does not come out 'naturally'. It emerges because the calculation incorrectly assumes that the speed of light is a constant on the spinning earth in the east-west direction, which it is not. Indeed, having stipulated that the speed of light is a fixed element in any calculation and having applied that rule, the 'time' must alter by the exact amount that is caused by this same error – in this case, the precise amount is the Sagnac effect $(4A\omega)/(c^2)$. This confuses people into thinking that the Sagnac effect 'magically' appears from some calculation! If the result were not that the 'time' is to be corrected by a compensating amount, there would be a mistake in the calculations.

The committees have my sympathy. They were led into the whole debacle many years ago by an acceptance by their predecessors, who did not consider the matter in depth, that SR was correct. How a committee could now extricate itself from the mess is difficult to imagine. They had warning signs 30 years ago in the earlier-quoted statement by Hafele that *"The standard answer that moving clocks run slow by the well known factor gamma is almost certainly incorrect."* The CCDS committee references Hafele and Keating in its publications.

2. In relation to the application of GR to metrology, the chairman of the working group of the CCDS wrote:

> *There are possibilities to interpret the Sagnac effect without reference to relativity. I agree with that.*
>
> *However, for accurate time comparisons, we have (a) to adopt a relativistic model, because the classical treatment leads to contradictions with experiment, (b) a convention on the meaning of clock comparison. As a model, we use Einstein's general relativity because this theory is the simplest which, up to now, agrees with all observed facts. The convention for clock comparison is based on the convention of coordinate simultaneity; the readings of the clocks take place at the same value of some specified coordinate time (geocentric in metrology on the earth).*
>
> *The question is not to distinguish in the theory of clock comparison some classical terms, some terms due to special relativity and some gravitational terms. General relativity is a self-contained theory and provides all the terms we need, as a consequence of the basic postulates. The separation of the various terms, as indicated above is a consequence of the choice of coordinates we have made and of the low level of approximation which is accepted.*

The critical statement here is *"of some specified coordinate time (geocentric in metrology on the earth)"*. Why is the centre of the earth stipulated? It is named because all atomic clocks run slow in proportion to their speeds with respect to that spot. It is just magically chosen without any explanation or justification.

It was generous of these persons to respond to this author. They must realise the tricky situation in which they find themselves.

The 1990 CCIR report concludes by remarking that *"additional definitions and conventions are under consideration"*. Clearly, the CCIR is trying to reconcile the conflicting facts. They do not seem to have reached a conclusive situation in relation to those definitions. Guinot (1997), as chairman of the CCDS Working Group on the Application of General Relativity to Metrology, published their report in *Metrologia*. This report has some interesting comments.

> *. . . everyone has the right, even the duty, to question the capacity of general relativity to represent the real world, but this question is outwith the scope of this report. The developments presented here suppose that one accepts the model of general relativity.*

Guinot says here that they are compelled to assume that relativity theory is correct and that, while that does not represent reality, the problem is for some other organisation to address. I suppose we cannot blame him for taking that attitude because the idea of one such organisation announcing that SR is wrong would bring all sorts of opprobrium down on their heads. They have a day's work to do and they want to do it in peace.

Here we have the experts on the topic of clock synchronisation warning us that all may not be as rosy as it appears. Guinot is honest in these remarks. There is much serious work to be done by the committee.

Again, Guinot writes, *"the use of geostationary satellites is especially convenient for the two-way time transfers. In that case, it is simpler and, even at picosecond accuracy, the only relativistic term to be evaluated is that for the Sagnac effect."* This agrees that in the transfer of time from one earth clock station to another by go-and-return two-way signals, it is only necessary to consider the Sagnac correction.

Discussing the use of a Newtonian space-time model versus the general relativistic model, where coordinate distance and coordinate time are utilised (as distinct from absolute time of the former), the report states that *"quantities built with coordinates have, in general, no simple physical meaning"*. It says that *"these coordinates are often considered as merely a system for labelling events"*.

Presetting of GPS Clocks

The setting of atomic clocks placed aboard a satellite is made in advance of launching the satellite. These settings allow for both the so-called SR and the 'height over sea level' corrections. In a typical case, these corrections can amount to setting the clock at –50,000 ns/day to correct for the increased reading that will emerge as a result of height over sea level and at +7,500 ns/day to allow for the decreased reading that will emerge because of the velocity of the satellite.

This 7,500 ns/day is computed from two elements: (a) the slowing of the satellite clock as compared with the centre of the earth and (b) the slowing of a clock on the surface of the earth as compared with a supposed clock at the centre of the earth. It is the difference between (a) and (b) that gives rise to the correction to be applied to the timing on a clock on a satellite versus a stationary clock on the surface of the earth.

The satellite clocks will then keep the same time as on the surface of the earth. These corrections are in accordance with the proposals put forward in this book. However, the CCDS and CCIR do not reproduce these simple rules because they do not reflect SR theory. These are huge corrections and are a precise confirmation that the two corrections are totally vindicated. Without making the corrections, the clock on the satellite would not keep an unaltered time as compared with a clock on the surface of the earth.

Remember that, as discussed above, the satellite clock does not run slow in proportion to its speed with respect to the clock on the earth's surface (the relative speed of the two clocks). However, whenever one has to compare the time on such a satellite with the time on another satellite or on the earth by interchanging information via electromagnetic signals, the time taken by the signal to travel from one place to the other has to be corrected because the signal travels at a different speed eastward from westward.

Atomic clocks increase in rate as their distance over sea level increases. More on this anon.

Other Tests

Sadeh et al. (1968) sent atomic clocks on a truck up and down the eastern coast of the U.S.A. They found that the further away from the base station was the position of the truck, the greater was the alteration in the frequency being received at the truck from the base station. They had three caesium clocks on the truck and supposed that all three kept the same time and could not have changed in frequency with respect to each other. Sadeh et al. commented, *"We are aware of the tremendous theoretical difficulties implied in the apparent results."* They claimed that because the rate of the three clocks was the same when they began the test and on their return to the starting point, this proved that no alteration in their rates had occurred. They concluded that *"this proved that there was no change in the frequency of the clock during the trip"* and that *"neither the Doppler shift nor the gravitational red shift can explain this"*. However, if all three clocks on the truck were altering at the same rate, which depended on the alteration in 'absolute' velocity of the clocks with respect to the geocentre as they travelled on the journey, this would just as well explain the anomaly. This possibility did not strike them.

These tests were done very carefully with teams of experts in this field. Sadeh et al. had proposed that their results showed that the rate of a clock increased with increase in the nearby masses. Their proposition that mass had an effect on the frequency seems to have been disproven by Markowitz (1968). Hurley (1980) analysed the Sadeh et al. results and proposed that the alteration in the position of the truck in relation to nearby space while the signal was travelling there was causing an alteration in the received frequency. Hurley attributed the alteration to the fact that *"the only motion between clocks was that caused by the variation with latitude of the earth's surface velocity. Hence the relative velocity vector is perpendicular to the meridian direction."*

A paper by Rudefer (1979) compared the performance of clocks at standard clock stations on the earth. The conclusion drawn by Rudefer from his experimental results is that atomic clocks evince a change in their rates depending on their velocity with respect to the earth's centre.

An earlier paper by Cannon and Jensen (1975) proposed the same connection, but the conclusion in that paper was refuted and withdrawn by the authors in a later paper (1976). The reason why they withdrew their conclusions was that they subsequently discovered that, during the period monitored, the clocks at the various stations had had their rates altered purposely to make them conform to the time being recorded at other clock stations. This invalidated their conclusions because they had not allowed for it.

Rudefer, on the other hand, took the clock station performances over some later years (1973–77) and only considered stations that were co-ordinated with each other and not altered in relation to each other. This made possible a comparison of the clock stations' long-term relative performances. Co-ordination of the relevant clock stations only began in 1972.

Sherwin (1960) shows that the 1960 experiments by Pound and Rebka can be explained as merely the time recorded by the atomic clocks slowing with increased velocity.

There is no relative motion between the various clock stations on earth because they are all fixed on the rotating earth. There is no relative motion between London and Rome. Therefore, any correlation between a difference in the long-time rates of these clocks that is shown to depend on their velocities in relation to the non-rotating centre can only be the result of their 'absolute' (using the term loosely) and not 'relative' velocities. Rudefer showed this correlation to be present. On the other hand, Alley (1979) concluded from tests on transporting clocks from Washington to Greenland that there was no evidence of a latitude effect. Which is correct?

As we saw earlier, Cocke (1966) showed that the timekeeping of atomic clocks anywhere on the earth at sea level is the very same. However, this does not apply to the time recorded on clocks that are not both at sea level.

No calculation was done to take account of the various heights over sea level of the atomic clocks as they were transported by Sadeh et al. or Alley; neither was account taken of the height over sea level of the various fixed clock stations by Cannon & Jensen or Rudefer. Any comparison between clocks whose height over sea level is different from zero must allow for the fact that there will be a constant difference being recorded between such clocks. This difference is because the clocks run slow in proportion to their speeds with respect to the earth's centre, as described above. Perhaps if account were taken of this factor, it would reveal a consistency between all these test results. The speeding up of clocks with height over sea level is a separate matter and will be discussed in a later chapter.

Pulsars

The pulse rate of some pulsars has been measured over at least a decade and found to be in confirmation of the above ideas. Hill (1995) gives the details and shows that the timekeeping of clocks on earth is not at all as consistent as the time depicted by the pulse rate of pulsars. The difference is shown to be explicable by the movement in space of the solar system and the earth. Pulsar time even picks up the slight variation caused by the motion of the earth and the moon around the earth-moon barycentre. Taking the pulsar timing as the most accurate time we have, there is one fascinating feature of this discovery. While talking about the annual alterations in time caused by the fact that the earth's orbit around the sun is elliptical rather than circular, Hill says, *"It is interesting (and probably significant) that the gravitational and the speed effects are equal and that they add rather than canceling each other even though the earth is in 'free fall'."*

Van Flandern says that there remain inexplicable 12-hour periods correlated to the sun's direction in the time recorded by satellite clocks. Who is going to solve that puzzle? This finding is significant in relation to the postulate in this book that light moves with the earth on its annual orbit around the sun. This would conform to the findings concerning the pulsar time that shows an outside view of the situation that exists.

So, pulsar timing shows how the time based on the non-rotating earth's centre, described above, is also subject to alteration with respect to a more consistent time given by the pulsar time. I wonder how that pulsar time in turn may be altering with respect to some more consistent time even further away from earth. Hill concludes that a universal time based on pulsar time is a rational concept and *"better than the time based upon the uncorrected earth based atomic clocks"*. Even such pulsar time, however, is not a genuine universal time as proposed in this book.

The ITU and the BIPM have these matters on their agenda. It will be mighty interesting to read what they eventually publish on this topic. One of their officers has already published a paper on the matter.

Just a reminder – this book is claiming that *'time'* does not alter. It proposes that the recording devices on atomic clocks change due to various influences such as speed with respect to the earth's centre or gravitation. This should be borne in mind throughout the debate.

Let us consider again the matter of the speeding up of clocks with higher gravitational potential and the slowing of clocks with higher speed. The orbits of GPS satellites are eccentric. At perigee, the lower sun's gravitational potential causes atomic clocks to run faster; the faster speed of the same clock at perigee causes the clock to run slower. These two effects exactly cancel out. It seems that energy is the determining factor. Increased potential gravitational energy causes clocks to run faster and increased speed causes them to run slower. These two causes are linked. This effect is allied to the fact that clocks on the earth at sea level run at the same rate from equator to poles.

Cocke (1966), as discussed in detail earlier, showed that the combination of gravitational plus centrifugal forces on the earth gives an equipotential surface on which all clocks should run at the same rate. Clocks on the earth do not, however, appear to be affected by the gravitational potential of the sun. This is shown by the fact that GPS clocks are not altered by the change in gravitational potential between their point of nearest approach to the sun and their point of greatest distance from the sun (about four earths' diameters). These points in their orbit do not orbit the sun at different speeds. This fact negates a potential explanation offered by Hoffmann (1961) – a point made by Hatch (2003) in an excellent paper entitled *Those Scandalous Clocks*; that paper concludes that SR theory is incorrect and that *"Such a conclusion is, of course, scandalous."* That is a beautiful transferred epithet because Hatch has proved it was SR that was scandalous. Various explanations havebeen offered for this strange fact. Ashby and Bertotti (1987) introduced a 'fictitious' gravitational field to try to explain the matter. Is this puzzle somehow associated with the proposition in this book that the behaviour of light on the earth is such that it is not affected by the earth's orbit around the sun? A similar effect was discussed earlier in this book whereby the two effects of gravitational potential and velocity also cancel out on the earth's actual surface. Surely this is no coincidence.

Clocks on earth do not run slow with any velocity 'relative' to an observer on the earth. They all run slow with respect to the non-rotating centre of the earth. Time is not relative. As measured by the most accurate pulsar beats, it is absolute.

Vigier

Professor J. P. Vigier published a paper in 1997 that was devoted to agreeing with this author's proposals. I never met Professor Vigier. He had read a copy of the 1995 paper by this author and telephoned my home as a result. I was off to play a game of golf and had no idea who the caller was. I asked him to call the next day, which he did. Had I known who he was, I would have postponed the golf! We had several long conversations and he subsequently published his paper on the theory forming the basis of this book.

Vigier quoted verbatim long sections, including the diagrams, from that 1995 paper. He agreed that there is one absolute frame in which light of a particular frequency *"moves in all directions with the same velocity"*. He says that, in relation to the atomic clock, were we to consider the periodic processes in a single atom, we would have to assume an absolute frame in relation to which the rate of those periodic processes would be affected in accordance with the absolute speed of the atom. That absolute frame is then, he says, assumed to be that where the 2.7° K microwave radiation is isotopic for all light velocities.

In his paper, Vigier gives two alternatives: either relativity theory has to be *"amended"* (a euphemism for abandoned) or some other solution must be found. As such an alternative, he proposed that the photon has a 'nonzero rest mass'. He opined to me that not many would swallow that. It was clear from our conversations that even the great Vigier had to cloud the issue and appear not to challenge relativity theory directly but instead give an 'out' in any publication. Indeed, the second part of his paper is not relevant to the debate on the Sagnac effect and was obviously dragged in as a red herring to get the paper published. This latter part of his paper contains several errors in the symbols used and also some non-sequiturs. Professor Vigier had sent me a draft of his paper. I had checked the first part carefully but had not bothered with the second part – I was being a bit lazy as I was only interested in the fact that he was supporting my publication. In any case, I have no view on the rest mass of the photon, on which Vigier has published many papers over the years. If that was the price to be paid to get my ideas backed by such an eminent person, why would I upset the apple cart?

Vigier discusses the fact that the Sagnac effect and SR are not in conformity. He remarks that if a photon has a zero mass ($m_0 = 0$), *"the Sagnac effect is evidently not compatible with the initial assumption of restricted relativity theory where the velocity of light is constant"*. Vigier then gives two alternatives as follows: *"(i) if one drops the assumption $m_0 = 0$; (ii) if one somehow modifies relativity theory"*. The second is in agreement with the proposals in this book. This is a satisfactory endorsement of the ideas propounded here. For a renowned physics professor to go so far as to endorse such radical proposals is indeed comforting.

Vigier had worked with and published papers jointly with the Laureate De Broglie. That non-zero rest mass idea has been published by Vigier many times in the past but not in relation to an explanation of the Sagnac effect.

Vigier, quoting Builder (1958), said that atomic clocks slow down with absolute speed: *"There exists a unique absolute inertial system which interacts with and affects, the behaviour of the clocks in a manner dependent on their speeds relative to it i.e. their absolute speeds."* Vigier also said that:

The fact that the clocks do behave differently when their speeds are different requires that they interact differently with something, in a manner which depends on their speeds. Thus any difference in their behaviour must be ascribed to a difference in their physical interaction with their environment.

Who was Vigier? He was Professor of Gravitation and Cosmological Relativity at the Pierre & Marie Curie University in Paris, France. He is acknowledged as one of the leading physicists in the world. Despite having conferences on relativity named after him (as already specified in chapter 3), he once modestly said to this author that he could not understand why he was held in such respect! As a young man, Vigier was on the Council of the French Resistance during the Second World War. He was eventually captured and sent on a train to Lyon on the way to almost certain extinction by Barbier (the Butcher), when the train was bombed by the U.K. air force and he escaped. He was luckier than the young German Harress (see Index), who was killed in the First World War.

Review of the Problem

Let us review the problem here.

1. The speed of light is defined as c (even though it is measured, as we know from the discussion on the Sagnac effect, as $c \pm v$) because SR demands that this be so.

2. This automatically introduces a correction factor that is supposed to apply to the 'time' taken for a clock to circumnavigate the earth. Instead of allowing for the variation in the speed of light, a false alteration in 'time' is introduced.

3. The alteration in the 'time' must exactly compensate for the real alteration in the speed of light ($c \pm v$). This is what SR is specifically designed to do.

4. The mathematics of SR theory is all about calculating by what amount the 'time' must be altered to bring about the false pretence that the speed of light is constant.

5. Why then should we be surprised that the calculation comes up with a correction to 'time' exactly equal to the Sagnac effect?

6. Had the answer not been 207.4 ns, then the calculation would be wrong! SR demands that we change the time taken for any such event by the gamma factor.

7. There is a snag. Carrying a clock physically around the earth (as done by Saburi et al.) to compare it with another clock at a second site shows that the alteration in the time recorded on the clock, as calculated under SR from the relative speed of the two clocks, does not give the correct answer. It is the comparison of the relative speeds of the two clocks with respect to the earth's centre that has to be compared.

8. The CCIR excuses the use of the earth's centre as a base by implying that it is a convenient frame from which to take measurements. Why on earth (excuse the pun) should that spot be used? The unstated reason is that all atomic clocks on the earth happen to run slow in direct proportion to their speeds with reference to that place. Nobody knows why this is so.

It is clear that the same results hold good of bodies at rest in the 'stationary' system, viewed from a system in uniform motion.

Albert Einstein (1905)

In 1905 Einstein published a paper which set forth the relativity theory of Poincaré and Lorentz, with some amplifications, and which received much attention.

E. T. Whitaker (1953)

Chapter 6

Universal Relativity

A new theory is needed that fits all of the experimental results described earlier in this book. Such a theory is outlined in this chapter and is named universal relativity (UR).

Any theory on the behaviour of light on earth has to satisfy the following conditions:

1. The speed of light as measured in different directions on the earth with respect to the surface of the earth does not show any measurable difference to the accuracy of the 1964 Jaseja et al. Michelson and Morley-type test.

2. Light that is generated on board a spinning disc and that is split and sent in opposing directions, with and against the direction of the spin of the disc, travels at a speed measured aboard the disc of $c \pm v$ against and with the direction of spin, respectively, where v is the peripheral speed of the disc in the path of the light. This was proven by the 1913 Sagnac experiment and by the 1993 Bilger et al. experiment (to an accuracy of 1 in 10^{20}).

3. It was confirmed by Wang in 2003 that light generated aboard an object travelling in straight-line uniform motion:
    *   travels at a speed of $c + v$ against the direction of motion of the object
    *   travels at a speed of $c - v$ with the direction of motion of the object

    Measurement was made aboard and with respect to the object.

4. In cases (2) and (3) above, the light travels at a speed of c with respect to the fixed laboratory in which the experiment is held.

5. Light generated on the earth and sent around the globe travels faster westward than eastward relative to the surface of the earth. The Michelson and Gale 1925 test and the Saburi et al. 1976 test, as well as the Global Positioning System (GPS) for clock synchronisation, prove this.

6. Light coming from a distant star subtends an angle to the orbital path of the earth around the sun relative to a frame set in outer fixed space. The orbital speed of the earth around the sun requires that a viewing telescope be tilted to allow for that orbital speed, just as is the case with falling rain being viewed from a moving vehicle. Bradley proved this. Airy proved that filling the barrel of a telescope with water did not affect the apparent position of a star as viewed from earth.

In UR, the following three postulates are put forward in relation to the behaviour of light:

1. Light generated on the earth moves at a speed of c with respect to the non-rotating centre of the earth as that centre moves on its large elliptical orbit around the sun.

117

2. Light generated on the earth does not move at a speed of c with respect to the surface of the earth on its daily spinning motion; in this case the speed is $c \pm v$ westward or eastward, respectively, where v is the surface speed of the earth at the relevant test site.

3. The speed of light generated in outer space is the constant c with respect to that space, independent of the motion of its emitter or of any observer.

It is proposed here that these three postulates fit the facts and also dispel the various paradoxes, discussed earlier, that derive from SR. We shall see later what is meant by outer space.

In 1897, Michelson wrote that there were three possible explanations for the zero test result that he attained in 1881 (the precursor of the famous Michelson and Morley zero result experiment). This is what Michelson said:

In any case we are driven to extraordinary conclusions, and the choice lies between these three:

1. *The earth passes through the ether (or rather allows the ether to pass through its entire mass) without appreciable influence.*
2. *The length of all bodies is altered (equally?) by their motion through the ether.*
3. *The earth in its motion drags with it the ether even at distances of several thousand kilometres from its surface.*

Michelson could think of no other possibility. The three choices are equally improbable. Indeed, they are individually incredible. Michelson did not think of the fourth simple possibility put forward in this book – that light travels with the earth on its orbit around the sun. The Irishman O'Rahilly (1938) and Beckmann (1987) did, however, mention that possibility.

SR has two requirements relating to the behaviour of light: (i) the speed of light is independent of the speed of its source and (ii) the speed of light is always measured as a constant (c) by any observer travelling at uniform speed with respect to the source of the light (see Einstein 1905 and 1922). As will be seen, neither of these requirements is compatible with the theory proposed here.

Michelson and Morley Test Yields a Difference

Having proposed the above new theory of the behaviour of light, a search was then undertaken to see if a very accurate Michelson and Morley-type test had ever been done. If so, a difference should show up between the east-west and north-south speeds of light because the daily spin of the earth should cause a resulting fringe shift at the measuring station when the light rays were reunited on completion of a circuit. If the theory proposed in this book is correct, the effect shown by the Michelson & Gale and Bilger et al. tests should eventually be picked up on a more accurate Michelson and Morley-type test. Following an exhaustive but not exhausting search, such a test was in fact uncovered.

At a site at mid-latitudes, the movement of the surface of the earth caused by the spin of the earth on its axis is about 350 m/s. This speed is about one hundredth of the orbital speed of the earth around the sun (30,000 m/s). As we saw at figure 1, the effect depends on the square of the velocity (v); therefore, the effect sought is about one ten-thousandth of the effect that would be caused by the orbital movement around the sun. It has only been in recent years that the required accuracy to measure to this level has been attained – it was outside the detection limit of the Michelson and Morley-type tests performed up to and including the Jaseja et al. test of 1964. Few were interested in the smaller daily spin effect. The original Michelson and Morley test yielded a zero result. Why should scientists waste their time trying to measure any effect from the daily spin of the earth on its axis when the much larger effect was not detected in the Michelson and Morley experiment?

A Michelson and Morley-type test by Brillet and Hall (1979) eventually reached the level of accuracy where the spin of the earth should show an effect. The accuracy was 4,000 times better than that of Jaseja et al. There is no comment in their paper on any measured effect, as was expected by the author of this book. This was very disappointing.

However, a further search showed that the Brillet and Hall test results were later analysed by Aspden (1981), who showed that the test indicated a diurnal variation that was, to within 3%, the spin velocity effect of the earth in the correct direction (355 m/s at the latitude of the test). This important scientific analysis by Aspden, which has virtually gone unnoticed over the intervening 24 years, could be termed the Bingo factor in the whole of this investigation. There have been but two references to Aspden's paper in the *Science Citation Index* over the intervening years to 2005 – the references did not allude to the analysis of the test results but merely cited it as a paper on the subject of light. This author had the pleasure of meeting Aspden in the autumn of 1996.

Relativity theory cannot accept that the movement of the surface of the earth, when measured in a test over a length of less than one metre (as was the Brillet and Hall test), should show any difference in an eastward and westward direction. It can only be explained by UR, which states that light moves with the orbital velocity of the earth's surface on its movement around the sun but not with the daily spin velocity of that same surface. How else could such a test show the daily spin velocity effect of the earth but not its orbital velocity effect?

Further confirmation is provided by Hils and Hall (1990), where a 'once-per-day' effect due to the rotation of the earth was detected in an accurate repeat of the Kennedy and Thorndyke (1932) test. Kennedy and Thorndyke had done a Michelson and Morley-type test with unequal arms. In that test, they had also detected a daily effect but had not identified the cause. The tests by Brillet & Hall, Hils & Hall and Kennedy & Thorndyke confirmed that the orbital motion of the earth around the sun did not affect the speed of light in these tests. However, those three papers showed a daily effect due to the daily spin of the earth on its axis – findings that tie in with UR theory.

A later analysis of the Brillet and Hall experiment was given by Hayden (1991), who concluded that *"the laboratory-based data of Brillet and Hall show entirely the incorrect signature for a model in which the speed of light is isotropic in the laboratory frame".* This agrees with Aspden.

Heretofore, the null result of the Michelson and Morley test has been viewed as sacrosanct no matter what the accuracy of the test undertaken. Stephen Hawking, who holds Newton's chair as Lucasian Professor of Mathematics in Cambridge University, states in his classic *A Brief History of Time* (1988), *"The special theory of relativity was very successful in explaining that the speed of light appears the same to all observers (as shown by the Michelson-Morley experiment)."*

SR rests on the assumption that no difference can be detected in a Michelson and Morley test. Now that such a difference has been recorded, SR is fighting a losing battle. However, its demise will be a long-drawn-out affair.

It is interesting to note that the results of direct measurements of the speed of light on earth undertaken over the years vary and do not agree to within the magnitude of the spin effect of the earth (about 350 m/s at mid-latitudes). Bates (1988) lists the direct method measurements of the speed of light results; these varied in the years 1950 to 1958 from 299,791.9 km/s to 299,793.1 km/s. The difference could be partially due to a different orientation of the line of flight of the light beam and partially due to the limit of the accuracy possible in the experiment.

Tests done on the speed of light on a north-south line would not have had any effect from the spin of the earth. An east-west test would have the maximum effect, with a lesser effect occurring in between these two extremes. This would help to account for the difficulty in getting a somewhat more consistent result in the various experiments over the years.

Therefore, the speed of light on the earth is not constant in all directions. It varies depending on the compass direction in which the measurement is being made. This statement directly contradicts one of the two postulates on the behaviour of light contained in SR. On the first page of his first paper on relativity theory (1905), Einstein stated that *"the unsuccessful attempts to discover any motion of the earth relatively to the 'light medium'"* suggested to him the idea that there was no such thing as *"absolute rest".* However, it is now possible to measure the motion of the surface of the earth relative to light.

In 1983, the speed of light was 'fixed' by measuring its frequency and wavelength. This method gave a value of 299,742,458 m/s, and it was defined as that value by the CCDS in 1983. Fortunately, just before that defining, the test by Brillet and Hall (1979) was performed, which shows the folly of defining the speed of light as a constant. The 'defining' of the speed of light for all time is tantamount to forbidding any further attempts to measure the speed of light.

When considering the difference between the null result of the Michelson and Morley test and the positive result of the Brillet and Hall test, light is shown to travel with the earth as it travels on its orbit around the sun. The speed of the earth on its orbit around the sun is transmitted to (or adopted by) the light, and the speed of the light is not, in all circumstances, independent of the speed of the source. This is because the light takes up the orbital speed (30,000 m/s) of the earth around the sun. The speed of the light is, in this particular case, affected by the speed of the object (the earth) on which it is emitted. This contradicts the postulate of SR concerning the behaviour of light – *"the constancy of the velocity of light must hold whatever may be the motion of the source which emits the ray of light."*

Straight-Line Interference

With the knowledge of all the foregoing, this is an appropriate place to discuss the behaviour of light signals reflected off mirrors on the earth. Figure 18 shows light beams being sent to the right and left from a starting point O. Point O is moving to the left at velocity v with respect to the laboratory. The two mirrors shown on the left and right are fixed in the laboratory and therefore move with the earth. The light beams sent to the left and right from O reflect off the mirrors. The time for the light to go from O to the left mirror is L/c, where L is the distance from O to the mirror at the start of the experiment.

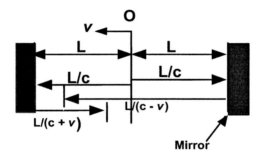

Figure 18: Mirrors in Laboratory

We arrange for the orientation of the apparatus to be in the north-south direction. Thus, the movement of the earth on its daily spin does not affect the result. That effect would be tiny but is eliminated from the test by the orientation of the apparatus. The time for the light that is reflected off the left mirror to travel from that mirror back to point O (which is approaching at a velocity v) is L/(c + v); this is because the light is travelling at a speed of c in relation to the fixed laboratory.

It also takes a time of L/c for the beam that goes to the right to go from the original position at point O to the mirror on the right. The time for that reflected beam to catch up with the receding point O is L/(c – v).

The difference between the times taken by the two beams to leave point O and eventually meet up with point O is L/(c + v) – L/(c - v); the two additional times of L/c to get from O to the mirrors cancel out. The difference between these two is $2Lv/(c^2 – v^2)$. The v^2 may be ignored (if v is much less than c), giving $2Lv/c^2$.

In figure 18, consider the position after the light has gone out to the two mirrors in equal times of L/c. Here we actually have a 'starting post' for a test just like the Sagnac test. We have the light subsequently going at speeds of c ± v with respect to point O in opposing directions. We can imagine that the two mirrors could be bent around on a circuit to meet and be glued together. In this case, we have the starting point for a Sagnac test without having to get to that 'starting post'. The ensuing shift of the light will be similar to that in the circular Sagnac test.

As discussed earlier, the debate has raged as to whether the Sagnac effect can be applied to straight-line motion. As described in their 1942 paper, Dufour and Prunier had a test in which the path of the light consisted of two straight lines with two radial connections, as shown in figure 19. They introduced the light at O and sent it out from there to B in a radial direction. The light was then split in two – one part went in the direction B–A–O and the other part in the direction B–C–O. The result of this test was to yield a Sagnac difference in the times taken to complete the circuit in opposing directions. There is no reason why a smaller, triangular path such as A–B–O would not also give the Sagnac result corresponding to the area of the triangle ABO. In that case, the only part of the circuit contributing to the fringe shift would be the straight line AB. It is clear that had there been but one straight-line portion, the Sagnac fringe shift would similarly be determined by the normal Sagnac formula. Here, then, we have confirmation that a straight-line out-and-back test would give a Sagnac result. Wang (2003) has confirmed this by an ingenious experiment.

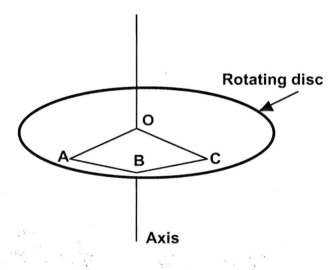

Figure 19: Light on Two Straight Lines

In the tests in figure 19, Dufour and Prunier had the portions between A–O and O–C off the disc. This was immaterial to the result, as described earlier. The portions that were off the disc were those that were towards and out from the centre of rotation. These radial portions do not contribute to the fringe shift, as shown in the general derivation of the Sagnac effect given earlier. It is solely the non-radial components that are with and against the direction of rotation that contribute to the fringe shift.

In their series of tests, Dufour and Prunier did tests in which the light beam was introduced to the circuit at the centre of rotation (or as near to there as was practicable) and then sent radially out to point C (figure 19) instead of at point B, as in their main tests. They had no success with that arrangement. They cite as the reason that the slightest movement upset the readings. It is a pity that the Dufour and Prunier apparatus no longer exists because a repeat of all those tests, with variations, would be very instructive.

An objection might be raised on the basis that the Sagnac laboratory test is too small to derive any firm conclusions. However, the Michelson and Gale test measured the Sagnac effect on a disc of radius of 4,250,000 m (of the cross section of the earth at the site).

Discussion on Universal Relativity

The timing of the investigation described in this book was fortunate. The Sagnac and also the Dufour and Prunier tests had been done. The Hafele and Keating test had been published. The direct tests on the speed of light had been done to the required accuracy – this last requirement was a close-run thing. All direct tests on the speed of light were suspended when the speed of light was 'defined' in 1983. Thereafter, there would be no further speculation or new tests to determine its (defined for all time) speed. Had those tests not been performed, no proof would be available, and the new theory put forward here could not be developed or proven. No research funding would be provided by any university or government to any 'idiot' who might propose to measure the speed of light in view of the fact that Einstein had said it was a constant and its fixed value had been internationally agreed upon.

Magnetism and gravity are obvious suspects when trying to explain the fact that light travels with the earth on its orbital path around the sun but not with the daily spin of the earth on its axis. The offset of the earth's magnetic field from geometric north-south would give a biased effect, so magnetism does not fit the bill. Gravity seems to meet all the criteria. The gravitational attraction between the earth and the moon does not rely on any spin of either body. The gravitational lines of force between the sun and the earth must move around with the earth as the earth moves on its orbit around the sun.

Van Flandern (1993) discusses the effect of gravity on light and says that the sun's force comes *"from its true, instantaneous position rather than its apparent, aberrated position, to a precision of one arc second (the two positions differ by 20 arc seconds)"*. He also says, *"An alternative way of viewing the gravitational redshift phenomenon is the slowing of atomic clocks in a gravitational field. This is again a reflection of the slowed propagator of all electromagnetic phenomena in such a field."* Furthermore, Van Flandern points out that the sun's light appears to come from where the sun was 8.3 minutes ago; the gravitational pull, however, is shown to be along the instantaneous line between the sun and the earth. This is a very important distinction.

Dabbs et al. (1965) showed that neutrons are subject to deflection by the force of gravity. Magnetic or electric fields do not affect neutrons. It is therefore likely that it is gravity that controls the behaviour of light when the light is within the sphere of influence of the earth.

The CCIR and CCDS reports use *"local geocentric reference frames"* for time comparisons. They have two methods of comparing time: (a) viewed *"from a geocentric, earth-fixed, rotating reference frame"* (i.e. at the centre of the earth, which is spinning with the daily spin of the earth as it travels on its orbit around the sun), or (b) viewed *"from a geocentric, non-rotating, local inertial frame"* (i.e. at the non-rotating centre of the earth as it travels on its annual orbit around the sun).

These methods recognise that in case (a), a Sagnac correction is applied, whereas in case (b), no Sagnac correction is required, and examples are worked to show this. This conforms to the theory proposed in this book whereby electromagnetic signals do not adapt to the spin of the earth. Here we have international bodies as far back as 1980 using an element of the theory put forward in this book but for a different reason, namely that they found in practice that this gives the correct method of synchronising clocks on the earth.

Signals coming from the Viking craft that was placed on Mars behave peculiarly when passing very near the sun. An electromagnetic signal that passes very near the sun (whose gravitational pull is about 300 times that of the earth) may, in a similar way, be grossly affected. In Shapiro et al. (1977), it is recorded that when the signal came to within three suns' radii of the centre of the sun, the data became erratic. Shapiro et al. asked, *"What of the other anomalous results? How can they be explained?"* Their analysis showed that the corona of the sun or any errors in measurement could not account for the erratic results. In Reasenberg et al. (1979), it is recorded that when the signal from Mars to earth was very close to the sun, the signals *"were markedly inconsistent with each other as well as with the rest of the delay data"*. They deleted these figures from the analysis while remarking that *"no definitive explanation has been obtained for these anomalies"*.

Is the change in the speed of light near the sun relative to fixed space or relative to the sun? The evidence from Mars shows that the alteration in speed must be relative to fixed space because the signal takes longer and longer to reach earth from Mars as it gets nearer to the sun (see Schwinger, 1986).

Electromagnetic signals, electrons, neutrons and atomic beams all ignore the spin velocity of the earth. All four travel with the orbital motion of the earth but do not take up its spin motion.

Comparison of Theories

Table 2 shows a comparison of UR with SR in relation to conforming to the results of various tests discussed in this book. Other tests have also been described that give similar results to some of the last eight listed in the table.

For the sake of gathering the important tests in one table for easy reference, there is repetition here of earlier conclusions. Let us briefly discuss again some of the tests listed. It will be seen that the new theory satisfactorily explains the experimental results of all the tests, whereas SR does not conform to eight of the twelve. Cases 1, 2 and 3 (Stellar aberration, Fresnel drag and Fizeau experiment) have been addressed earlier. All

Michelson and Morley-type tests done between 1887 and 1964 gave results consistent with the original Michelson and Morley test of 1887 (4).

Table 2: Comparison of theories

Case	Test	Year	UR	SR
1.	Stellar aberration	1725	Yes	Yes
2.	Fresnel	1814	Yes	Yes
3.	Fizeau	1851	Yes	Yes
4.	Michelson and Morley	1887	Yes	Yes
5.	Sagnac	1914	Yes	No
6.	Michelson and Gale	1925	Yes	No
7.	Dufour and Prunier	1942	Yes	No
8.	Macek and Davis	1963	Yes	No
9.	Macek et al.	1964	Yes	No
10.	Saburi et al.	1976	Yes	No
11.	Brillet and Hall	1979	Yes	No
12.	Bilger et al.	1993	Yes	No

In the case of the laboratory Sagnac test (5), UR states that light moves relative to the laboratory (not to the moving object). In a Sagnac test, there would also be a tiny distortion due to the fact that the light is not turning with the daily spin of the earth, but this is not measurable in such laboratory tests on small discs. SR claims that time aboard a moving object is observed as shorter than when observed in a stationary frame. This is not in accordance with the Sagnac test results on a rotating disc or travelling in a straight line.

The Michelson and Gale test (6) shows that light does not take up the spin movement of the earth. This is in accordance with UR, which postulates that light moves with the earth on its orbit around the sun but not with the earth's daily spin movement. SR has a grave difficulty with the Michelson and Gale test because the light is shown to go around the globe at different speeds eastward and westward. Is this why that pioneering and extraordinary test is rarely mentioned in university physics textbooks?

Dufour and Prunier (7) showed further positive proof that light moved at a speed of c relative to the laboratory and not relative to any moving object. The Dufour and Prunier test conforms solely to UR. As quoted earlier, in a furious debate with Langevin, Dufour and Prunier recorded that their test results were not in conformity with SR.

Macek and Davis (8) carried out a very accurate Sagnac test. This answers any objection to the Sagnac test that implies that the accuracy of a test done so long ago is not sufficient to be taken seriously.

Saburi et al. (10) carried out a test comparing the time recorded on a clock that was flown on an aeroplane from the U.S.A. to Japan with the time recorded via an electromagnetic signal also sent from the U.S.A. to Japan. The test showed that a signal sent around the earth does not travel at the same speed eastward and westward. This conforms to UR because if the light does not take up the daily spin velocity of the earth (as proposed by UR), this will be the result. Adherents of SR, on the other hand, claim that SR is not relevant because of the element of rotation. This is despite the statement by Einstein to the contrary in his 1905 paper, where he specifically stated that SR applies to motion on a closed circuit. Adherents of SR cannot abide the thought that light is travelling at speeds of $c \pm v$ going westward and eastward around the earth, where v is the surface speed of the earth caused by the spin.

The Brillet and Hall test (11), as analysed by Aspden, shows that on a very accurate Michelson and Morley-type test, the daily spin velocity of the earth is detected. This shows that the velocity of the surface of the earth at the location of the test affects the result of a measurement of the speed of the light.

Bilger et al. (12) carried out a very accurate Michelson and Gale test in the southern hemisphere. Again, this answers the criticism that the Michelson and Gale 1925 test was not sufficiently accurate because it was done so long ago. UR conforms to the Bilger et al. test, but SR does not.

The eight tests listed in table 2 that are not satisfied by SR were performed many years after that theory was promulgated in 1905. Einstein's theory satisfied all the known phenomena at the date of its publication. It should be noted that these eight tests confirm that it is possible to detect absolute motion from a test done solely within the earth's frame; such a detection is an anathema to SR.

UR shows that the speed of light is not, in all circumstances, independent of the speed of the source of the light. That this is true is deduced from the fact that light emitted on the earth takes up the orbital motion of the earth around the sun but does not take up the daily spin motion of the earth.

Could it be that the earth is really the centre of the universe after all? This idea fits many of the requirements set out above. It could explain why light travels with respect to the centre of the earth but not with the orbital movement around the sun. However, this explanation does not fit all the facts. Van Flandern has said (in private correspondence) that:

Nearby stars show parallax compared to distant ones. This means the earth is moving back and forth in an annual cycle. The Sun doesn't see such a parallax. Spectra of all distant astronomical objects have their lines shifted by a component of the earth's orbital speed (30 km/s) that depends on their direction relative to earth's direction of motion. Objects in the earth's orbital plane all show a +30 km/s shift at one time of year, and −30 six months later. With precise observations, one can even see the small effect of the ellipticity of the earth's orbit.

So the recently deceased Pope John Paul II was right when he apologised for the treatment meted out to Galileo!

When writing to Schrödinger in 1935, Einstein advocated reliance on experimental results rather than theory.

All the other fellows do not look from the facts to the theory, but from the theory to the facts; they cannot extricate themselves from a once accepted conceptual net, but only flop around in it in a grotesque way.

Einstein said that a theory that does not fit the experimental facts should be superseded. We can conclude from the above discussion that SR does not fit the experimental evidence and that UR does. Therefore we should, as Einstein said, discard SR.

Light Escaping from Earth

Under UR theory, when light escapes from the influence of the earth, it would travel at a speed of c relative to the point where it escaped. The yearly orbital motion of the earth around the sun would influence the angle at which it escapes. At what precise stage would light escape from the influence of the earth? This is a problem to be solved.

The behaviour of light in outer space would not be as heretofore assumed. UR gives speeds of c ± v for the speed of the light, where v is the straight-line speed of an observer relative to the spot in fixed space where the light was emitted. SR, on the other hand, predicts that the speed will be measured as c by the observer who is travelling in a straight line at constant speed. It seems reasonable to assume (as an interim unproven assumption) that light in outer space is influenced by gravity. Because, as we have shown earlier, light generated on the earth moves with the earth's gravitational field, it seems reasonable to assume that it moves with gravity in general.

It is proposed that light in space speeds through empty space at a velocity of c in relation to absolute space. If light escapes from the earth's atmosphere (as does the reflected light from the sun) and thus escapes from the influence of the earth, the light is then in outer free space and travelling at a speed c relative to the spot where it left the earth's influence. This is like throwing a ball off a train that is speeding through a railway station; once the ball gets free of the train, its subsequent behaviour is to travel until it hits a platform of the station. After leaving the train, the ball is not influenced by any in-between change in movement of either the train or the platform. It travels relative only to the last spot where it left the train (ignoring the influence on the ball of the air, gravity and so forth).

Activities on earth are sometimes referred to as being observed from an inertial frame 'fixed in the stars'. However, this idea is suspect. As Bondi puts it in his book *Relativity and Common Sense* (1964), *"how it is that the distant masses fix the state of no rotation, is not wholly clear"*. He refers to it as *"this very mysterious fact"*. It is proposed later in this book that space in infinite, that it is homogenous in every direction and at all places and that the galaxies are in a steady state with respect to each other, apart from their orbital and random local movements. So, it is with respect to this infinite space that rotation is determined and not with respect to any particular category of stars or the 'distant masses', as they are termed.

The speed c is loosely used for the speed of light in a vacuum and air because the difference is insignificant in most cases. The speed of light in a vacuum is about 300,000 km/s (c). In air, it is slightly less (0.9997c). In water, the speed is about 0.75c. In the gem rutile, light travels at 0.33c. In tellurium, it travels at 0.16c. Any test that sends an electromagnetic signal out to a distant planet and measures the time until the reflected signal returns has sent the signal out of the influence of the earth. The signal travels at close to c in the atmosphere of earth and at that speed relative to the emitter until it leaves the influence of the earth. It then assumes a speed of c in free space relative to the spot where it left the influence of the earth. The return journey is the reverse of this. The difference between having a speed relative to the emitter and relative to the spot where the signal leaves the influence of the earth will not be sufficient to be detected with current technology.

One of the proofs that SR was correct lay in the explanation of the fact that the frequency of light arriving to earth from rotating double stars (one approaching and one receding) was the same from the approaching as from the receding star. There is a difficulty with observing light from such faraway sources. French (1968) points out that a phenomenon known as 'extinction' (as discussed earlier) means that light that passes through a thickness of 10^{-4} mm of glass or 0.1 mm of air has obliterated any memory of the incoming light. The light observed beyond that distance will have no record left of the characteristics of the incoming light. This, unfortunately, gives no proof of the invariance of light speed or frequency coming from the faraway binary stars. Fox (1962) pointed out that *"Double stars, especially close binary pairs, are surrounded by a common envelope of gas which may contain enough matter to extinguish direct light from the stars."*

There have been a number of other (unsuccessful) attempts at explaining the behaviour of light. Being one of the great mysteries of physics, it is not surprising that many authors have attempted to come up with a valid explanation. One is by Ritz (1908), who claimed that light was affected by the movement of the source, which means that a light flash would travel towards an observer at a speed of c plus the movement of the source of the light at the moment of emission (assume a stationary observer in relation to the source). This would be quite unlike the behaviour of sound. We have referred earlier to experimental results that show that Ritz's idea is not correct. On the other hand, work has been carried out (in 1964 by Babcock and Bergman, for example) that convincingly confirms that light in laboratory tests is not affected by the speed of its source.

It is worth remarking that the following phenomena apply to sound: reflection, refraction, interference, the Doppler effect and our famous Sagnac effect. So sound behaves like light with respect to these observable facts. Interesting?

As explained earlier in this book, the instantaneous movement of the source of the light does not affect the instantaneous speed of a light flash. As also shown, light emitting from a moving source always has the origin of the light at the centre of the globe of light that expands from the sequential spots that are the origins of those globes of light. This is just like sound coming from a moving source.

More on Universal Theory

To conform to all the experimental results discussed earlier in this book, we have to invent 'universal theory'. Under this theory, universal time holds sway. All universal clocks record the same time everywhere in the universe. All such clocks record the 'actual' time of any occurrence anywhere in the universe at the instant of the occurrence.

Such clocks will record right now an occurrence that occurs right now at a spot a distance of 1,000 million light-years from here. Information concerning that event will not arrive via the speed of light for another 1,000 million years to that spot in the universe where we happen to be at this instant.

To define universal time (UT for short), which is recorded by our universal clock, we should take the earth as a reference point because it is the human race that is concerned with the problem.

We look out at the sky and see a mixture of events that occurred at various times in the past, some a few seconds ago and others millions of years ago. Our viewing is very interesting in that we can actually look back into the past and see something that occurred so long ago. We can see a cross section of time from now to over 15,000 million years ago. We are lucky that this is our panorama. It is more interesting than looking at a cross-cut of one of the old cedar trees from the Lebanon, which shows us events of some thousands of years ago. Had the transfer of information been at infinite speed, we would not be able to see into the 'past' by looking out into space and observing things that occurred long, long ago. In fact, we have far more knowledge and fun this way because our information is coming in gradually over the millennia.

Let us choose the midpoint of O'Connell Bridge, which spans the River Liffey in Dublin, capital city of Ireland, as the spot in the universe to consider when defining UT. The time from which we shall measure all events in UT is 00.00 a.m. on 1-1-2000 AD. (zero UT). UT starts from the beginning of the century at that spot. Unfortunately, that was the only time in the history of the universe when UT could have been accurately recorded for any spot in the universe. This is because the earth is moving, as is our galaxy, and possibly our universe, and to get back to the same spot again is highly unlikely. Never again can anyone compare their time with zero UT because the spot in space where UT began will never again be occupied by the midpoint of O'Connell Bridge in Dublin. To compare with UT it would be necessary to know the distance from where you are now to the place in the universe where Dublin was at zero time, and that is just about impossible!

All UT timepieces will be (theoretically) synchronised at zero time and will ever afterwards keep UT accurately. At any recording station in the universe, UT will (in theory) always correct the arriving information for the distance through which the information has travelled at the speed of the signal (light or other electromagnetic phenomenon) and will then record the UT of the occurrence of the distant event.

For example, information about an event that occurred at a distance from earth of 7,000 million light-years and at zero UT will be supplied in 7,000 million years to the spot where the earth currently resides, and attached to the information will be the fact that the UT of the event is zero. The information could be attached somewhat like the time shown on a video camera as the time of the recording! I wonder will anyone be on earth to receive the news? Indeed, will the earth be in existence? It will certainly not be where it was on 1-1-2000 AD. Dublin will be the only place in the universe where UT was ever recorded, and that record was solely for the instant of 00.00 a.m. on January 1st 2000 AD. Like Greenwich Mean Time (GMT), which is now largely superceded, this concept has no practical daily use.

129

Application of These Concepts

Let us now apply these conclusions to the concepts discussed in chapters 1 and 2. Going back to figure 5 in chapter 1, consider the definition of 'contemporaneous' as defined by Russell. Figure 5 is reproduced here as figure 20a for ease of reference. We will refer to figure 20b shortly.

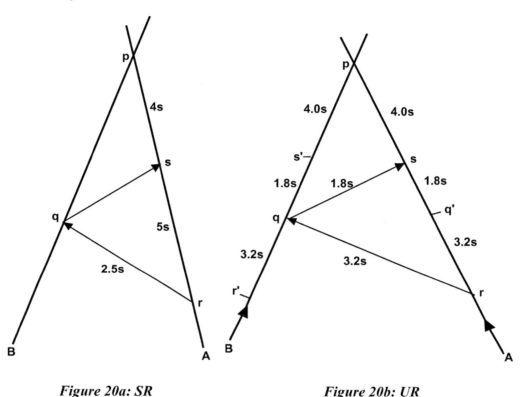

Figure 20a: SR *Figure 20b: UR*

Figure 20: Space-Time Diagrams

The whole of the time between the sending of the first signal from r and its arrival back at s would be defined as 'contemporaneous' i.e. a period of 5 seconds from a total consideration of 9 seconds from the beginning of the events to the end.

If this 'contemporaneous' definition is to be believed, then the time taken by A and B would, according to some texts, have some peculiar results. Geroch makes the following deductions (which the general reader may skip):

- *A would think that B took 6 seconds √(9 x 4), to get from q to p, because the reading on the clock of B would be seen by A at s, and taken as 6 seconds earlier than the reading that is later seen at p.*

- *A on the other hand would take the time for oneself to get from s to p as 4 seconds, from the moment that the reading on the clock of B was recorded (at s).*

130

- *thus A would think that the clock of B had speeded up in the ratio of 6:4*
- *B on the other hand would observe the time on the clock of A when seen at q, as being 9 seconds before the reading that is later seen at p. But B's own clock only shows 6 seconds, from q to p, so B will believe that the clock of A is going faster.*
- *the ratio of 9:6 is the same as 6:4, so each has the same idea as to the speeding up of the clock of the other.*

The derivations done by Geroch for the above deductions are not reproduced here. The derivation derives from the assumption that the time taken by light to travel from one point to another point (r to q) is the same as for the light to travel the reverse journey (q to s) where the observer will again meet the signal.

Geroch then computes the difference between the two clocks in another way, as follows. (This calculation was reproduced beneath figure 5 in chapter 1.) A will deduce that B has come towards A by a distance of 2.5 light-seconds because the light signal went from r to detect where B was and returned 5 seconds later. This shows A that B is 2.5 light-seconds away when the light signal hit B. Therefore, in accordance with SR, A calculates that $t = t'\gamma$, where t is the time as observed by A and t' the time as recorded by B. Because B travelled a distance of 2.5 light-seconds while A travelled from halfway between r and s to p (6.5 seconds, figure 20a), $v = 2.5/6.5$. The slowing of the clock of B is calculated by Geroch to be 7.7%, i.e. the percentage difference between the times 6.0 and 6.5. We thought we had enough of the abstruse gobbledegook in chapter 1. This Geroch piece is a reminder that SR can be invoked at any time to cause utter confusion – just in case we were beginning to think we had got rid of it.

Geroch discusses the two contradictory results by remarking that one result shows that the clock of B speeded up by 50% while the other shows it slowed down by about 8%. He remarks that *"physics never finds any final explanations or real reasons"* and *"one becomes accustomed to accepting gratefully those small glimpses into the workings of nature that one is able to glean"*. Does this read like an admission of failure? Put more bluntly, it reads like a 'load of cobblers', 'tommyrot' and just plain 'bunkum'! We may recall Geroch's statement when we come to consider the twin paradox in further detail in a later chapter.

Builder (1979) stated the problem clearly in relation to SR:

> . . . *the 'velocity of light' must always be interpreted as 'the velocity of light measured in an inertial system' and it must be understood that this value is the average speed measured over a go-and-return path. The principle can then be stated in the form 'The principle of relativity precludes any possibility of ascertaining how light is propagated relative to any inertial reference system. Measurements made in inertial reference systems, using the methods of measurement prescribed by the restricted theory, always give the same value for c for the speed of light irrespective of the direction of its propagation and irrespective of the motion of its source'.*

By 'restricted theory', Builder means SR. He could have added that the speed of light was also irrespective of any motion of the observer making the measurement.

Universal Space-Time Diagram

The following is the usual calculation that would be done without any thought of SR. There is nothing complex or abstruse about the calculation but it is comforting to do it. Going back to figure 5 again (figure 20a above), consider the problem with the aid of the concept of UT, which lets everyone know what occurs exactly as it occurs, no matter where the various observers are situated and no matter what their relative speeds. Remember, we are now applying UT in full to all the following measurements and observations.

From figure 20a, the time for the light signal to go from r to q is believed by A to be 2.5 seconds. Take this as correct for the moment – it will be corrected later by the universal clock. B would have moved a considerable distance in that 2.5 seconds. The distance travelled by B equals 2.5 seconds multiplied by the speed of B, which is taken by A as being $2.5/6.5c = 0.385c$. Therefore, the distance is 0.96 light-seconds, i.e. 0.385 x 2.5c. This is almost one light-second (300,000 km) and is no small distance.

Let us completely redraw figure 5 as figure 20b, which represents the UR interpretation of events. If we begin to allow for these movements and use UT, we can show what is actually happening. As the discussion progresses, figure 20b should be compared in detail with figure 20a.

Figure 20b is a universal space-time diagram. It depicts the movement of two parties A and B as they approach each other travelling through fixed space. We first come across party A at point r and party B at point r'. A and B eventually meet at point p. The distances on the diagram are shown in light-seconds (1 light-second = 300,000 km); this is a convenient measure when large distances are involved. (We could just as well have used kilometres, but the numbers would be cumbersome.)

The diagram is drawn to separate out the parts of the events that occur with respect to starting points, sending of signal, receiving of signal, and meeting at p. The UT system has infinite speed of transfer of information (as we earlier defined it), which is why the diagram can show the 'actual' position in the universe of A and B at all times.

The diagram allows for the timing on the universal clock as follows: At the start of the experiment, when A sends the light flash off from r, B is at r' at that time in UT. Because A is the person who sends out the signal to measure where B is (B sends out no signal), it is from the point of view of A that the diagram is drawn.

The light signal going from r towards q will take longer than on the return journey (q to s) because A and B are approaching each other at a very fast speed. As we saw above, the speed is such that B would be about a distance of one light-second nearer to A while the (presumed) 2.5 second time for the light to travel was elapsing (in figure 20a). This 2.5 s is contradicted in figure 20b and is shown to be greater (3.2 s). The return from q to s (1.8 s) is less than the 2.5 s assumed under SR – again, see figure 20a.

Let us show an approximate timing on figure 20b. Because B is nearer to A at q than when the light signal was sent out from r, the return signal going from q to s takes less time than the outgoing signal going from r to q. Now, all the mystery has disappeared.

All of the following is measured in UT. A is at r and B is at r' at the same time. B is at q and A at q' at the same time. A is at s and B at s' at the same time. Both A and B have a total time from start to finish (from r and r' to p) of 9 seconds.

Notice that the signal going from r to q and back from q to s goes at the speed of light. The other speeds (the movement of A towards p and of B towards p) are less than the speed of light. Also, rq and qs are in light-seconds of time taken by the light to travel those distances. All other numbers on the diagram are times in seconds for A and B to travel the various distances.

Looking at the diagram, we see the following times:

rq	=	3.2 seconds	r'q	=	3.2 seconds	rq'	=	3.2 seconds
qs	=	1.8 seconds	qs'	=	1.8 seconds	q's	=	1.8 seconds
sp	=	4.0 seconds	s'p	=	4.0 seconds	r'p	=	9.0 seconds
rp	=	9.0 seconds	rs	=	5.0 seconds	r's'	=	5.0 seconds

The separation distance qq' is more than 1.8c and less than 3.2c light-seconds, say about 2.5c light-seconds. This is because light travels faster than the travellers and therefore the distance rq' must be less than the distance rq. Furthermore, the distance qs must be greater than q's. The speed of approach of A and B is then not 2.5/6.5c (0.385c), as derived from figure 20a, but closer to 2.5/5.8c (0.43c). This is because qp = 5.8 and q'p = 5.8, and the distance of separation of A from B is qq', which is about a distance of 2.5 light-seconds. Applying this 0.43c in place of the 0.385c derived under SR (see figure 20a), we derive that B will have got nearer to A by a distance of 0.43 x 3.2 = 1.376 light-seconds, while the signal going from r to q travelled a distance of 3.2c light-seconds.

Let us show these results together as follows. At the start of the experiment, r and r' are a distance of 3.87 light-seconds apart. The relative velocity of A and B is 0.43c. In 3.2 seconds, A and B get to be 3.2 x 0.43c = 1.376 light-seconds nearer (at q' and q). In the next 1.8 seconds, they get to be 1.8 x 0.43c = 0.77 light-seconds nearer (at s' and s). In the final 4 seconds, they get to be 4.0 x 0.43c = 1.72 light-seconds nearer (where they meet at p).

Adding all these, we get 1.376 + 0.77 + 1.72 = 3.87 light-seconds separation at the start of the 'experiment'. This distance of 3.87 light-seconds cannot be confirmed by any measurement because while a light signal would be travelling to try to confirm the position of B, B would have moved from the position we are trying to confirm. In UT, the positions of A and B at the start of the experiment are confirmed from the above calculation as placed at a distance of 3.87 light-seconds apart and positioned at r and r' respectively.

'Space-time' as defined under relativity theory is therefore eliminated as a concept by UR.

Distortion Observed

A distortion is caused by the finite speed of light.

Figure 21 depicts an apparent change in length of a rod that exists because of the finite speed of light. This distortion will, as previously indicated, have a correction applied to the length of the rod under UR. The distortion will be a shortening or lengthening depending on whether the rod is recessing or approaching the observer. We shall now analyse the first case. A rod A–B of length L is travelling to the right in the $+x$ direction at a velocity of v. A stationary observer is situated at O. What is seen by the observer at O is whatever is depicted by the light that arrives simultaneously at O. Therefore, we must consider the light that leaves the two ends of the rod and eventually arrives at O at the same instant. Light that leaves the nearer end of the rod (A) to travel to the observer at O will be joined by light that left the far end (B) at an earlier time, so that light from both ends will arrive at the eye of the observer at the same time. The relationship between these two signals is $(L − x)/c = x/v$ because the light signal from the far end of the rod goes at a speed of c and the rod travels forward at a speed of v. The light signal that arrives at point P with the information on the far end of the rod then travels to O simultaneously with the information on the near end of the rod. (End B will have to be slightly thicker to enable the observer at O to see both ends.)

From this equivalence, $x = Lv/(c + v)$. The rod appears shorter by that miniscule amount x.

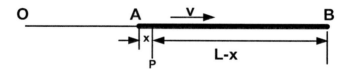

Figure 21: Apparent Rod Shortening

In the case of a very wide rectangular object, there will be a very slight distortion because of the fact that the light from the far corners of the object will travel 'inside' the path of the light from the near corners. Such contraction and distortion are not real but, as far as the observer is concerned, are the only things that can be observed and can be falsely portrayed as 'real'.

The contraction under UR is apparent. It is not a real contraction but is due to the fact that light travels at a finite speed c, the maximum speed at which information can travel. This (apparent) contraction is far greater than that supposed to occur (actually) under SR. The ratio is as follows: The difference in length of the rod (apparently) under UR is $Lv/(c + v)$ as derived above. The supposed (actual) shortening under SR is $L(v^2/2c^2)$ – see Index under 'gamma'. The ratio is approximately $2c/v$, which is the same as the ratio of the Sagnac effect to the SR prediction for that same effect as derived earlier.

References to this facet of the problem are to be found in many texts. The possibility that this is the core of relative motion is dismissed as not worth pursuing. An

134

example is the textbook *University Physics* by Young, in which it states, *"The finite speed of information transmission is not the real issue."* Indeed, as shown in this book, it is the real issue. All this is corrected in UR and no distortion of distance occurs. UR (magically) corrects for all apparent distortions.

Einstein stated that:

The theory of relativity is often criticised for giving, without justification, a central theoretical role to the propagation of light, in that it founds the concept of time upon the law of the propagation of light. The situation, however, is somewhat as follows. In order to give physical significance to the concept of time, processes of some kind are required which enable relations to be established between different places. It is immaterial what kind of processes one chooses for such a definition of time. It is advantageous, however, for the theory, to choose only those processes concerning which we know something certain. This holds for the propagation of light in vacuo in a higher degree than for any other process which could be considered, thanks to the investigations of Maxwell and H. A. Lorentz.

This is certainly true as there is no better way known to measure time. However, the disadvantage caused by the limited speed of light does not give light an absolute right, as assumed by Einstein. Light gives a distorted view, but it is the only view we can get. In the above passage, Einstein is, to an extent, apologising for selecting the propagation of light as the basis of 'time'. Perhaps he appreciated that it was a convenient, if not an ideal, selection. The 'something certain' he mentions is the speed of light, and that is anything but certain, as proven in this book.

Consider the problem associated with a light signal that emanated from a galaxy that was at a distance of 5,000 light-years from the earth's current position when the signal was sent out. The signal arrives here today. According to SR, no time elapsed for the signal itself to get here, i.e. if a clock could have travelled along with the signal, no time would be recorded as having elapsed for the whole journey. According to UR, however, the time elapsed is 5,000 years. It will be seen later that UR can lead to further speculation on the history of the universe.

There is no way in which UR time can be checked in practice. However, its difference from time as calculated under SR can be shown to be correct by observing practical events that tie in with the universal method of timing. Several of these will be discussed below.

Observing Versus Seeing

Terrell (1959) discussed the possibility of photographing the effect of SR on moving objects. He quotes a reference to a 1922 publication by Lorentz (who devised the mathematics of the Lorentz transformations used by Einstein) as stating that the contraction could indeed be photographed. In his first paper on relativity in 1905, Einstein stated:

Whereas the Y and Z dimensions of the sphere (and therefore of every rigid body

135

of no matter what form) do not appear modified by the motion, the X dimension appears shortened; . . . the greater the value of v, the greater the shortening. For v = c all moving objects - viewed from the 'stationary' system shrivel up into plane figures.

What could be clearer? Einstein stated that the shortening could be viewed. Many authors wriggle out of this by implying that Einstein did not really mean that. They play on the words 'observing', 'seeing' and 'appearing to'. Terrell points out that the first paper on relativity theory by Einstein in 1905

> *. . . leaves the intention, perhaps unintentionally, that the contraction due to relativistic motion should be visible. The usual statement is that moving objects "appear contracted" which is somewhat ambiguous. The special theory predicts that the contraction can be observed by a suitable experiment, and the words 'observe' and 'see' seem to be used interchangeably in this connection.*

Terrell proposes an explanation of the difference between 'observing' and 'seeing' as follows:

> *There is however a clear distinction between observing and seeing. An observation of the shape of a fast-moving object involves simultaneous measurement of the position of a number of points on the object. If done by means of light, all the quanta should leave the surface simultaneously, as determined in the observer's system, but will arrive at the observer's position at different times. Similar restrictions would apply to the use of radar as an observational method. In such observations the data received must be corrected for the finite velocity of light, using measured distances to various points of the moving object. In seeing the object, on the other hand, or photographing it, all the light quanta arrive simultaneously at the eye (or shutter), having departed from the object at various earlier times. Clearly this makes a difference between the contracted shape which is in principle observable and the actual visible appearance of a fast-moving object.*

Terrell's 'observing' cannot ever be recorded because the information on different parts of the object arrive at the observer at different times. Here, Terrell says that the appearance of an object moving rapidly across one's line of vision will appear (or be photographed as) distorted. Terrell concludes that *"the Lorentz contraction is effectively invisible"*. Unfortunately, having gone thus far, Terrell adds at the end of the paper, *"None of the statements here should be construed as casting any doubt on either the observability or the reality of the Lorentz contraction, as all the results are derived from the special theory of relativity."*

For more than 50 years following the first 1905 Einstein paper on relativity, it was believed that the shortening of the length of an object in motion relative to an observer could be photographed (Terrell). Lorentz stated it in 1922, and it was not challenged by anyone, including Einstein, until after Einstein's death in 1955. During this period, none of the proponents of SR objected, and therefore it must be assumed that they agreed with that belief. The subject has been largely ignored in recent times. It is a somewhat futile debate because it is unlikely that a photographer will succeed in snapping an oblong object travelling at a speed of 0.99c and be able to compare that snap with the shape at rest.

It is to be noted that the relativity contraction described here is different from the contraction described above under UR. The former was invented to explain the null result from the Michelson-Morley experiment. The latter is merely the result of the finite speed of light.

Moving Clock in Universal Relativity

Figure 22 is a reproduction of figure 4 (chapter 1), which was discussed when describing SR. A flash of light is emitted at point 1. According to the observer travelling with the rod that is moving to the right, as defined by SR, the light travels up the rod and down again at a speed of c.

Using UR, we can analyse the behaviour of the clock as follows. In figure 22b, a light signal sent out from point 1 that goes up towards the top of the rod (which is moving to the right at a speed of v) will not travel the length L along the rod at a speed of c. The light takes the path 1–2. It will ignore the movement of this rod clock and will travel relative to the laboratory and outward from point 1 at a speed of c in all directions.

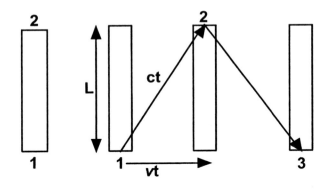

Figure 22a   *Figure 22b*

Figure 22: Moving Clock Under Special Relativity

Let us now redo the problem of the moving clock, as depicted in figure 23. In this diagram, a tiny object acts as a reflector at point 2. Light spreads out in ever-increasing spheres from the origin at point 1. The rod 1–5 moves at speed v in the +x direction, passing through the position 4–2 on its journey.

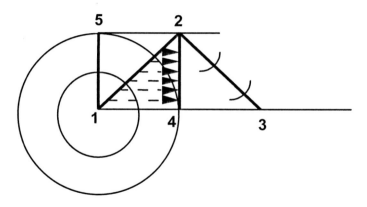

Figure 23: Moving Clock in Universal Relativity

It is a misconception to think that the light in free space travels at a speed of c as measured by a moving observer starting at point 1 and moving with the moving rod to point 4 and then to point 3. To the observer, the speed of the light in the direction 4–2 will not be c.

When light from the pulse emanating at point 1 hits the reflector at point 2, it spreads from there in a sphere, which expands out in all directions allowed by the reflector. The light spreads towards 3 without any impediment. The arcs of this sphere, as it expands, are shown along the line 2–3. Here we have a 'moving clock' where the light goes at speed c from to 2 to 3 but not from 4 to 2.

The horizontal dashed lines with arrowheads show the corresponding points along the vertical rod-clock 4–2 at which the light has arrived. If, for example, the speed of the rod moving to the right is 180,000 km/s, then because the speed of light (along 1–2) is 300,000 km/s, the speed of the light signal up along 4–2 will be 120,000 km/s; this is because the right-angled triangle has sides in the ratios 3, 4 and 5.

The sloping lines 1–2–3 are the lines along which the light travels at the speed of light. The distance 1–2 is made equal to 2–3. The rod takes a time of t to travel from its initial position 1–5 to get to 4–2. Therefore, 1–2 is a distance of tc in light-seconds and 2–3 is also a distance of tc because the light travels along 1–2 and 2–3 at a velocity c. The line 4–2 has the signal travelling at the speed $c\sin\theta$ (θ = the angle 2–1–4) i.e. the vertical component of the line 1–2. Therefore, 4–2 = $tc\sin\theta$ distance measured in light-seconds. The time for the light signal emanating from the origin at 1 to pass along the line 4–2 is $(tc\sin\theta)/c\sin\theta = t$ because the distance is $tc\sin\theta$ and the speed of the signal is $c\sin\theta$.

This result is quite different from that deduced from SR, which concludes that the light going up and down the moving rod clock (see figure 4) travels at the speed of light (c) relative to an observer who remains stationary at point 1 and also to an observer who travels along with the moving clock. UR corrects for the 'moving clocks run slow' syndrome, and it also does away with the twin, or clock, paradox (which will be discussed in further detail in a later chapter).

138

The Lorentz Equations

This section is for those interested in the mathematics of transferring an observation from one frame of reference to another. The Lorentz transformation equations describe how the observations of two observers, moving relative to each other at constant speed, are related. It is not necessary to derive these equations here – indeed, even Einstein, in his 1922 book, assumes that the reader knows the results. In his 1905 paper, Einstein derived (some references say independently) the same equations without any reference to Lorentz. However, in the 1922 book, he named the equations *"Lorentz transformations"*. To quote Einstein from that book:

> *Maxwell-Lorentz equations have proved their validity in the treatment of optical problems in moving bodies; no other theory has satisfactorily explained the facts of aberration, the propagation of light in moving bodies (Fizeau), and phenomena observed in double stars (De Sitter). The consequence of the Maxwell-Lorentz equations that in a vacuum light is propagated with a velocity, at least with respect to a defined inertial system K, must therefore be regarded as proved. According to the principle of Special Relativity, we must also assume the truth of this principle for every other inertial system at rest relative to each other.*

A sphere whose radius is growing at a speed of c may be represented by the equation $x^2 + y^2 + z^2 = c^2t^2$, t being the time elapsed and x, y and z the three-dimensional coordinates. If this equation is valid to the stationary observer, then for the sphere of light to spread as a sphere as observed by a moving observer, the following equation must also be valid, where x', y' and z' are the coordinates and the time elapsed is t' for the moving observer:

$$x'^2 + y'^2 + z'^2 = c^2t'^2$$

The x' is moving with speed v in the $+x$ direction. There is no movement assumed in the y or z directions. For both equations to be valid, Lorentz worked out that the relationships should be as follows. As y and z are not varying, then:

$$y' = y$$
$$z' = z$$
$$x' = \gamma(x - vt)$$
$$t' = \gamma[t - (vx/c^2)]$$

The term γ (which has been derived in chapter 1 following figure 4) is used to transform the expanding sphere of light from one frame to the other, and vice versa. Lorentz got the mathematics right, but the conclusion that he and the Irishman Fitzgerald drew from it was that bodies shortened in the direction of their motion. This idea was subsequently replaced by SR.

It is worth repeating here what was said earlier. The fact that such mathematical equations can be derived does not, in any way, prove that an expanding sphere of light really does give the same speed relative to observers who are moving in relation to each other. Many authors seem to believe that the fact that the mathematics can be calculated proves the physical certainty of the existence of such a phenomenon. Such authors appear to be mesmerised by the beauty of mathematics!

Notice that c is defined as unchanged in the above two formulae for the spheres. Because that speed was defined as unchanged, it was not the mathematical equations that derived or concluded that it was a constant. It was already built in as a precondition! Mathematics is indispensable for describing what occurs. However, just because we can write down a mathematical equation does not mean that it represents reality.

Faster Than Light?

If things go faster than the speed of light, what is the result? It is fascinating to contemplate this possibility. If something is travelling towards us at a relative (not an absolute) speed of 10c, then the information brought to us by such an object would be in advance of the information that we usually get. In a sense this is equivalent to seeing into the future – just a look at information about something that occurred in the past and of which we would, in any case, have knowledge when the normal light signal comes to earth. In this respect, we are not really looking into the future but finding out more quickly about the past.

Assume, for example, that something is coming towards us at a speed of 4,000c. After one light-year, we would see something that would not otherwise reach us at the speed of c for another 3,999 years. This would let us know what was 'going to happen' later on in the past. Such speculation is good fun. However, under UR, it is proposed that the maximum relative speed of light is 2c. There are superluminal sources that seem to be separating at speeds greater than the supposed maximum speed of electromagnetic phenomena. The name 'superluminal' implies travelling faster than light. Things that are said to go faster than light are also referred to as 'tachyons'.

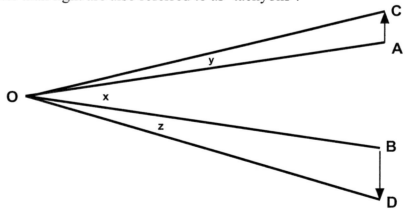

Figure 24: Superluminal Objects

140

Consider the problem in figure 24. An observer is positioned at O. Objects A and B are observed in outer space. The distance of these two objects from earth is known. Later observation shows A and B to have moved to positions C and D, respectively. The difficulty is that to get to C and D in the elapsed time, A and B would have to travel at a speed in excess of the speed of light. The angles measured (x, y and z) are such that the speed of separation must be greater than c.

In *Lectures on Special Relativity*, Bowler (1986) says:

> *A number of very distant radio sources appear to be expanding transverse to the line of sight with velocities in excess of 5c. The best evidence comes from the V.L.B.I. (very long baseline Interferometry) observations of the Quasar 3C 273, where a knot of radio emissions was observed at a transverse distance of 62 Light Years from a central core in July 1977. By July 1980, the knot was 87 Light Years from the central core; the observations gave a constant transverse velocity of 9.6c.*

In *Cosmic Discovery* by Harwit (1981), we read:

> *The compact radio galaxies may well represent two quite distinct classes, a fairly stable group, and a set of sources that seem to consist of components that rapidly expand and move at velocities that incredibly enough, appear to exceed the speed of light; . . . if the quasar was at the large distance indicated by its high red shift expansion at this rate indicated an expansion velocity ten times in excess of the speed of light.*

Cohen et al. (1977) state that *"Nearly half the strong compact sources show a superluminal effect."* So, the effect is not an isolated peculiarity but a common feature. The explanation depends on the accuracy of the measurement of the distance to the objects being observed. If the estimate for the distance to the galaxy is far too great, then speeds in excess of c would not result. We shall consider this matter further in a later chapter on galaxies.

Bowler (1986) also says:

> *The pulsar in the Crab nebula is about 5000 light years distant from earth. It emits a light beam of radio frequency electromagnetic radiation and light which sweeps across the earth every 33 ms. The velocity with which the beam passes over the surface of a sphere of radius 5000 light years centred on the pulsar is $3 \times 10^{13}c$.*

The light referred to here passes across our eyes at billions of times the speed of light! Kiang (1995) measured speeds of close to 5c. When considering the Sagnac effect earlier (see discussion at figure 7, chapter 3), we deduced that light can travel relative to an observer at speeds in excess of c but not in excess of 2c.

Another problem for SR is the so-called scissors experiment (figure 25). One blade is clamped and the other is free to move. If a scissors has a small angle α between the blades, what is the velocity v' with which the tip of the scissors moves along the clamped blade if the velocity of the moving blade is v downwards?

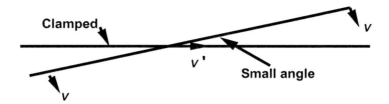

Figure 25: Scissors Experiment

The velocity of the tip $v' = -v/\text{Sin}\alpha$. For modest values of v and small angles, the velocity of the point of contact between the blades exceeds the value of c. For example, for an angle of 0.001 of one degree when $v = 0.001c$ (approximately), $v' = c$. For any value of v greater than 0.001c, v' is greater than c.

Consider the problem where (in figure 24) C and D are both diverging from A and B, respectively, at speeds of 0.1c and the point O is moving to the right at a speed of 0.1c. Then, as deduced in figure 25, the 'scissors' effect would give the speed of separation as apparently far greater than c. This is because the angles subtended from O to A and B are rapidly changing.

If the line A–B (figure 24) had simultaneously approached O, then the objects A and B would appear to have separated by a greater amount. For such movement towards O to explain an apparent transverse movement of 9c, the approach speed would need to be great. However, as far as could be identified by this author, no such approach speed has been identified.

Quantum theory has no problem with considering speeds faster than c (Feynman 1985), particularly at subatomic level. If the reader is interested in objects that appear to go faster than light, there is a bibliography in Feldman (1971) that gives 76 references to articles on tachyon phenomena.

Absolute Versus Relative Velocity

If we have a static universe, the speed of any object can be absolute, and not just relative, to other objects. We can then differentiate between (a) the attainment of an absolute speed of c and (b) the attainment of a speed of c relative to some other object.

Einstein (1922) states *"that material velocities exceeding that of light are not possible, follows from the appearance of the radical $\sqrt{(1 - v^2)}$ in the special Lorentz transformation"*. Einstein does some mental 'sleight of hand' here. He first defines the speed of light as a constant 'c' for observers moving at uniform velocity in relation to each other. Next he does some mathematics on the assumption that this is correct. He finds that $\sqrt{(1 - v^2)}$ is the direct result of the assumption and the mathematics. Then he declares that the result proves that the speed of light cannot exceed c. However, having made the assumption, why be surprised that the result comes out in agreement with the assumption made? This is a perfect example of a 'circular' argument.

On the question of speeds in excess of c, Rothmann (1960), perhaps trying to confuse the issue, says that Einstein did not say that *"nothing could go faster than light"* but that *"no message and no energy (including that contained in the mass of material bodies) could be transmitted faster than light"*.

Figure 26 depicts two objects, A and B, that are diverging at high speeds. Starting together at point O, A goes off to the left at a speed of, say, 0.9c, while B goes off to the right at the same speed. This gives a relative speed of separation of 1.8c. One is not supposed to draw a diagram like this because it seems to contradict the fact that nothing can go at a speed faster than light relative to anything else. To draw such a diagram is supposed to indicate that the person doing so has a limited view and is confined by *"having absolute time at the back of one's mind,"* as Hawking puts it. However, the diagram is now drawn in the sure knowledge that light can be observed as travelling at speeds in excess of c relative to oneself, as shown earlier under the section dealing with the Sagnac tests. If, on the other hand, we do not have SR at the back of our minds, we have no problem looking at two objects that behave as in figure 26.

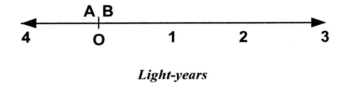

Light-years

Figure 26: High-Speed Separation

Consider what would happen if A and B were photons, each diverging at the speed of light (c). After one year, A and B are two light-years apart, A at point 4 and B at point 1. We cannot see this happening because the speed of light limits the amount of information we can receive. If we stay at the origin where A and B began their journeys, we cannot appreciate what is happening. Even if A stops after one year, A cannot know where B is at the end of one year. Three years would need to go by from the start of the journeys to the time when A would know where B had been after one year. The news of B's whereabouts has to travel from point 1 to point 4 (a distance of two light-years).

Now, following the first year, let B continue for another year at a speed of c. This time, A remains stationary at point 4. The information that B has reached point 2 after two years will reach A after five years from the beginning of the journey – the two years B was travelling plus a further three years for the information to get back to where A has stopped. If B continues for a third year and arrives at point 3, the information regarding B's new position would reach the stationary A at point 4 after seven years.

Consider what would happen had the two photons continued to diverge without stopping for two years:

- After one year, because information can travel only as fast as A and B travel, each would only know that the other had been at the origin a year previously.

- After two years, the same applies. No information regarding what has happened the other since it left the origin can reach either A or B. In this case, A and B might be forgiven for thinking that nothing can travel directly away from them at a speed in excess of c because they know they never identify anything that does. They might conclude that the other party had remained at the origin.

However, the information could accurately reach an observer who is located at right angles to the origin. This observer could observe (many years later) A and B appearing at places that indicate that they must have diverged at a relative speed of 2c.

Universal Length

With UR theory, the problem of the 'ladder in the garage' as posed by Zukav (1979) is eliminated (see the section on length contraction in chapter 2). There is no change in the length of anything, no matter who is looking at it and no matter what their speed relative to the item being measured. A five-metre ladder will not fit into a three-metre garage, no matter what the velocity of the ladder-bearer. You can try sending the bearer at a speed of 0.999c, but the ladder will still not fit into the garage. Under UR, the ladder is the same length to all observers, including its bearer and anyone who is travelling in a remote galaxy at any speed you care to invent.

The 'apparent' shortening of an object that is receding or approaching an observer was discussed earlier in this chapter. Such apparent alteration is 'corrected' by UR, letting the observer 'know' that the real length has not altered.

Universal Energy

In arriving at the famous equation for the relationship between mass and energy, Einstein came from the Maxwell equations relating to electricity and magnetism. Maxwell determined that electromagnetic waves travelled at the speed of light and deduced that they travelled through space. The famous deduction by Einstein yielded the relationship between energy, mass and the square of the speed of light, which is usually written as $E = mc^2$. (However, look up 'De Pretto' in Index.)

In developing SR and the famous equation, Einstein came from the relationship between electric and magnetic effects. He stated that *"the electric and magnetic fields lose their separate existences through the relativity of motion. A field that appears to be purely an electric field, judged from one system, has also magnetic field components when judged from another inertial system."* From his derivation of the mathematics of this strange relationship, Einstein derived in a few paragraphs the relationship between energy and mass.

In figure 27, rest energy is depicted on the vertical axis as E_0. This is the energy corresponding to what we term the 'rest mass'.

144

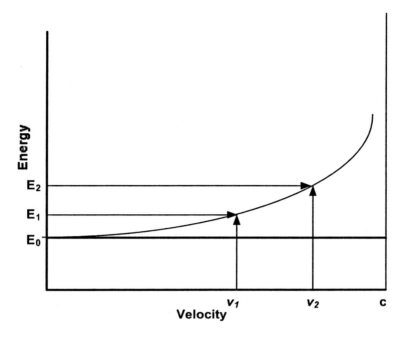

Figure 27: Energy Versus Velocity

If we now accept that it is the 'total energy' that has to be accelerated in every case, then we see that, as energy is added, the total energy that has to be accelerated increases as the velocity increases. At a velocity of v_1, the total energy is E_1; at a velocity of v_2, the total energy is E_2 and so forth.

The relationship between the rest energy E_0 and energy at a given velocity is now derived (from French, 1968). Accept that $E = mc^2$ and that for light, $E = cp$, where p is the so-called 'momentum' of the photon and c the speed of the photon. (Note that a photon has no known mass that has been identified but still has 'momentum', which is defined as mass by velocity.)

From the above two relationships, we get mc $= p$. In Newtonian terms, we have $mv = p$, i.e. mass by velocity = momentum. If we then accept that $E = cp$ for the photon as a particular case of $mv = p$, we can say $Ev = c^2p$, or $cp = Ev/c$.

Under Newton's laws, the increment of kinetic energy corresponds to the work done by external forces, i.e. *dE = Fdx = (dp/dt)dx*, or *dE = vdp*, where F is the force and *dx* the increment of distance. *Ev = c²p* and *dE = vdp*. Multiplying the left and right sides of these two equations together and then integrating *EdE = c²pdp*, we get $E^2 = c^2p^2 + E_0^2$. The E_0^2 is purposely written like this instead of just a constant of integration K because we want to get a particular relationship below. This is because E at $v = 0$ is E_0.

Next we combine $E^2 = c^2p^2 + E_0^2$ with $cp = Ev/c$ and get $E(v) = E_0/[(1 - v^2/c^2)^{0.5}]$. Here we have the Einstein relationship between energy when at rest and energy when in motion. We have derived this relationship directly from the normal relationships between energy, mass and momentum without calling on SR.

145

We describe the phenomenon in figure 27 as being the incremental addition of energy as we increase velocity. This is perfectly understandable when we accept that 'mass' and 'energy' are interchangeable. In all cases of moving objects, we have rest energy plus kinetic energy as total energy. This total energy has to be accelerated if we wish to increase velocity, which leads directly to the situation shown in figure 27. The total energy required to get to a velocity of c is infinite.

The velocities shown in figure 27 are the velocities measured in the inertial frame of the earth. When we release a light photon from a very fast-moving particle (as occurs, for example, when a neutral π meson, which is an unstable particle travelling at a velocity of 0.99975c, emits a photon), the photon moves forward with a slightly higher velocity. This, however, is now attributable to the effect we measured earlier in the Sagnac tests. The photon simply travels at its speed relative to the laboratory and not to the moving meson.

It is interesting to note what French said concerning the laws of magnetism and electricity: *"What is surprising – indeed astonishing – is that Maxwell's laws of electricity and magnetism have required no changes at high velocities."*

It is clear that the relationship between what we traditionally call 'mass' and 'energy' is in accordance with the equation $E = \gamma mc^2$. Lewis (1908) shows a derivation of the same equation, which ties in exactly with figure 27. He purports to show that the kinetic energy accumulated by a body in motion varies from $1/2mv^2$ to mv^2 as the speed of light is approached. He derived the result from a consideration of the fact that a light beam moves a black body in the direction of the beam of light. Lewis quotes Maxwell as deriving this from his electromagnetic theory and from Boltzmann by application of the laws of thermodynamics. He also ascribed it to Poynting and to tests by Nichols and Hull (1903) on the momentum of light.

π Paradox and Length Contraction

The 'Ehrenfest', or 'π', paradox (Ehrenfest, 1909) is now also dispelled because there is no difference in the ratio of the circumference to the radius of a large circle compared with a smaller circle aboard a spinning disc. There are several articles on this paradox. Sama (1972) said that the misconception is the result of the *"imprecise use of notation"*. Pauli (1921) said that *"Ehrenfest has shown that a rigid body cannot be set into rotation"*. Stachel (1980) gives a chapter on the efforts by Einstein to explain the π paradox.

It is not only the twin paradox that leads to nonsensical claims. Dewan and Beran (1959) posed a hypothetical problem concerning the contraction of lengths with increasing speed. They send two rockets off by accelerating them in the same direction. The rockets always have the same speed, which means that the distance between them remains the same even when they speed up to relativistic velocities. *"Since this fact confuses some students,"* comment Dewan and Beran, *"we discuss it at some length."* They say:

> *At first sight the fact that the distance between the two rockets will not change might seem to be in violation of the Lorentz transformation because the latter*

implies that a fast-moving object contracts in the direction of its velocity.

This statement assumes that some stupid students get confused but clever lecturers do not! Dewan and Beran debate the consequence of assuming that the distance between the two rockets would lessen, which would lead to the daft conclusion that there would have to be a relative motion between the rockets. Dewan and Beran conclude that because this contradicts their original stipulation that the two rockets always had the same speed (relative to the earth), the shortening of the in-between distance is too horrible to contemplate. When launching another outrageous suggestion that *"in certain circumstances relativistic contraction can cause measurable stresses"* in any connecting tie, they have the grace to add, *"if this argument is not convincing"*. From all that gobbledygook, Dewan and Beran conclude that the distance between the two rockets does not alter even though each rocket contracts in the direction of its velocity! They continue:

> *Now suppose that one end of a silk thread is attached to the back of the first rocket and the other end to the front of the second rocket. According to the special theory of relativity the thread must contract with respect to S because it has a velocity with respect to S. However, since the rockets maintain a constant distance apart, the thread cannot contract; therefore a stress must form until for high enough velocities the thread finally reaches its elastic limit and breaks.*

Mind you, this all happens while the distance between the two rockets is said to be always the same! Dewan and Beran next consider three rockets all tied together and launched in a straight line and ask *"which ones have the larger and smaller velocities to give the contractions?"* They see no problem with having a rigid rod connecting the two rockets and having that rod contracting with increased velocity. They add the following mysterious distinction:

> *The fact that the rod is 'connected' allows the possibility for it to define a rest length. Two unconnected objects which move in the prescribed manner with respect to an inertial frame need not satisfy constraints which are defined with respect to an instantaneous rest frame.*

It is small wonder that some students are confused; for 'some', read 'all'! The peer review system of approving articles for publication in reputable journals allows such stuff to be published while articles that argue that such conclusions are arrant rot will never see the light of day.

Consistent Theory

In proposing any theory, we should look out for inconsistencies, both internal and external. In the case of SR, an internal inconsistency appears in the twin paradox while an external inconsistency appears in the practical results of the Sagnac test. In that test, the light is not observed as travelling at the same speed relative to an observer aboard the spinning disc. We have shown how this also applies to uniform motion in a straight line.

In such cases, we have to come up with an explanation that will eliminate inconsistencies or else come up with an amended theory. It is a euphemism to name such inconsistencies as 'paradoxes' and to try to put the blame on the reader for not understanding the matter. Instead, we should try to correct the inconsistencies.

In any amendment to existing theory, the impact takes many years to be felt. This is natural because all texts need to be superseded and all the unfortunate lecturers need to relearn their trade and amend their lecture notes. A rearguard action is natural. Indeed, even if it is more correct in its description of nature, ignoring the new theory is what usually happens. So, UR had better look out for storms ahead. This author is satisfied to launch the theory and to allow others to take up the implications in all branches of science.

Even if UR conforms to all the tests quoted in this book and successfully does away with all the so-called 'paradoxes' that are thrown up by SR, this may not be viewed as sufficient. Critics may reasonably demand an explanation as to how UR fits with other phenomena that are explicable by SR. The main ones are addressed in this book. Once the basics of UR are accepted as explaining and removing all the paradoxes mentioned here, the physics fraternity should address the other phenomena with which they are familiar.

Doppler Effect and Relativity

When an ambulance speeds by, you hear a change in tone from its siren. This is known as the Doppler effect and is caused by a change in frequency of the sound that reaches your ears as the ambulance approaches and then recedes. Light behaves in the same way. SR has a method of applying the Doppler effect to light and to all electromagnetic phenomena. This is done as follows (Young).

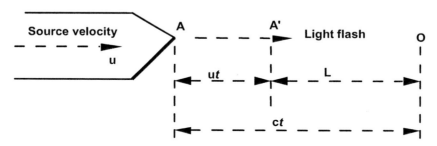

Figure 28: Frequency Changes

In figure 28, a source of light is moving with constant velocity u towards an observer who is stationary at O. The source emits light pulses with a frequency of f_0 and period of t_0 ($=1/f_0$) as measured in its rest frame. With what frequency do the pulses arrive at the observer? Let t be the time interval between the arrival of successive pulses at the observer's position. During the time t, a pulse moves a distance ct and the source moves forward a distance of ut towards O. The second pulse is emitted when A has reached A'.

148

The distance L between successive pulses as measured in the stationary observer's frame is $L = ct - ut = (c - u)t$.

If one pulse arrives at the observer at a certain time, the next pulse arrives after an interval of L/c, which is the time a pulse takes to travel the distance L at speed c. The time between the arrival of successive pulses at the observer's position is then $L/c = (c - u)t/c$. The frequency f with which these pulses are received by the observer at O is the reciprocal of this, i.e. $f = c/L = c/[(c - u)t]$, where f is the frequency received at O. So far, this is exactly the same method as used for the derivation of the Doppler effect for sound from a moving source.

Under SR, the general relationship between the time as measured by the stationary observer and the time t as measured in the rest frame of the moving source is (as derived earlier in this book) $t = \gamma t_0$. To get a general relationship in terms of only c and u and the frequencies, we proceed as follows:

$$t = t_0/(1 - u^2/c^2)^{0.5}$$
$$= ct_0/(c^2 - u^2)^{0.5}$$
Now, $t_0 = 1/f_0$
$$f = 1/t = (c^2 - u^2)^{0.5}/(ct_0)$$
$$= f_0(c^2 - u^2)^{0.5}/c$$

Substituting this expression for $1/t$ above, we get:

$$f = [c/(c - u)][f_0(c^2 - u^2)^{0.5}]/c$$
$$= (f_0)[(c + u)/(c - u)]^{0.5}$$

When $u = 0$, both frequencies are the same; when u approaches c, the frequency received at O approaches infinity. This shows that when the source moves towards the observer, the observed frequency is greater than f. The difference df is the Doppler frequency shift under SR. When the source moves away from the observer, $(c + u)$ and $(c - u)$ reverse positions in the final equation above.

We have a problem with the Doppler effect on light from galaxies. Dingle (1972) discusses this point in detail. If the Doppler effect seems simple, then have a browse through Dingle's 1960 analysis, where he gives a step-by-step run through the problem of the finite speed of light and an assumption of immediate transmission of information as required by relativity theory.

Signals coming from the Pioneer 10 and 11 spacecraft act as if there is an acceleration of the spacecraft towards the sun. This effect is the subject of speculation by Renshaw (1999) as to its cause.

This raises a problem with Maxwell's equations, which say that any speed greater than c is impossible. We have a 'Hobson's choice' here – either we assume an infinite speed for the transmission of the information concerning the recession of a galaxy or we assume that Maxwell's equations, which require that light travels no faster than a speed of c, are incorrect. This is often referred to as one of the unsolved problems of SR (another euphemism!). With UR, there is no problem because the information comes to earth at a speed of c.

Another phenomenon is the fact that under UR, caesium clocks should run slow with increasing absolute speed ('absolute' being in relation to the centre of the earth for all clocks on the earth, as discussed earlier). This is because it has been shown by Ives and Stilwell (1938, 1943) that the frequency of a moving atomic clock reduces asymptotically to zero at the speed of light.

Ives carried out an experiment in which he used canal rays (positively charged hydrogen atoms) whose frequency can be determined from the light they emit. He compared the frequency of a stationary hydrogen atom with that of a hydrogen atom moving with high speed. He attained this by subjecting the atoms to a high voltage and ejecting them through a perforated plate in a stream. He was able to prove that the frequency depended on the velocity of the atoms. Ives presented a paper at the Royal Dublin Society in 1951, which was published in the society's proceedings in 1952. The paper is also to be found in the book *The Einstein Myth and the Ives Papers*, edited by Turner and Hazlett (1979). A very important distinction is to be made here. Because of the null result from the Michelson and Morley experiment, Ives was assuming that the Fitzgerald contraction in the direction of travel was true. He could not devise a way to measure the supposed contraction of any dimension with speed. He set out to determine if the 'time' was slowed with motion – this would be required to back up the Fitzgerald contraction. As we saw earlier in this tome, a more accurate Michelson and Morley-type experiment showed that the result was not null at all.

Now we see that the experiment by Ives proves something entirely different. It showed that the frequency of the hydrogen ray varied downwards with increased speed. In relation to what was the speed having this effect? As we saw earlier in chapter 5, atomic clocks run slow with respect to the non-rotating centre of the earth. Ives's experiment conforms to this idea. The way the clocks run slow is in accordance with the formula $f = f_0(1 - v^2/c^2)^{-0.5}$, where f is the frequency of the moving clock, f_0 is the frequency of the stationary clock and v is the velocity of the moving clock with respect to the non-rotating centre of the earth. In the Ives experiment, the velocity was measured with respect to the laboratory in which he was working. As we saw earlier, this is the correct measurement in the case of a laboratory experiment.

We could be puzzled as to why the formula looks exactly like the 'gamma' factor that is so prevalent in the theory of relativity. However, that formula is very common for other things, such as kicking a football against a glass window and photographing from the other side of the glass the disc that forms where the leather of the ball flattens against the window (assuming no slippage). Gamma will give the radial contraction of the leather at each point on the disc. Therefore, gamma is not peculiar to relativity theory. It is not just about the projection of planes onto planes – it also shows up when we project spheres onto planes.

We could protest that the geocentre is a very strange spot in the universe for atomic clocks on earth to regard as their base. However, that is the way it is and someone will have to come up with an explanation as to why this is so. This book puts forward the idea that light on the earth travels with gravity – time will tell if this idea holds up. A very important fact is that an atomic clock on earth runs slow depending on its speed in relation to the non-rotating centre of the earth. This matter is later described at greater length when discussing the synchronisation of atomic clocks on the earth.

Synopsis to Date

1. SR requires that, with uniform relative motion, time runs slow and objects contract in the direction of travel. UR theory contradicts SR. UR gives an explanation that is compatible with absolute time and distance.

2. Light pulses sent around the circumference of a small rotating disc in opposite directions will not travel at the same speed relative to an observer aboard that disc. The explanation put forward in this book for this effect is that light on the earth travels relative to the laboratory, even when it is generated aboard a spinning apparatus. The same applies to light pulses sent around the earth in the east and west directions. In this case, the earth is a huge spinning disc – the geocentre travelling with the earth on its orbit around the sun corresponds to the laboratory.

3. This leads to the conclusion that distances and time aboard a spinning disc are the same as in the stationary laboratory. They are also the same aboard any object moving in a straight line with constant speed relative to the laboratory. This does not agree with one of the postulates of SR on the behaviour of light.

4. Light generated on the earth travels with the earth on its orbit around the sun. In this particular case, therefore, light has a speed that is not independent of the motion of the emitting source. This fact contradicts the other postulate of SR on the behaviour of light.

If you have followed the discussion so far in this book, you will appreciate that SR, and with it the theory of GR, is disproven. In Einstein's own words, *"the theory of relativity resembles a building consisting of two separate storeys, the special theory and the general theory. The special theory, on which the general theory rests, applies to all physical phenomena with the exception of gravitation."*

A paradox has the same significance for the logician as the smell of burning rubber has for the electronics engineer.

Sir Peter Medawar, Nobel Laureate (1941)

It is clear that the same results hold good of bodies at rest in the 'stationary' system, viewed from a system in uniform motion.

Albert Einstein (1905)

Chapter 7

Twin Paradox Revisited

Dingle Versus McCrea

Let us revisit the twin, or clock, paradox. Not everyone accepted the unequal ageing of the twins. Perhaps the premier advocate of the unacceptability of the twin paradox was the English professor H. Dingle. The author of this book had never heard of Dingle until well into this investigation. My first reaction was disappointment that someone else had trod much of the same path before me. However, on reflection, it was consoling to find that Dingle, an eminent scientist, somewhat like St. Paul on the road to Damascus, had had second thoughts concerning what he had been preaching for years.

Who was he? Dingle was no amateur in the field of relativity. Unlike an engineer who had merely proven that a siphon could lift water to a height greater than the equivalent of atmospheric pressure (Kelly, 1966) or that Faraday's Law (Kelly, 1997) was not correct in all circumstances (me!), Dingle was an expert in this field. He had published standard university textbooks on relativity in 1922 and 1940. He had taught the subject in university undergraduate courses for many years. He was the expert used for decades by the Encyclopedia Britannica to write the section on relativity. Indeed, when he began to doubt the veracity of Special Relativity (SR), he proposed that he would no longer write for the encyclopedia. They asked that he record his doubts in the continuing article, which he did.

Dingle was well known to all the early workers in the field and was praised by Max Born for his second book on relativity. This book was much used in four editions over several decades in universities throughout the world. Dingle had discussed relativity theory with Einstein, Eddington, Tolman and Born. Indeed, Tolman's book *Relativity Thermodynamics and Cosmology* has 'Dingle's formulae' from 1932–3, when Dingle worked for Tolman on the production of the book.

Einstein's book *Relativity* was issued in an English edition in 1920. In an enlarged edition in 1954, which includes a preface by Einstein, Dingle's book *The Special Theory of Relativity* (1940) is listed at the top of the reference list. The books were not listed by date of publication, indicating that Dingle's book did not top the list by coincidence. Apart from books by or about Einstein, books by Eddington, McCrea, Schrödinger, Tolman, Pauli and Møller are also listed. We can assume that these were 'approved' texts. This shows that Einstein considered both Dingle and McCrea as experts on relativity theory. Dingle first saw the problem with SR in the same year that Einstein died (1955).

It was because of Dingle's eminence in the field that he was taken seriously. Unfortunately, nobody would answer his simple query on the twin paradox, and all the experts ran for cover and remained silent.

Professor McCrea, an Irishman, had written the foreword to the English edition of

Einstein's *The Meaning of Relativity*, which was published in 1967. At the time this author was starting this book, McCrea was well into his 90s, but has since died.

Dingle began by showing the danger of accepting a mathematical solution to a problem as inviolate. He gave the example of trying to calculate the length of the side of a cube of volume 8 units. This has three mathematical results: 2; $[\sqrt{(-3)} - (1)]$; and $[-\sqrt{(-3)} - (1)]$. We are so used to such nonsensical results in our mathematics classes that we just ignore the second and third solutions and accept the answer of 2 units. Remember that the second and third results have a mathematical validity but have no physical meaning whatever. Dingle pointed out that in mathematics we can have nonsensical results as well as sensible ones and that we have to decide between the real and the bogus results.

Dingle set out the problem very simply:

The problem here is to find the relation between the rates of two exactly similar clocks, A and B, of which one is moving uniformly with respect to the other, on the assumption that the motion is truly relative, i.e. that there is no justification for ascribing it to one rather than the other. Now this is a problem that can be solved mathematically, and we find that there are two solutions, known technically as the 'Galilean Transformation' and the 'Lorentz Transformation'. According to the first the clocks work at the same rate, and according to the second they work at different rates. The special theory of relativity regards the second as true and the first as false; the usual expression is that 'a moving clock runs slow'. But, as we have said, it is a condition of the problem that either clock can be regarded as the 'moving' one, so this second solution (subject, of course, to the truth of the postulate that the motion is truly relative) requires equally that A works faster than B and that B works faster than A, and just as we know enough about measuring rods to know that they cannot read $\sqrt{-3}$ - (1), so we know enough about clocks to know that one cannot work steadily both faster and slower than another.

Dingle asks, *"How is it possible that such an obvious absurdity should not only have ever been believed but should have been maintained and made the basis of almost the whole of modern physics for more than half a century. . .?"* For 'half' now read 'whole'! Dingle eventually poses the question simply as:

How does one determine, consistently with the theory, which clock works the more slowly? Unless this question is answerable, the theory unavoidably requires that A works more slowly than B, and B more slowly than A - which it requires no super-intelligence to see is impossible.

Dingle was met with complete silence from the scientific fraternity. We all know how keen scientists are to demolish a colleague who is thought to be in error. Indeed, that is the spice of scientific debate. You would have to read Dingle's book *Science at the Crossroads* (1972) to get a flavour of the way in which the scientific establishment tried to ostracise him for asking a simple straightforward question that could be understood by any 10-year-old.

A president of the Royal Society tried in vain to get one single authority on relativity to comment on Dingle's poser. He wrote to Dingle as follows: *"My blood will boil if I am unable to do something about it."* Dingle eventually thought that he would have had success had he been more focused in his questioning and stuck with repeating the simple question with which he had begun. I do not think that this would have made a whit of difference. He certainly got into a morass once he widened the debate, as we will see below. The whole matter is largely one of theory and few facts are brought to bear on the mathematical issue. It is a bit like two theologians from different religions debating the veracity of their beliefs.

Indicative of Dingle's tenacity is what Professor Max Born wrote in *Nature* in 1963 when challenged by Dingle to respond: *"Though former experience has taught me that discussing relativity with Dingle leads to no agreement, I have to answer a challenge which is directed against the 'scientific integrity' of myself and of others."* Undeterred, Dingle responded that Prof. Born's response did not answer his query. One can, with hindsight, have sympathy with both of them. Born had to assume (as is required by SR) that the speed of light must be measured as constant by all observers in all inertial frames. He had a beautiful diagram illustrating this in his response to Dingle. Dingle did not accept the response. He repeated the twin paradox and could not accept that either twin would simultaneously be younger than the other. Neither of the authors referred to the fact that Einstein had actually stated that the time on the clocks would slow *mutatis mutandi,* as quoted above. Had this been uncovered and highlighted, I wonder how the debate would have progressed.

Dingle persevered and tried to make the opposition see sense. He was, as it turned out, wasting his time. His questions became more complex. He was correct when he bemoaned the fact that he had not continued repeating the original simple question.

Here is more of what Dingle published (figure 29). Four people, X, Y, A and B, are moving at velocity v to the right:

Figure 29: Dingle's Puzzle

A and X are twins who separate at birth at a speed v such that $\sqrt{(1 - v^2/c^2)} = 1/5$. Each carries a clock which reads 0 at the moment of separation and thereafter reads the age of the bearer. Ahead of A, in the direction of X's motion, and keeping at a constant distance from A, is another child B, born at the same moment as A in A's and B's common time system and carrying a similar clock synchronised with A's. Likewise, in the rear of X, and keeping at a constant

155

distance from X, is a child Y, born at the same moment as X, in X's and Y's common time system and carrying a similar clock synchronised with X's.

When X is 6 years old he passes B and they exchange photographs which they have just taken. B, and therefore A, is then 30 years old according to the Lorentz transformation. Further, when A is 6 years old Y passes him and they exchange recent photographs. The Lorentz transformation then shows that Y, and therefore X, is then 30 years old. All assemble later and agree, on the evidence of the photographs, that A is 30 when X is 6 and X is 30 when A is 6. I call this a contradiction.

Dingle discusses as follows the consequences of accepting the paradox as a disproof of SR:

Even a brief reflection on the consequences of a disproof of the special relativity theory shows how fundamental they are. In the first place, 'space-time', as something having objective significance, is abolished, and 'universal time', independent of space, is restored - not, however, as a necessity of thought as in the old days, but as the only concept of time that makes possible a consistent description of nature. There is no limit to the velocities attainable by material bodies, and - unless there is, in fact, an ether of the Lorentz type which modifies bodies moving through it - there is no contraction of rods, slowing down of clocks, increase of mass, and so on, accompanying motion.

In Dingle's book *Science at the Crossroads*, full details of the debate are recorded, together with Dingle's later unsuccessful attempts to get his ideas published in scientific journals. He quoted the correspondence published in *Nature* in 1967 and 1968 and included an editorial from the October 1967 edition, which contained the two papers written by Dingle and McCrea. There was a further paper by Dingle the following year.

On reading *Science at the Crossroads*, it was clear that Dingle had already covered the following points unearthed in this book: (i) Einstein had not referred in his 1905 first paper on relativity to the reverse situation when discussing clock 'A' going slower than clock 'B'. Dingle did not mention nor seem to know that Einstein did refer to this in his 1922 book; (ii) using that reverse situation, each clock must go slower than the other, which is not possible.

Having got over the shock of seeing that Dingle had predated my derivation by more than 20 years, it was comforting to see that another author had noticed the omission in the first 1905 Einstein paper. Had Dingle noticed that Einstein had said in his 1922 book that the situation applied *mutatis mutandi*, his debate with McCrea would have been even more heated. It would still probably not have gone in Dingle's favour because most scientists believed that relativity theory just had to be right in view of the fact that no refutation was forthcoming from any tests done over the years. The opposition might still have come back with ever more convoluted (purely theoretical) responses and would have carefully avoided the nub of the query, or more likely maintained silence.

McCrea dismissed Dingle's argument concerning the reverse situation of the two clocks moving in relation to each other by saying that they *"concern two different sets of events, and so they cannot contradict each other"*. All Dingle was saying was that the reverse situation must apply, i.e. that to an observer travelling with clock B, the clock at A must also appear to run slow. Even though Einstein actually stated this to be the case in his 1922 book, McCrea defended the opposite view to the bitter end.

Dingle states in his book that because SR *"is based on two postulates and a definition,"* one of three things had to be incorrect. He argued that if these three items are accepted, *"the rest follows logically, so there must be incompatibility in these foundations"*. He states the two postulates and the definition as follows:

1. *The postulate of relativity - that nature contains no absolute standard of rest, that would enable a unique state of uniform motion to be ascribed to a single observable body.*

2. *The postulate of constant light velocity - that the velocity of light, with respect to any chosen standard, has a constant value c which is independent of the state of (uniform) motion of the source from which it is emitted i.e. that if, from two sources in uniform relative motion, light pulses are emitted in the direction of motion at an instant at which the sources are adjacent to one another, those pulses will thereafter remain adjacent and reach a distant point at the same instant.*

3. *The time (instant) of an instantaneous event, occurring at a distance r from a clock which is accepted as a standard (r being measured by a standard scale at rest with respect to the clock) is given by subtracting r/c from the clock reading when a light-pulse, emitted at the time (instant) and place of the occurrence of the event, reaches the clock.*

Dingle then argues that the third item, the definition, follows from the second postulate so that at least one of the postulates must be incorrect: *"Our problem is to determine which of these is wrong; possibly, of course, both are wrong, but at least one must be so."*

However, Dingle does not clearly highlight here the strangest claim made by Einstein – that the speed of light as measured by observers travelling away from or towards the source of that light is also a constant 'c'.

Dingle proposed that if SR were left unchallenged, the direst consequences could result for the human race. He stated the following warning:

Directly or indirectly - at present chiefly the latter, though none the less inseparably - special relativity is involved in all modern physical experiments, and these are known to be attended by such dangerous possibilities, should something go wrong with them, that the duty of ensuring as far as possible that this shall not happen is imperative.

Understandably, this scare-mongering got Dingle nowhere with his peers because no problems were evinced with any experiments or observations made.

McCrea states, *"The first thing that relativity does is to deny any operational meaning to the notion of simultaneity at two different places."* On this argument he decried Dingle's logic. This is like the Einstein Train puzzle (see chapter 1), where simultaneity is said to be relative. Two events that are simultaneous to one observer are said not to be so to another observer who is in uniform motion with respect to the first observer.

Let us go back to the definition by Einstein of 'simultaneity' in his first 1905 paper. He devoted no less than 10% of the whole paper to this definition. He wrote:

If at the point A of space there is a clock, an observer at A can determine the time values of events in the immediate vicinity of A by finding the position of the hands which are simultaneous with these events. If there is at point B of space another clock in all respects resembling the one at A, it is possible for an observer at B to determine the time value of events in the immediate neighbourhood of B. But it is not possible without further assumption to compare, in respect of time an event at A with an event at B. We have so far defined only an 'A time' and a 'B time'. We have not defined a common 'time' for A and B, for the latter cannot be defined at all unless we establish by definition that the 'time' required by light to travel from A to B equals the 'time' it requires to travel from B to A. Let a ray of light start at the 'A time' t_A from A towards B, let it at the 'B time' t_B be reflected at B in the direction of A, and arrive again at A at the 'A time' t'_A.

In accordance with definition the two clocks synchronise if $t_B - t_A = t'_A - t_B$.

We assume that this definition of synchronism is free from contradictions, and possible for any number of points; and that the following relations are universally valid:

1. If the clock at B synchronises with the clock at A, the clock at A synchronises with the clock at B.

2. If the clock at A synchronises with the clock at B and also with the clock at C, the clocks at B and C also synchronise with each other.

Einstein continued:

We have settled what is to be understood by synchronous stationary clocks located at different places, and have evidently obtained a definition of 'simultaneous' or 'synchronous', and of 'time'. The 'time' of an event is that which is given simultaneously with the event by a stationary clock located at the place of the event, this clock being synchronous, and indeed synchronous for all time determinations, with a specified stationary clock.

In agreement with experience we further assume the quantity $2AB/[t'_A - t_A] = c$ to be a universal constant - the velocity of light in empty space.

It is essential to have time defined by means of stationary clocks in the stationary system, and the time now defined being appropriate to the stationary system, we call it 'the time of the stationary system'.

Einstein was convinced that the speed of light had to be a constant 'c' as measured by any two observers who were travelling with uniform motion with respect to each other. As we now know, this is untrue. Taking the distance AB and dividing it by the total time for light to travel from A to B and back again is not always a constant as Einstein assumed.

The correspondence between Dingle and the scientific journals became somewhat ludicrous. At one stage, the editor of *Nature* wrote to Dingle saying, *"I agree with you that what McCrea says is mystifying,"* but did not comment further. The editor of *Nature* had promised a subsequent editorial saying precisely what the supposed error in Dingle's approach was. This eventually appeared in 1972, quoting the Hafele and Keating test as the final answer to Dingle's objections. Unfortunately, as seen earlier, that test proves no such thing. The Royal Society declined to publish an article by Dingle because their two referees (anonymous) had written, *"in the present case the fallacy is so elementary that I must recommend the rejection of the paper"* and *"my view is that the Society would make itself ridiculous by publishing this paper"*. It is highly unlikely that the Royal Society will open its files to the public to determine who were the referees!

At least McCrea tackled Dingle in print, even though the end of the controversy was very unsatisfactory. One scientist who gave a modicum of credence to Dingle was the Irish professor J. L. Synge, quoted by Dingle as *"by common consent one of the leading authorities on the mathematical side of the theory, and advocates of it"*. Synge debated the problem in *Nature* in 1968 and said that Dingle's ideas were *"equivalent to Newton's concept of absolute time, and since relativistic physics appears to me to represent nature more closely than Newtonian physics I cast my vote in favour of relativity theory"*. At least Synge rejected Dingle's theories with the casting of a vote and not with an absolute dismissal.

The U.S.A. journal *Science* also declined to enter the debate by refusing an article by Dingle in 1969. They wrote to him saying that *"We have consulted two distinguished physicists in this country who feel that your letter adds little to the discussion in Science in 1957-8."* Interestingly, Dingle said that nobody had questioned the veracity of the theory in *Science* in 1957–8, whereas he himself was now questioning it.

The president of the British Association wrote to Dingle as follows:

Perhaps, in the end, you will have been proved right and I, with all my colleagues, wrong, and a sorry lot of fools we will seem. However life is full of such gambles and I am prepared to take my chance on it.

Sir Bernard Lovell, the eminent astronomer, after whom the observatory in England is named, replied to Dingle when the latter wrote to him looking for support: *"I have never been one of those who pretended to understand either the theory of relativity or its implications."* At least he was honest. Dingle thought that Lovell was avoiding the problem as Lovell's knowledge of science was very wide. If Lovell did not understand it, then why was it being taught as gospel to undergraduates all over the world?

All the controversy creates the distinct impression of a 'cult' that will not brook any interference with its beliefs. My late brother, a cleric, said that he spent his life teaching things he did not understand, but at least he taught them as 'mysteries' that we are not supposed to comprehend. We hope that science is not a religion with mysteries that can never be explained. Several of those who excused themselves to Dingle on the grounds that they were not experts and had not an in-depth understanding of relativity were eminent university professors who had been teaching this subject to undergraduates for many years. The unfortunate students are the victims of this nonsense. Dingle was suitably scathing on this point.

Interestingly, no physicist, with the single exception of McCrea (and leaving aside the letter from Born), replied to Dingle; all the others remained silent. If they were all so sure of their ground, why did they not respond? In general, scientists are only too eager to rush into print whenever they see what they believe to be an error.

Dingle tried every avenue, including the Press Council in the U.K., to try to get the Royal Society to do more. Not surprisingly, his efforts were all in vain. As described above, SR was proving completely coherent and useful. Why then should anyone listen to the bleatings of one (by now old) former member of the 'cult'? I tried to contact Dingle by writing to his address. I was too late. I got a reply from the new owners of the house that he had died. They wrote that they knew from the neighbours that he had been a very friendly and helpful person.

Dingle did not know of Sagnac's work. Had he known of it and of Dufour and Prunier's tests, perhaps the debate would have gone on longer. The only way he could get the matter into the open was to publish *Science at the Crossroads*, where the whole sordid affair is given in detail. The reader should get that book from a library and make up his or her own mind about the rights and wrongs of the issue.

The standard trick in dealing with Dingle has been to brand him as 'that well-known crank'. This avoids answering the question that he posed.

Einstein and the Twins

Be prepared for more gobbledegook. You see, Einstein was concocting a convoluted but nonsensical article to cloud the issue for 13 years; he has to date got away with the supposed explanation, with the single exception of Dingle's refutation. Read on. In 1918, after 13 years of avoiding the problem, Einstein eventually answered the challenge concerning the one-sided ageing of the twins who are in uniform relative motion. It is worth following the argument that he made as a so-called explanation of the paradox in order to appreciate what a 'con trick' he pulled.

In an article in German in *Natürwissenschaften*, Einstein postulated that *"the speeding up of a moving clock in the acceleration phase was exactly twice the slowing down that is occasioned in the steady-speed state"*. This is quoted in translation in Dingle's book (p. 194).

The following bizarre incorrect bluff of a supposed 'proof' of one-sided ageing has been buried in the archives. It is surely another huge embarrassment to believers of relativity theory. If Einstein's explanation were palatable, would not everyone quote it whenever any doubts were raised? Apart from Dingle, no other author seems to have referred to that Einstein article over the past 87 years.

As this article by Einstein is very important in the paradox debate, it is quoted here in full. In a supposed discussion between a sceptic and a relativist, the sceptic raises the paradox of the two clocks (U_1 and U_2), each of which is supposed to be running slower

160

than the other.

Let K be a Galilean system of co-ordinates within the meaning of the special theory of relativity - that is, a reference frame relatively to which isolated mass points move uniformly in a straight line. Further, let U₁ and U₂ be two exactly similar clocks, free from external influences. They work at the same rate when at rest relatively to K, either immediately next to one another or at an arbitrary distance apart. If, however, one of the clocks, let us say U₂ - is in a state of uniform translatory motion relatively to K, according to the special theory of relativity - judging from the system of co-ordinates called K - it is supposed to work more slowly than the clock U₁, which is at rest relatively to K. This seems odd in itself. It gives rise to serious doubts when one imagines the following familiar thought-experiment.

Let A and B be two points of the system K at a distance from one another. To depict the situation more precisely, let us assume that A is at the origin of K, and B at a point on the positive x-axis. Let the two clocks at first be at rest at A, so that they work at the same rate, and let their readings be the same.

We now impart to U₂, a constant velocity in the direction of the positive x-axis, so that it moves towards B. At B we imagine the velocity reversed, so that U₂ returns towards A. When it arrives at A its motion is stopped, so that it is now again at rest relatively to U₁. Since the change in the reading of U₂, judged from K, which might occur during the acceleration of U₂, certainly cannot surpass a definite amount, and since U₂ works more slowly than U₁ during its uniform motion along the line AB (judged from K), then, if AB is sufficiently long, U₂ must lag behind U₁ on its return.

Now comes the rub. According to the principle of relativity the whole process must surely take place in exactly the same way if it is considered in reference frame K' which shares the movement of U₂. Relatively to K' it is U₁ that executes the to-and-fro movement while U₂ remains at rest throughout. From this it follows that, at the end of the process, U₁ must be behind U₂ which contradicts the former result. Even the most loyal adherent of the theory surely cannot maintain that, of two clocks at rest beside one another, each is behind in time compared to the other.

The relativist, after accepting the last statement, objects that the special theory is inapplicable in this case, since it deals only with unaccelerated reference frames, while K and K' are at times accelerated. The critic points out that the general theory does deal with accelerated frames, and the relativist is forced to agree.

It is certainly (he says) that from the point of view of the general theory of relativity, we can use the co-ordinate system K' just as well as the system K. But it is easy to see that, in their relation to the process under consideration, the systems K and K' are by no means equivalent; for while the process is to be conceived as above from K, it presents a completely different aspect when looked at from K', as the following comparison shows:

A. Reference Frame K

1. *The clock U2 is accelerated by an external force in the direction of the positive axis until it reaches the velocity v. U1 remains at rest.*

2. *U2 moves with constant velocity v to the point B on the positive x-axis. U1 remains at rest.*

3. *U2 is accelerated by an external force in the direction of the negative x-axis until it reaches the velocity v in the negative direction. U1 remains at rest.*

4. *U2 moves with constant velocity v in the direction of the negative x-axis to the neighbourhood of U1. U1 remains at rest.*

5. *U2 is brought to rest by an external force.*

B. Reference System K'

1. *A gravitational field, oriented in the direction of the negative x-axis, is set up, in which the clock U1 falls with an accelerated motion until it reaches the velocity v. An external force applied to U2 in the direction of the positive x-axis prevents U2 from being moved in the gravitational field. When U1 has reached the velocity v the gravitational field disappears.*

2. *U1 moves with constant velocity v to a point B' on the negative x-axis. U2 remains at rest.*

3. *A homogeneous gravitational field in the direction of the positive x-axis is set up, under the influence of which U1 is accelerated in the direction of the positive x-axis until it reaches the velocity v in this direction, whereupon the gravitational field disappears. An external force applied to U2 in the direction of the negative x-axis prevents U2 from being moved by this gravitational field.*

4. *U1 moves with constant velocity v in the direction of the positive x-axis into the neighbourhood of U2. U2 remains at rest.*

5. *A gravitational field in the direction of the negative x-axis is set up, which brings U1 to rest. The gravitational field then vanishes. U2 is kept at rest during this process by an external force.*

Einstein stressed that we must bear in mind that exactly the same process is described in the two sets of itemised occurrences under the two reference systems K and K', but that the description in the top list refers to the coordinate system K while the lower list refers to K'. To continue the quotation:

According to both descriptions, at the end of the process the clock U2 is retarded by a definite amount compared with U1. With reference to K' this is explained as follows: It is true that during the stages 2 and 4, the clock U1 moving with velocity v, works more slowly than U2, which is at rest. But this retardation is overcompensated by the quicker working of U1, during stage 3. For, according to the general theory of relativity, a clock works the faster the higher the gravitational potential at the place where it is situated, and during stage 3, U1 is indeed situated in a region of higher gravitational potential than U2. Calculation shows that the consequent advancement amounts to exactly twice as much as the retardation during stages 2 and 4. This completely clears up the paradox which you have propounded.

This attempted explanation by Einstein is arrant nonsense. On the journey of a twin who goes off and then turns around and comes back again, the acceleration phase can be of any duration and magnitude and the deceleration phase can also be of any duration we like. The return journey could have entirely different acceleration and deceleration. Therefore, we cannot say that the magnitude of any acceleration or deceleration effect would exactly balance out the slowing that is supposed to happen during the (arbitrarily chosen) steady-state phases. As an example, in reference system K', we could have the steady-state phases going out and back each of duration 100 years, while phase 3, which reverses the motion, could take 10^{-100} s. How could the slowing that took place over 200 years ago be exactly balanced by a quickening that takes place in 10^{-100} s? An alternative example could have the steady state, out and back, taking 10^{-100} s, with the acceleration and deceleration parts taking 100 years each.

As for the statement by Einstein that *"U1 is indeed situated in a region of higher gravitational potential than U2,"* Einstein had laid down that a gravitational field was *"set up"* acting on both of the clocks. He also said that *"an external force applied to U2 prevents U2 from being moved by the gravitational field"*. Therefore, both clocks are in the same 'even' gravitational field.

Einstein's analysis used a supposed gravitational field to reverse the motion of one twin. This field is then used to introduce GR (whereby a clock goes faster in such a field). However, the reversal could just as well be achieved by a force rather than introducing a fictitious field. In the first example being discussed, the clock that goes away from the 'laboratory' frame is said to be accelerated *"by an external force"*. Why not use the same idea in the reverse situation in the second case? Why change to a supposed gravitational field, which is 'magically' turned on and off and which complicates the example with intermittent added forces to counteract the gravitational field, to keep the clock U2 from also moving in the supposed gravitational field?

Consider the statement by Einstein that *"Calculation shows that the consequent advancement amounts to exactly twice as much as the retardation during stages 2 and 4."* This statement is, to put it mildly, bunkum. No second-level student would swallow that nonsense, but dare anyone speak out?

Einstein did not show the mathematics of the analysis because it is impossible to concoct mathematics that would hold true for varying assumptions on the duration of the steady state and of the mysterious phases of gravitational fields. Indeed, the above statement by Einstein cannot hold water and must be seen in the light of the firm belief by him that SR was really true and sacrosanct and that some explanation was needed, no matter how outlandish, to stem the tide of any possible attack on that theory. Maybe

Einstein was more of a politician than was thought to be the case. His explanation had the desired effect as it was so complicated that it mystified any potential critics. Who was it that was reputed to have said to an eminent scientist that there were only three persons in the world who understood relativity theory, only to get the reply, *"Who is the third?"*?

It is insulting nonsense to suggest that the two phases always balance exactly no matter what the duration of the steady-state phase or the acceleration phases. Why did Einstein not simply repeat the five steps used for reference frame K and label them reference frame K' and substitute U1 for U2? Remember that he had said the slowing of time was *mutatis mutandi*.

In the introduction to the problem, Einstein said that *"the change which might occur during the acceleration certainly cannot surpass a definite amount"*. Later he conveniently forgets this obvious fact and pretends that the acceleration phase magically contributes exactly twice the steady-speed phases.

It appears that the reputation of Einstein was such that he could publish such convoluted nonsense and get away with it. It is interesting that none of the proponents (including McCrea) who defends the twin paradox quotes Einstein's 1918 analysis. Because the article was published in German, it is likely that it escaped the attention of some.

Dingle quotes Møller as giving the mathematics purporting to back up Einstein's statement. Dingle took those calculations as being accurate and then proceeded to demolish them on similar arguments to those given above. However, we shall now see that Møller's analysis is nonsense.

Møller (1952) takes the case of two clocks, one of which remains stationary (C1) while the other moves away (C2). In the usual way, C2 accelerates to a uniform speed and continues at that speed for a while. Next, it decelerates and stops, reverses and comes back again with the same uniform speed to where the original uniform speed phase started on the outward journey. Finally, it decelerates and stops at the origin, where it began the journey. Møller shows that the phases of acceleration and deceleration do not count because they can be taken as instantaneous. Einstein, on the other hand, relies on those phases as contributing what he terms *"exactly twice the slowing down that is occasioned in the steady-speed state"* to get the result that he required. Møller rejects the reasoning used by Einstein's 1918 paper. Møller actually references that 1918 paper in his book, but does not mention it in his discussion on the twin paradox or anywhere else in the text; this is very strange because he annotates every other reference in the book to the page where it is used.

So far, so good. The problem is now reduced to the standard SR case where only uniform motion is concerned. Møller derives the usual SR claim that the moving clock runs slow compared to the stationary clock. Having (properly) reduced the consideration solely to the uniform motion phases, the problem is very simple. If clock C2 moves off (consider only a steady velocity), it is deemed to run slow.

The result Møller gets in the case where the stationary twin on the earth considers the problem is $t = \gamma t'$, as derived in chapter 1 of this book. Møller's symbols are different but we make them the same as in this book for the sake of comparing results. We define t as the time as observed by the observer who is stationary on earth, and t' as the time as observed by the travelling observer; $t = \gamma t'$ means that the travelling twin ages less.

If, however, clock C1 is considered as moving off in relation to clock C2, then of course the clock that is considered as moving is the one that goes slow in relation to the 'stationary' one! This is the *mutatis mutandi*, or vice versa, situation.

To claim that either of the twins would be older and younger than the other at the same time is untenable. To salvage SR from such a ridiculous conclusion, Møller has the problem of trying to prove that, as considered by the twin who goes off from the earth, the one fixed to the earth also ages by more instead of by less. Because it is solely the 'relative' motion that has to be considered, this is impossible to prove. How could Møller wriggle out of this impossible quandary?

Møller next considers the case where clock C2 is taken as the stationary one and clock C1 is considered to be moving and states that the acceleration and deceleration phases are not relevant to the solution in this case either. This disposes of the whole of Einstein's 'gravitational fields' notion (quoted above). We agree with that. Møller opines that it is solely the uniform motion parts of the journey that contribute to the result. We also agree with that.

However, Møller then does a strange thing. He takes the result of the first case, where clock C1 is stationary, and uses it in the second case, where clock C2 is stationary. From this he concludes that in both cases the one clock (C2) runs slow!

In the reverse situation, as considered by the travelling observer, the result should, of course, be $t' = \gamma t$, i.e. the twin who stays on the earth ages less. However, Møller blithely uses the result $t = \gamma t'$ from the first case and, with no explanation whatever, jumbles it in with a number of factors that are rightly ignored and discarded and thus magically gets the result he wants for the second case as $t = \gamma t'$. This procedure is a nonsense.

To cover up the swindle, Møller says *"we get"* this result without saying how it was got. This is the same as the statement by Einstein in his 1918 publication, where he said that *"calculation shows"*. Calculation could not 'show' the result in Einstein's case, and we do not 'get' the result in Møller's case.

Møller's book was completely revised in 1972 for the second edition, and the numbering of the equations was altered. Therefore, the hoax cannot be said to be a slip that was perpetrated in 1952 and left there inadvertently. I wonder how many tens of thousands of lecturers and students have been fed that nonsense. Møller's book has been a standard textbook for university students for nigh on half a century. Students are keen to pass their examinations and will hardly pause to consider the verity of such sections in the text. It will be mighty interesting to watch whether or not the next edition of the Møller text quietly omits that section!

Anyone interested in further reading can read Møller's textbook on the topic. As both Møller and Einstein were expert mathematicians, we can but conclude that they both knowingly perpetrated a momentous confidence trick in the case of the twin paradox. Einstein, one of the greatest scientists of the 20th century, must have known well that his explanation was a hoax. I wonder if he chuckled at the joke he had perpetrated. That hoax has lasted for 87 years to the present day.

Multiple Explanations of the Paradox

Before leaving the twin paradox, let us have a look at the comments given in various papers and texts over the years (excluding Einstein's 1918 analysis and Dingle and McCrea, to whom we referred in detail above). Many try to come up with a plausible explanation that might concur with SR – any one of those is as confusing as the next! Some use the general theory to try to explain the problem. Quite a few point out that the reciprocity of viewing from the stationary and moving frames gives a nonsensical result.

There is a sample of 54 published 'explanations' of the paradox given in chronological order in Appendix 2 at the end of this book. The reader may be amused to dip into these. The only excuse I have for listing them and giving a short note on the conclusion in each case is that I went to the trouble of finding them! However, reading them will show how ludicrous are the attempts to pretend that one twin ages less than the other.

Each of these papers refers to yet other books or papers that contain yet other so-called explanations that they claim to have superseded. One journal (the *American Journal of Physics*) published more than half of the quoted papers. That journal is devoted to the teaching profession and aims to give good explanations of matters on which the profession lectures. Their editorial policy is to publish *"papers that meet the needs and intellectual interests of college and university physics teachers and students"*. The unfortunate students must be totally confused. Nobody seems to be allowed to fight back or to imply that the explanations of SR are nonsensical. An advertisement for an editor of the *American Journal of Physics* that plainly debars anyone who might consider publishing any criticism of SR is reproduced elsewhere in this book.

It would seem that everybody and nobody is an expert on this topic. The more abstruse the argument, the more strident the implication of the stupidity of others. What most of these authors attempted to do was to invent a correction factor that would automatically allow for one of the twins to age more slowly than the other, no matter which twin was considered to be stationary. To do this, they had to bias the answer in one direction. This they did in numerous ingenious ways and subsequently got their enigmatic efforts published. This was much to the chagrin of Dingle, whose continued refutation was eventually cut off from publication. It is very strange that very few (if any?) of these authors referred to Einstein's 1918 attempt to get the same result. That is significant because the 1918 article by Einstein is referenced in at least two texts (Møller and Dingle). It seems that any convoluted nonsense that is in tune with the current theories will be published with alacrity.

The so-called explanations break down as follows: eight of them say the paradox is inexplicable, six say acceleration alone explains it, nine say acceleration has nothing to offer, four say GR is the sole answer, five say 'jumping inertial frames' are the answer, one says the uniform relative velocity is sufficient to explain the matter, two use a

166

cylindrical universe to explain it and seven (including this author) say SR is wrong and that the twins age by exactly the same amount. The remainder just comment on the matter.

It is worth dwelling on what Essen, the famous inventor of the caesium clock, said. This is listed in Appendix 2. He pointed out that in Einstein's first paper in 1905, Einstein said that a clock that was sent around the earth at the equator would run slow in relation to one at the pole. However, Einstein conveniently forgot to mention that, in relation to the pole clock, the one at the equator should also run slow. He forgot his own *mutatis mutandi* rule. Here the nonsense started.

So, dear reader, if you want to see your name in print, you now know what to do – just pen a nonsensical treatise concluding that one twin ages more than the other. It does not matter what your reasons are; you can refer to more than 40 other papers in building your case. Nobody will understand what the paper is all about, and surely your peers will think that you are very intelligent!

Going back again to the original 1905 paper by Einstein, let us see what the definitions are of the clocks being used. In the book *The Principle of Relativity*, we read about clocks that have the peculiar attribute of remaining synchronised with a stationary clock (in the laboratory) while at the same time travelling with the moving rod. This anomaly is quoted by MacRoberts (1980): *"In Einstein's description of the moving rod experiment he places two clocks on the rod which have the curious (for SR) characteristic of remaining synchronised with the clock at rest in K regardless of their motion."* The problem with quoting such an anomaly is that there is the danger that some physicist will initiate an abstruse discussion around this one point, thus avoiding the core of the synchronisation problem! MacRoberts continues:

> *We might consider these clocks simply an oversight on Einstein's part if he were not so meticulous in describing them, even adding a superfluous footnote to emphasise their synchrony with the rest clocks... the only thing we can conclude with certainty is that Einstein thought there were clocks which would not suffer time dilation because of motion.*

The reader will see that the various explanations of the twin paradox contradict one another and in turn deny the veracity of the explanation of other authors. Not one of the 'explanations' mentions the *mutatis mutandi* statement by Einstein in 1922. All of this is surely sufficient to show that the best efforts of physicists around the world have failed to come up with any explanation of the twin, or clock, paradox in 100 years. If any one solution held water, everyone would have latched onto it long ago.

Concerning the so-called explanations, including that put forward by Einstein in 1918, one is tempted to remark, *"If you believe that, you'll believe anything!"* One gets the distinct impression that if an author dares to try to publish a contrary view, that author will certainly not get published. Offering a mild innuendo seems to be the best approach, as was done by Abolghasem et al. in their 1989 paper, as quoted earlier in the Sagnac test discussions. They dared to suggest that the speed of light was 'locally' different, as if it were an insignificant matter.

Let us give the last word to Professor H. Dingle (1957):

The principle of relativity - i.e. the principle that nature allows of no criterion for deciding which of two relatively moving bodies is the 'moving' one - necessarily means that the clocks in question shall agree on reunion; otherwise the prohibited criterion would be found.

In this book, a proposed solution based on universal relativity (UR) is put forward whereby there is no slowing of time due to any motion, and therefore no twin paradox.

Chapter 8

Critics of Special Relativity

Let us recall some of the authors who tried to put sense on the inconsistencies in SR. We have quoted Dingle earlier – he was the one who went the furthest with his ideas. Other authors were not as persistent. As will be seen in this chapter, Dingle's name has become associated with being unreasonable. It is convenient to refer to such eminent critics as 'well-known cranks' – this neatly gets rid of the facts that support their arguments. If you do not like the message, shoot the messenger.

O'Rahilly

Eminent among the critics was a compatriot of mine, Alfred O'Rahilly, who published the 900-page book *Electromagnetics* in 1938. O'Rahilly was Professor of Experimental Physics at University College Cork, Ireland. At the time of his death, O'Rahilly was reputed to have been working on a second book, which would directly challenge SR. O'Rahilly's papers were destroyed some years after his death in a fire in Blackrock College, Dublin, which is one kilometre from my home. The 1938 book is actually very critical of SR. While it set out to avoid specific comment on what was planned to be the subject of the second book, lengthy comments were added at the proof stage that are scathing, indeed vitriolic, in relation to SR.

Oddly, in *Electromagnetics*, O'Rahilly had not uncovered Sagnac's or Pogany's work, although he referenced other publications that appeared in the same journals as did the salient articles by those authors. O'Rahilly mirrored several conclusions in his book. Indeed, he mentions in passing that light seems to travel with the earth on its orbit around the sun! He says, *"It has been shown that electromagnetic phenomena require the framework to move with the earth (at least on its orbital movement)."* O'Rahilly also says that any assumption of an ether must consider the ether to be earth-convected and not stationary in space.

O'Rahilly also criticises SR on the basis that all the laws of physics are supposed to be invariant under SR. When commenting on the relative movement of two frames K and K', he asks, *"Well, why not also the laws of elasticity? If the coordinate system has nothing to do with the object described, why should the wave be a sphere in K' and an ellipsoid in K?"* O'Rahilly continues:

> *Whether we are advancing towards the light or are receding from it we always find that its measured velocity is 186,000 miles per second. Einstein was led to this statement by the fact that the earth's motion round the sun makes no difference to the observed speed of light.*

O'Rahilly says that the claims by Einstein that the relative speed of light is always measured as the same value by observers in uniform motion with regard to each other *"not only sound like, but really are, sheer nonsense"*. He does not put a tooth in it – O'Rahilly was totally dismissive of Einstein!

Other Critics

Another critic, S. J. Prokhovnik (1979), stated that *"Editors of Journals (and their referees) have simply rejected out of hand any article critical of Special Relativity or its conventional presentation, and made individuals think that they were simply isolated eccentrics."*

Marinov, another frustrated author, once threatened to immolate himself outside a British consulate if his writings on SR were not published. This author met him at a conference in 1997 in Athens, Greece and discussed his experimental work on the rotation of magnets in a complimentary manner. This was a few weeks before he apparently committed suicide.

Essen, the inventor of the atomic caesium clock, wrote several articles critical of SR. One was entitled *Relativity – Joke or Swindle* and appeared in *Wireless World* in 1978. Essen quotes a president of the Royal Society as saying that he did not understand relativity but that *"it must be right, because he found it useful"*. Imagine the president of any other worldwide representative organisation proclaiming such ignorance. Suppose that the president of the Institution of Mechanical Engineers (U.K.) or the American Society of Mechanical Engineers proclaimed ignorance of thermodynamics – would not that person be ridiculed and requested to resign? In the *Relativity – Joke or Swindle* article, Essen quotes the splitter of the atom (Rutherford) as treating relativity as a joke and quotes Soddy as thinking of it as a swindle. If these eminent people have been ignored, what chance has this author of changing the 'swindle'?

The renowned Essen was warned by his employers that *"to persist in his criticism of relativity may affect his career and hence pension prospects, and he was told to use his private address on all correspondence on the subject of relativity"*. This is from private correspondence from a close relative of Essen. Essen was not forced to retire early as has been rumoured; he even worked part-time beyond the retirement age for the National Physical Laboratory (U.K.), where he invented the caesium clock. His clock was used to get the accuracy of the measurement of the second to one part in 10^{-9} and is recorded as being used to do that in the 1999 records of the BIPM (see chapter 5).

Another author who implied the same notion – that of light moving with the earth on its orbital movement around the sun – is Ideström (1948), controller of the Swedish state telegraph system. Ideström said that *"The Michelson-Morley experiment seems to show that the light-wave follows the movement of the earth through space. Einstein does not view this as due to the fact that the earth carries with it the electromagnetic field of force."* Yet another author who agrees with this is Professor Petr Beckmann of the Electrical Engineering Department at the University of Colorado, U.S.A., who published the book *Einstein Plus Two* in 1987. So we see that this is a simple idea that has been considered many times but has yet to be formed into a comprehensive theory and accepted as an alternative to SR.

The writings of O'Rahilly, Idestrōm and Beckmann on this particular point were uncovered after this author published in 1996 the idea that light travels with the earth on its orbital movement around the sun. It is such an obvious explanation of the Michelson and Morley experiment that it is likely to have been published by many others.

John E. Chappell (1979) complained that Einstein's theory was *"the most appalling set of errors in all the history of science and philosophy"*. Chappell wrote that he was denied the opportunity to complete a Ph.D. thesis in 1965 at the University of Kansas, U.S.A. He claims that he was threatened that if he dared to write a thesis critical of Einstein, he would never receive his doctorate. He later went to Yale, and there he claimed that:

> *The professor I met listened to me politely for about ten minutes, and then as soon as I had mentioned Herbert Dingle, probably the best known critic of Einstein then living, he lost his composure and flew into a rage, and loudly demanded that I get out of his office at once.*

Chappell then met another professor at Yale who promised to publish an article by him in a magazine of which that professor was editor. This never happened because the professor could not get any physicist to write a review of the paper. The professor then asked Chappell to release him from his promise.

Chappell also records that the editor of the *American Journal of Physics* told him that articles critical of relativity could not be published *"given the current situation in physics in the late 1970's"*. Chappell claims that the *American Journal of Physics* had *"an editorial policy which explicitly forbade any criticism of special relativity within its pages"*. This policy continues to the present day, as illustrated by the recent advertisement, quoted elsewhere in this book, for a new editor of the journal. One can almost see the steam rising off the pages of Chappell's writings. He was clearly a very frustrated author. Chappell gives a clear example, as follows, of the incompatibility of the argument that light travels at a constant speed relative to all observers.

> *If the velocity of system X relative to system Y is to be undetectable within system X, then the relative velocity must be added to all motions occurring within X, insofar as X is considered to be moving relative to Y. But then if an observer in Y sees light sent to him from X, this light cannot have a fixed velocity relative to Y; it must change its velocity depending on the velocity of X.*

Chappell also states that *"no imputation of extra-sensory perception was quite as pathological as the assumption that photons in effect adjust their velocities, all by themselves, in such a way as always to keep them constant relative to moving observers."* Chappell was founder and director of the Natural Philosophy Alliance, an organisation devoted to the discussion of topics not permitted in the mainstream physics journals. He died in 2002.

John Maddox, the editor of *Nature* who was involved in the controversy with Dingle, retired in 1995. In August of that year, Maddox wrote an editorial entitled *"Is the*

Principia Publishable Now?" in which he questioned whether or not Newton would get his ideas published today, given the current practice of peer review. Maddox speculates on what a reviewer would have written on receiving the script of Newton's *Principia*. He toys with the idea that Huygens (a contemporary of Newton's and an opponent of Newton's ideas) would have written caustically about the gravitation ideas of Newton – *"by what means, pray, does the author fancy that this magic can be contrived over the great distance between the Sun and Jupiter and without the lapse of time?"* Perhaps Maddox had on his conscience his tussle with Dingle almost 30 years earlier.

The peer review idea makes sense. It helps to eliminate papers that are nonsensical or incorrect. However, it is dangerous in that a new idea may often be reviewed (in secret because the reviewer's name is never released) by the person who launched or is an ardent advocate of the extant theory that is being attacked or disproven in the paper.

Many papers and books have been penned that are critical of relativity theory. It is extraordinary that all this criticism can be ignored without specific demolition. Is there any other topic in any discipline that has attracted such a continual attack? One physics professor in Canada remarked that his department gets one critical paper on relativity every week. That may well be an exaggeration but, if typical, adds up to a huge mass of criticism!

Sagan, Cornell University's professor of astronomy, wrote that he gets a letter every week or so from people unhappy with relativity theory. We could extrapolate from this that a total of 500,000 such letters are received on a yearly basis by university physics professors worldwide. If we add to this letters sent to physics lecturers and professors and lecturers in related disciplines, we would be justified in guessing that 1 million letters per year are written objecting to the scam of relativity theory. However, the voice of the objectors is not allowed to be heard.

Ives published many papers showing flaws in the theory. In fact, he published an alternative theory that indicated that the Fitzgerald contraction is real. This author does not agree that Fitzgerald's contraction is real (even though he was an Irishman). Another example is Keswani (1965). He remarked that:

Einstein (pp. 44-45) uses velocities of light propagation equal to (c − v), (c + v) and $\sqrt{(c^2 − v^2)}$ in utter disregard of his own second postulate. We must note that these velocities of light-propagation, in Einstein's derivation, are physically measured (i.e. observable) velocities and not certain quantities in algebraic calculation.

Keswani further comments:

When considering the energy contained within the expanding wave front of light as observed in the two systems, Einstein (p. 57) asserts: "the spherical surface - viewed in the moving system - is an ellipsoidal surface" ... and then proceeds to work out the equation of the expanding ellipsoid.

This all followed the assertion in the text that light expands as a sphere in the two frames that are in uniform relative motion.

This is what it says in another book critical of relativity, *The Case against Einstein* by Dr. Arthur Lynch (1932):

I was led to the point where I had to accept the conclusion that a clock would go fast or slow according as it moved relatively to imagined systems of coordinates. Now I believe that the motion of a clock depends on the operation of physical forces and that these, as the constructors of clocks know, have nothing to do with the influences imputed to Nature by the Einsteinists.

Lynch records that a Professor Grant from Australia criticised his book before reading it, on the grounds that it must be wrong because Einstein had to be correct since so many university professors endorse him. Lynch quotes Charles Lamb as having remarked that *"reading a book before criticizing it prejudices one"*. Lynch also asserts that *"the great majority of scientific men reject Einstein's theory"*. Lynch concludes his book by saying:

Yet, as I cast my eye over the whole course of science, I behold instances of false science, even more pretentious and popular than that of Einstein, gradually fading into ineptitude under the searchlight; and I have no doubt that there will arise a new generation who will look with a wonder and amazement deeper than now accompany Einstein, at our galaxy of thinkers, men of science, popular critics, authoritative professors and witty dramatists, who have been satisfied to waive their common sense in view of Einstein's absurdities. Then to these will succeed another generation, whose interest will be that of a detached and half-amused contemplation, and in the limbo of forgotten philosophies they may search for the cenotaph of Relativity.

The problem with the critics was that few put forward an alternative theory. Without an alternative, why should anyone pass a remark? Everyone is far too busy to stop and examine every objection to a theory that has served for so long and has apparently been confirmed by so many tests.

There are about twenty current journals that publish some articles that criticise relativity. These are listed by the National Philosophy Alliance, and the better-known ones are *Galilean Electrodynamics*, *Physics Essays*, *Infinite Energy*, *Foundations of Physics*, *Journal of New Energy*, *Meta Research Bulletin* and *Apeiron*. Formerly, *Wissen Im Werden* and *Speculations in Science & Technology* ran for many years. The latter publication published reviewers' comments and allowed authors to respond – that was an interesting experiment. The existence of such journals is, in part, a reaction to the 100% rejection of papers critical of SR and the publication by mainstream journals of any nonsense that, for example, supports the twin paradox.

One might speculate that all the criticism of relativity is somewhat like the publications of the Flat Earth Society. However, the critics are eminent. They include no less than Lorentz, who opposed relativity until his death in 1928, and the famous Michelson, who did the tests quoted in this book. We have professors of physics, the author of the standard university textbooks on relativity theory used for decades (Dingle), professors of electrical, mechanical and electronic engineering, Ph.Ds, presidents of large corporations, the famous inventor of the caesium clock and director of the Time & Frequency Division of the U.K.'s National Physical Laboratory (Essen), and the controller of the Swedish state telegraph system (Ideström). Why are they so vociferous? These people cannot all be brushed aside as 'cranks'.

A reasonable proposition demands a response. When all articles critical of relativity theory are banned from publication, surely suspicion should be aroused. The silence is becoming deafening. How much longer can the fortress be defended? Relativity theory has assumed the status of a religion whose mysteries are to be believed without question. For how long can nonsense stave off common sense?

Nobel Prize

There is a danger that critics of relativity could be accused of anti-semitism because Einstein was hounded out of pre-war Germany. Einstein was one of the great thinkers and philosophers of the past century and a winner of the 1921 Nobel Prize for his work on the photoelectric effect. He was a monumental genius.

While most people think that Einstein won the Nobel Prize for his relativity theory, the prize was actually awarded to Einstein *"for his services to Theoretical Physics, and especially for his discovery of the law of the photoelectric effect"*. The citation stated:

There is probably no physicist living today whose name has become so widely known as that of Albert Einstein. Most discussion centres on his theory of relativity. This pertains essentially to epistemology and has therefore been the subject of lively debate in philosophical circles. It will be no secret that the famous philosopher Bergson in Paris has challenged this theory, while other philosophers have acclaimed it wholeheartedly. The theory in question also has astrophysical implications which are being rigorously examined at the present time.

The citation then discusses Einstein's work on Brownian motion.

In 1905 Einstein founded a kinetic theory to account for this movement by means of which he derived the chief properties of suspensions, i.e. liquids with solid particles suspended in them. This theory, based on classical mechanics, helps to explain the behaviour of what are commonly known as colloidal solutions.

The citation then continues with a description of the work for which Einstein was awarded the prize.

A third group of studies, for which in particular Einstein has received the Nobel Prize, falls within the domain of the quantum theory founded by Planck in 1900. This theory asserts that radiant energy consists of individual particles, termed 'quanta', approximately in the same way as matter is made up of individual particles, i.e. atoms. This remarkable theory, for which Planck received the Nobel Prize for Physics in 1918, suffered from a number of drawbacks and about the middle of the first decade of this century it reached a kind of impasse. Then Einstein came forward with his work on specific heat and the photoelectric effect.

An historical description of how Einstein explained Stokes's rule is then given. The citation concludes as follows:

> *Einstein's law of the photo-electrical effect has been extremely rigorously tested by the American Millikan and his pupils and passed the test brilliantly. Owing to these studies by Einstein the quantum theory has been perfected to a high degree and an extensive literature grew up in this field whereby the extraordinary value of this theory was proved. Einstein's law has become the basis of quantitative photo-chemistry in the same way as Faraday's law is the basis of electro-chemistry.*

Henri Bergson, who is quoted in the citation as objecting to the theory of relativity, is best known for his book *Creative Evolution* (1907); he later won the Nobel Prize for literature. Here is what Hawking (2001) said about Einstein's Nobel Prize:

> *When Einstein was awarded the Nobel Prize in 1921, the citation was for important work but (by his standard) comparatively minor work also carried out in 1905. It made no mention of relativity, which was considered too controversial. (I still get two or three letters a week telling me Einstein was wrong). Nevertheless, the theory of relativity is now completely accepted by the scientific community, and its predictions have been verified in countless applications.*

As we see above, there was a specific reference to the theory of relativity in the Nobel citation, but it was not for that part of his work, nor for his work on Brownian motion, which was also mentioned, that Einstein was awarded the prize. It is a good rule that one should always go back to the original source when debating any topic; quoting others (even for someone as famous as Hawking) can be dangerous. Incidentally, it would be natural that the famous Hawking would get more than the average number of letters per week that are critical of relativity theory.

Einstein could not attend the ceremony but went to Sweden the following year to make an acceptance speech in a lecture to the Nordic Assembly of Naturalists at Gothenburg. The title of his lecture was *Fundamental ideas and problems of the theory of relativity.* Einstein did not mention the photoelectric effect. A footnote on the first page of the record of the lecture says, *"The lecture was not delivered on the occasion of the Nobel Prize award, and did not therefore concern the discovery of the photoelectric effect".*

Hoffmann (1975) records that *"When Einstein gave his Nobel Prize lecture in Sweden, he ignored the cautious wording of the citation and spoke on the theory of relativity".*

There appears to have been a bit of gamesmanship between the Nobel Institute and Einstein. Einstein appears to have thought that the Institute should have given the prize for his work on relativity, whereas the Institute went to some pains to emphasise that the prize was *"especially for his discovery of the law of the photoelectric effect".* Einstein ignored this and based his Nobel lecture solely on the topic of relativity. The Institute responded by publishing the lecture as the official lecture by the winner of the prize but added the footnote quoted above as a slap on the wrist for Einstein.

Debate in the Media

When the ideas in this book were first launched at two public lectures in Dublin University (Trinity College Dublin) in Ireland in 1995 and 1996, a furious debate ensued over a three-month period in *The Irish Times* daily newspaper. It all began when there was widespread publicity in the world press (notably by Reuters) on the day following the second lecture. Silence ensued from the physics fraternity.

A very short letter to *The Irish Times* on February 26th 1996 set the debate in motion. Dr. Anthony Quinn of the Department of Electronic and Electrical Engineering at Trinity College wrote:

> *The response of Ireland's defenders of Modern Physics to Dr. Alphonsus Kelly's lecture at Trinity College (February 15th) has been one of silence, in marked contrast to the response of the media. In the 'light' of this fact, are we to interpret the silence as grudging acceptance that Einstein was, indeed, wrong?*

I never met Dr. Quinn.

On March 7th a short letter signed by four Ph.Ds (Charles Nash of the Department of Mathematical Physics, St. Patrick's College, Maynooth; Denjo O'Connor of the Dublin Institute for Advanced Studies; Michael Tuite of the Department of Mathematical Physics, University College Galway; and Brian Dolan of the Department of Mathematical Physics, St. Patrick's College, Maynooth) appeared in *The Irish Times*. It read:

> *We are disturbed by the recent publicity surrounding the claim by Dr. A. G. Kelly 'refuting' Einstein's theory of special relativity.*
>
> *Special relativity has many fascinating and profound consequences and has been found to be in agreement with all the numerous experiments which have tested it since its inception. It is a well established corner-stone of modern physics. Dr. Kelly's principal monograph The Institution of Engineers of Ireland Monograph No 1 Jan. 1995 is unfortunately erroneous and is based on a number of serious misunderstandings of theory and experiment.*
>
> *It is regrettable that these claims have been presented without an accompanying response from the physics community.*

It was not long until a letter appeared pointing out to these four people that Monograph No. 2 (not No. 1, which was the subject of Dr. Quinn's letter) had several tests listed that refuted Einstein's theory. The four contributors referred to the first monograph (No. 1) and must have taken exception to some statements therein that did not accord with the conventional method of describing matters. However, they were careful to imply that they were not the 'experts' who should be commenting on Kelly's work. Why did they write at all if they were not experts? What a cop-out!

This author wrote in response that Nash et al. were welcome to read the second paper, which gave the fully developed theory (as distinct from the earlier paper, which left

176

the puzzle unanswered).

Earlier, on March 4th, the following letter appeared from Dr. Cormac O'Raifeartaigh of the Physics Department, Trinity College Dublin and Dr. Lorraine Hanlon of the Physics Department, University College Dublin.

As members of the Irish physics community, we are mystified by the intense interest shown by the Irish media (including the Irish Times) in the writings of Irish engineer, Dr. A. Kelly, on the subject of relativity. Comment from established experts in the field has not been forthcoming, perhaps due to the fact that Dr. Kelly's 'theory' has not been published in any recognised journal concerned with the subject and therefore does not merit their consideration.

Two points should be clarified: (1) To report that Dr. Kelly gave a lecture in Trinity College (the Irish Times, February 16th) without pointing out that he was invited by undergraduate students to give a talk to a student society, creates an entirely misleading impression of acceptance of his work on the part of the academic staff. (2) The publication of scientific work in internationally recognised journals through a process of peer review is the tried and tested method of introducing bona-fide work into a forum for informed scientific debate. Until the work of Dr. Kelly has been published in a journal of repute in this field, it must be regarded with the utmost scepticism (remember cold-fusion). Public interest in science is always welcome; however, the active promotion in the media of a 'relativity theory' which has not been recognised by professionals in the field does not mirror the cautious objective approach of scientists, and does little for the reputation of Irish physics abroad.

This author responded (sarcastically) that *"Perhaps, because they are Irish, they would make an exception and study the paper,"* even though it was published by an engineering institution. The lectures were published and distributed on the occasion as monographs by the Institution of Engineers of Ireland.

So far there was no reference to what was proposed in the new theory. It is to be wondered what these critics thought when the famous Professor J-P. Vigier of Paris published a long article in *Physics Letters A* in 1997 saying that Kelly was right. (Someone made sure they each got a copy of Vigier's paper!) They commented no further. By the way, cold fusion is far from dead in 2005, as is evident from the number of organisations currently funding research and publishing results on that topic.

There were a few letters backing Kelly's ideas (W. Browne and Jonathan Cooney). K. Holland of M.I.T. in the U.S.A. sat on the fence and left the question open: *"Maybe Einstein will one day be supplanted by an Irishman, but let's not get carried away."*

Then the fun began in earnest. Professor Sen and Dr. Sexton of the Mathematics Department of Trinity College wrote a long letter in which they said, *"Dr. Kelly's main thesis is that an experimental effect known as the Sagnac effect cannot be explained by Einstein's theory. This effect involves the comparison of speed-of-light measurements by two observers who rotate relative to each other."* Anyone who has read this book thus far will appreciate that this statement is incorrect. Naturally, this author replied by saying,

"That is not correct. The effect is measured solely by a measuring device which rotates with the disc and records the fact that the light takes different times to go around the spinning disc clockwise and anticlockwise."

There was some irony in the letters. Sen and Sexton wrote, *"With considerable regret we must accept that there is no mystery to excite our attention and research."* To that, this author responded, *"They need not be so sad; their analysis is incorrect."*

At this time, the late Dr. Christine Somers, Director of Education at the Institution of Engineers of Ireland, who was dealing with the meeting that launched the paper at the Institution, got phone calls from four professors in four different Irish universities who complained bitterly at the publication of Kelly's paper. What collusion and discussion was going on in the concerted attack and in the penning of joint letters to *The Irish Times*? Obviously, there was much debate and concern behind closed doors.

One of these professors went so far as to threaten the Institution director that he would see to it that the Institution's representation at the Royal Irish Academy would be cancelled. (The Institution is a descendant of the Institution of Civil Engineers and has been associated with the Academy (founded in 1785) for over 100 years.) The irate professor was asked to pen what he thought was wrong with Kelly's theory and was told that his comments would be published in the journal of the Institution of Engineers (*The Engineers Journal*). His response was that such a journal was not 'peer reviewed' and would not be a suitable place for comment. This drew the scathing response that it was all right to write letters to *The Irish Times* but not to *The Engineers Journal*! The professor put down the telephone at that stage. One can but wonder why such anger and attempted intimidation was directed at an officer in the Institution. Why the panic? The Institution of Engineers of Ireland is not easily intimidated.

The debate continued. Sen and Sexton responded concerning the Sagnac effect as follows:

We remain unconvinced by Dr. Kelly's comments, and we have no difficulty in explaining this effect within Einstein's theory. In support of his view Dr. Kelly refers to a 1993 paper by Hasselbach & Nicklaus which referenced 21 theoretical explanations for the Sagnac effect. What is not clear from Dr. Kelly's comments, however, is that all these explanations are completely successful in predicting the experimental results achieved.

They continued:

The multiplicity of explanations partly reflects the fact that the Sagnac effect has now been observed in many different experimental situations each of which required a slightly different analysis. Partly, however, it reflects the depth, the richness and the complete interdependence of the scientific ideas involved in the effect. If we tamper with Einstein's theory in the manner suggested by Dr. Kelly, then the interdependent structure collapses and the different analyses become illogically inconsistent. 'Things fall apart; mere anarchy is loosed upon the world'.

Here Sen and Sexton were quoting from *The Second Coming* by the Irish Nobel Laureate poet W. B. Yeats. Here is more from their letter:

> *Dr. Kelly suggested in his comments that we produce the subtle analysis we claimed was necessary to explain the Sagnac effect, and send it to the Institute of Engineers of Ireland for publication. There is no need to do so since the analysis is well known and standard, and is available in the literature.*

What Sen and Sexton did not say was that the Hasselbach and Nicklaus paper states that *"This great variety (if not disparity) in the derivation of the Sagnac phase shift, constitutes one of the several controversies that have surrounded the Sagnac effect since the earliest days of studying interference in rotating frames of reference."*

The final letter came from this author and cannot have pleased Sen and Sexton. It referred to the 21 explanations they said were completely in accordance with relativity theory.

> *Take two examples. Dieks and Nienhuis (1990) state that 'seen from the rotating system, the two signals have equal speeds'. That is incorrect; otherwise no difference would be measured. This error like that of Prof. Sen and Dr. Sexton discussed earlier (April 2nd), is typical of the many futile attempts to explain the effect. A second example is the useless flying clock experiment which is erroneously quoted as proof of the Sagnac effect, with which it has no connection whatever. On a disc the diameter of the earth, the speed of a lazy snail (0.5 mm per hour) would produce Sagnac's result, which is 4,000,000,000,000,000 times larger than the result forecast by Special Relativity; Prof. Sen and Dr. Sexton say the two are in agreement.*

The letter then included an extract from the poem by Yeats already quoted by Sen and Sexton: *". . . the worst are full of passionate intensity. Surely some revelation is at hand."* The letter ended as follows:

> *Are we discussing a religion or trying to explain the results of accurate scientific experiments? As this debate has become rather technical for newspaper columns, I am signing off and suggest that further discussion would be more appropriate in the Engineers Journal.*

There was no further correspondence. All very entertaining, but not a serious debate on the facts. We can have sympathy for the letter writers; having SR demolished before their eyes is too awful to contemplate. A standard comment is *"But it fits all these other things so well and until you disprove all those, we will not listen to you."* Such comments come from those who have not read Karl Popper. Millions of experiments that agree with a theory do not prove that theory. Unfortunately, however, one solitary reliable experiment (repeated by independent experimenters) that disagrees with a theory demolishes that theory, no matter how beautiful and no matter how much trouble its demise will cause, no matter how many reputations will suffer and no matter what pride is hurt.

The defenders of relativity theory are besieged and feel threatened. How long will their fortifications hold? Fifty years would be a reasonable guess.

One further episode occurred that is worth recording here. Later in 1996, this author was invited by an undergraduate society to repeat the lecture at the University of Limerick. A delegation of ten members of the mathematics department visited the office of the Vice President and objected on the grounds that their careers would be severely damaged if they were to be associated with a university that allowed such a lecture to proceed. Most had degrees from U.S.A. universities and said that papers contradicting Einstein were regularly rejected in those colleges. The VP reluctantly cancelled the lecture in the teeth of such an attack and explained to me what had happened.

Why the abject terror that undergraduates might debate such a matter? It seemed as if this author was officially 'excommunicated' and that no contact should be made with him in case of contamination. Undergraduates can debate whether or not there is a God or whether or not humans have a soul but cannot be trusted to discuss relativity theory! Undergraduate societies thrive on controversial topics such as euthanasia, abortion, ethnic cleansing, corruption in government, in the church and in banking, corporate greed, the mafia, fascism, genetically modified foods, global warming, the cloning of humans – the more contentious the better – but there is one exception. Students must be protected from the heresy of criticism of relativity theory. Why?

Expert Opinion

At an early stage in the investigation, one of my sons, who had read what was penned and could not see any flaw in the conclusions, suggested I consult some expert in the field in case I might have missed some elementary aspect of the topic, thereby possibly avoiding the danger of an ambulance filled with men in white coats coming to my house to take me away! Shortly afterwards, I was lucky to meet an eminent central European professor of physics. This person listened attentively and politely to my arguments and agreed to correspond by fax. We had a few meetings whenever the subject matter became too difficult for remote contact. This went on for a year, with long faxes being exchanged every few days. The debate was furious, fascinating and invigorating. There was no trace of condescension or anger, just a search for the truth.

At the end of that investigation, the professor penned a careful hand-written note stating what I had proved satisfactorily, which agreed with what I claimed. The only point of disagreement was that the professor claimed the effect of SR existed *as well as* the Sagnac effect. As discussed earlier, Post had proposed this idea, which has been addressed and disproven in this book. Because I had read of dreadful treatment meted out to others who had dared to question relativity theory, I asked if I could associate the professor's name with what I intended to publish. I was politely asked not to and have complied. I suppose this is another indication of the terror that even the most eminent people feel when associating their names with any critique of relativity theory. I must acknowledge a great debt of gratitude to this anonymous professor for the kind reception and infinite patience bestowed on me. I was very lucky indeed to have met such an honourable person.

Chapter 9

Unipolar Induction

History

This chapter gives a description of a series of novel experiments undertaken by this author on the relative motion of conductors and magnets. The tests were undertaken because the results previously published were said to contradict SR. Indeed, for many years, a paper claiming just that was to be found on the Natural Philosophy Alliance (NPA) website but was dropped when the experimental results detailed below were published in 1998. As it turned out, the matter of the relative motion of a magnet and a conductor was otherwise explained and shown not to contradict relativity theory. This might persuade sceptics to accept that this author is not anti-relativity or anti any other theory but simply seeks the truth in all instances.

The word unipolar is used to describe the behaviour of one single pole of a magnet in relation to a conductor. Magnets are peculiar things. Every magnet has two poles – north and south. Nobody has ever isolated a magnet's north or south pole. No sooner is a magnet cut in half than each half becomes a new magnet, complete with its own north and south poles. No plausible reason for this has been proposed. It is somewhat like cutting an earthworm in two, thereby making two new worms!

The current experiments were undertaken because there was distinct evidence in the literature that the relative motion of a magnet and a conductor did not, in all cases, give the same result. This is in direct contradiction to SR, where relative motion should give the same result whether it is the magnet or the conductor that is moved. The results of the experiments carried out will, ironically, fit relativity theory but disprove another basic theory of physics.

In 1832, Faraday showed that a current is generated in a conductor when:

- one pole of a magnet is moved laterally near a stationary conductor.
- a conductor is moved laterally near the pole of a stationary magnet.
- a conductor is rotated on the north-south axis of a nearby stationary magnet.

However, Faraday also showed that:

- when a magnet and conductor are rotated in unison about the north-south axis of the magnet, a current is generated in the conductor. This is surprising because there is no relative motion between the magnet and the conductor and therefore there should be no effect.
- when a magnet alone is rotated about its north-south axis, no current is generated in a nearby stationary conductor. This result is astonishing and is not mentioned in many textbooks – it could lead to embarrassing questions from students.

Faraday (1832) concluded that *"rotating the magnet causes no difference in the results; for a rotating and a stationary magnet produce the same effect upon the moving copper".* Weber (1841) quoted Ampere as saying that the effect applied *"only . . . to the rotation of the conductor about the magnet; discovered by Faraday and not at all to the rotation of the magnet on its axis".* In 1851 (test No. 3090), Faraday again described this phenomenon by stating:

> *When lines of force are spoken of as crossing a conducting circuit, it must be considered as effected by the translation of a magnet. No mere rotation of a bar magnet on its axis, produces any induction effect on circuits exterior to it. The system of power in a magnet must not be considered as revolving with the magnet; the magnet may even, in certain cases, be considered revolving amongst its own forces.*

In this latter statement, Faraday was referring to the Faraday generator (see below for an explanation of this phenomenon). Faraday's pronouncement has been accepted over the intervening 173 years.

Wesley (1991) stated that Faraday had changed his mind in 1851 and decided that the lines of force actually rotated with the magnet. However, this is not true (as quoted above). Preston (1885) claimed that Faraday's experiments did not settle the matter and that Weber, Ampere and Lord Raleigh agreed with his (Preston's) competing analysis. Preston said that:

> *When a magnet rotates on its axis, the field of force must (in regard to the inductive effect) be considered as moving with the magnet and intersecting external conductors, in the same sense as it would do if the magnet were bodily translated.*

Later, Preston (1891) partially retracted this claim, saying that *"it may be that the magnetic field partly partakes of the motion of the revolving magnet".* This is the same Preston that we met earlier in the discussion as to who was first to derive the famous equation $E = mc^2$.

This is what Einstein wrote in the first paragraph of his first paper on relativity in 1905:

> *Take, for example, the reciprocal electrodynamic action of a magnet and a conductor. The observable phenomenon here depends only on the relative motion of the conductor and the magnet, whereas the customary view draws a sharp distinction between the two cases in which either the one or the other of these bodies is in motion.*

Einstein did not distinguish between translational and rotary motion. He seemed unaware of the peculiar phenomenon described above.

The following tests that reproduced Faraday's results have been identified: Lecher 1895; Barnett, 1912 and 1918; Fehrle, 1913; Pegram, 1917; Kennard, 1917; Cramp and Norgrove, 1936; Then, 1962; Das Gupta, 1963. All of these experimenters confirmed

Faraday's conclusions. Even more recently, Montgomery (2004) says that there is no way of determining whether or not the lines rotate with the magnet – Montgomery had not sourced the 1998 paper or later papers on unipolar induction published by this author.

The anomaly where the rotation of a conductor and a magnet about the north-south axis of the magnet does not produce reciprocal results has been the subject of much controversy over the intervening years. Miller, the author of the article on the NPA website, claimed that the experiments contradicted relativity theory.

The current experiments were carried out to investigate this phenomenon in more detail because the results achieved by those earlier experimenters directly contradict relativity theory and indeed contradict what could be termed 'common sense'.

Preliminary Experiments

This section describes the preliminary series of experiments referred to above.

The apparatus (figure 30) comprises two concentric shafts. An aluminium disc, which forms the 'conductor', is mounted on one shaft and a magnet (for 'magnet' read 'solenoid' as appropriate) is mounted on the other. A disc is the equivalent of a rotating single conductor, as can be seen from the fact that the voltage generated on each radius of the disc is in the same direction (say from the axis to the rim) and therefore equates with a single rotating conductor. A test was done using a single conductor on one radius alone. The voltage reading was taken from a cylindrical rim and gave the same result as would have been achieved from a solid disc.

The magnet or the disc can be rotated independently or in unison. A galvanometer is connected between two carbon brushes, one rubbing on the rim and the other rubbing on the axis of the disc. The galvanometer's sensitivity is 1.42 microvolt and 0.066 microamp/mm.

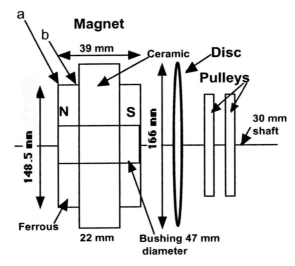

Figure 30: Magnet Apparatus

183

The apparatus, which uses a permanent magnet of short length but sizeable diameter, is shown with the north-south axis of the magnet on the axis of the driving shaft. N denotes the north pole and S the south pole of the magnet.

The distance between the disc and the magnet can be adjusted by sliding the magnet along a keyway on the shaft. The magnet has a head-and-shoulders shape and is 39 mm in length; the central portion (22 mm long in the north-south direction) is of ceramic material and the two side portions (each 8.5 mm long) are of ferrous material. The diameter of the ceramic portion is 166 mm and that of the ferrous parts 148.5 mm. The disc is 155 mm in diameter and 5 mm wide. The magnet is of an annular shape with a 47 mm hole in the middle. A brass bushing was fitted to the hole and was fitted to a driving shaft connected to one of the pulleys.

The magnet is on the left and the aluminium disc on the right. This peculiar shape is merely because such magnets, which are very powerful, were readily available from old loudspeakers. The shafts driving the magnet and the disc are separate. Two pairs of driving pulleys are used, one pair connected to an electric motor (not shown) to drive the apparatus and the other pair (shown in figure 30) connected to the shafts to drive the disc and the magnet respectively. By having one belt twisted, the disc could be rotated in one direction and the magnet in the opposite direction. By bolting the two pulleys together, the magnet and the disc could be rotated in unison.

In an alternative arrangement, two separate motors are employed, one to drive the magnet and the other to drive the disc. In this case, either the magnet alone or the disc alone could be rotated in the same or opposing directions.

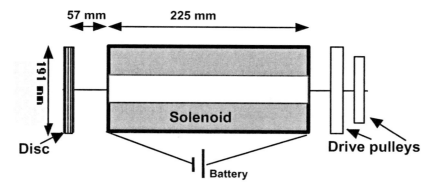

Figure 31: Solenoid Apparatus

Figure 31 illustrates the apparatus using a solenoid. The aluminium disc (191 mm in diameter and 7.5 mm wide) is on the left. The solenoid consists of 1,250 turns of copper wire of total resistance 2.09Ω. It is 225 mm long and 220 mm in diameter and is wound on a spool of inner diameter 76 mm and outer diameter 220 mm. The centre line of the disc is fixed at a distance of 57 mm from the end plate of the solenoid. A 12-volt battery supplies the current to the solenoid. A 12 KΩ resistance was connected between the negative of the battery and earth.

184

The results of the experiments are shown in figures 32 and 33. The galvanometer readings are in millimeters (mm) on the *y* axis, and the speed of rotation in revolutions per minute (rpm) is shown on the *x* axis.

Figure 32 gives the results of the magnet tests. This shows that when the disc alone is rotating or when the disc and magnet rotate together, the galvanometer's deflection varies directly with speed. The fact that these results differ from each other will be discussed later. When the magnet alone is rotating, no effect is recorded, which is astonishing. How can it be that the rotation of the magnet does not give the same voltage as the rotation of the conductor? This does not seem to make sense.

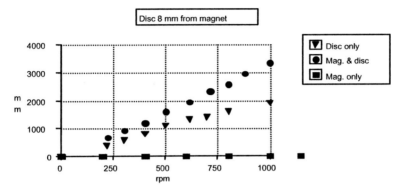

Figure 32: Magnet Tests

Figure 33 shows similar results using the solenoid. Because the apparatus was vibrating slightly at speeds over 2,000 rpm and so to conserve it for future use, tests to rotate the disc and solenoid in unison were not carried out at higher speeds. The apparatus was capable of being operated up to 2,900 rpm.

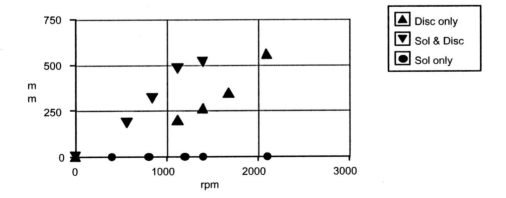

Figure 33: Solenoid Tests

Because the contact between the carbon brushes and the rotating surfaces (rim of disc or

185

shaft surface) was not consistent, the absolute values of the voltages generated altered slightly from test to test. During the tests, the current through the solenoid varied by 12% from maximum to minimum. The current usually increased slowly as the test progressed, indicating that the contact was improving with time. The gradual heating of the coils would increase their resistance. The absolute values of the voltages are probably accurate to about 15% on the tests in general. The maximum voltage in the magnet tests (figure 32) is 1.6 millivolts. The voltages in the solenoid tests (figure 33) were less than 10% of those in the permanent magnet tests; the permanent magnet was far more powerful than the solenoid.

Moving the galvanometer or the leads to any position or shielding them with mu-metal while the disc alone was spinning made no difference in the readings. In a similar test, Cramp and Norgrove altered the length and positioning of the leads and obtained no difference.

In the current experiments, a permanent magnet or a pure solenoid (devoid of a core or any ferrous parts) was used. Only Kennard, Pegram and Cramp & Norgrove previously used a solenoid devoid of a ferrous core. Using a pure solenoid dispels the idea that, at microscopic level, small magnets behave in a different way than a large magnet, which might explain the fact that no effect was evident when rotating the magnet alone (as proposed by Then).

Since Faraday's original work, the accepted explanation of the results given in figures 32 and 33 is that the 'lines of force' do not rotate with a rotation of the magnet about its north-south axis. This explanation fits the results because, if this is the case, rotation of the magnet causes no lines of force to cut the conductor (in our case, the disc) and no voltage is generated.

Several authors tried to explain the fact that the effect is not reciprocal for the movement of the magnet and the conductor. Panofsky and Phillips (1964) conclude that *"unipolar induction is fundamentally a relativistic effect"*. They say:

> *Here we have been dealing with the special (inertial) frames in which the laws of special relativity are valid. Which frame is an inertial frame is presumably defined by gravitational forces, and therefore 'a preferred frame as to rotation' is defined by the location of the bulk of the masses in the universe. Strictly speaking, there is no frame in which special relativity is exactly valid, since no frame can be found in which gravitational acceleration or 'equivalent' (i.e. indistinguishable) inertial accelerations vanish. For all electrical phenomena however, the surface of the earth is a satisfactory Lorentz frame to a very good approximation.*

Panofsky and Phillips then discuss the problem of unipolar induction: *"Many paradoxes result if one assumes that such phenomena should be reciprocal in the rotating frame and that of the earth."* They assume here that what happens in linear motion on the surface of the earth will not happen in a rotating condition in the laboratory. They continue: *"In particular, the important conclusion is retained that motion (rotation in this case) of the source of magnetic field does not affect any physical process, so long as such motion does not produce a time-varying field."* At the same time, Panofsky and Phillips say that the device is an indicator of the absolute rotational motion of the disc, yet relativity hardly allows for any discovery of absolute motion. Their conclusion is that GR is required to explain the dilemma but, tellingly, do not say how this is to be achieved. This is all very intriguing. The introduction of 'distant masses' in the universe or of GR to explain a simple experiment in the laboratory is suitably mysterious.

Moon and Spencer (1955) described how authors in the field of electrical engineering *"exchanged rapier thrusts"* in 1949 and 1950 on the (unsolved) subject of unipolar induction. Cohn was one of these. 'Rapier thrusts' could be translated as insults! Cullwick (1966) said that *"the emf is due, not to a motion of the circuit as a whole, or to a changing magnetic field, but to relative motion between two parts of the circuit (e.g. between the rotating disc and the connecting leads)."* Shadowitz (1975), while discussing why the rotating magnet causes no effect, said that the lines are *"not defined with respect to the magnets but are defined with respect to the stationary observer".*

Mencherini (1993) said that the fact that rotating the magnet gives a different result from rotating the nearby conductor causes no problem for relativity theory. He excuses the result as being *"explained exactly within the cybernetic approach to relativity by the fact that the rotation of the source of B does not have any influence on the computation of the emf because of the symmetry of the problem".* The word 'cybernetic' lends an air of mystery to the (supposed) explanation! None of the above ideas is correct, as will be explained later. Valone (1994) gave a useful list of references on the subject.

Figure 34 shows the effect of varying the distance between the disc and the permanent magnet. As would be expected, the nearer the disc to the magnet, the greater the voltages. Increasing the gap from 8 mm to 16 mm appreciably decreases the voltages. There is very little difference between the results for the 16 mm and 24 mm spacing. Increasing the gap from 24 mm to 48 mm again appreciably decreases the voltages. A test of the magnetic field strength at various distances from the magnet shows the reason for these variations.

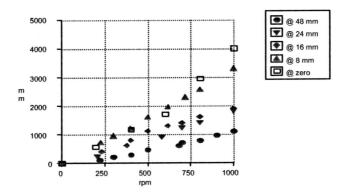

Figure 34: Variation of Distance from Disc to Magnet

Figure 35 shows the field strength at different distances from the face of the permanent magnet. The gaussmeter used was a Bell Model 600AV. The gauss reading is given on the *y* axis; the distance measured radially inwards from the outer rim of the magnet towards the axis is given on the *x* axis; the zero reading is at the outer rim. With the disc at 8 mm from the magnet, the strongest field was at the outer rim of the magnet. With the disc situated at 48 mm, the strongest field was at the inner edge. With the disc at the in-between distances of 16 mm and 24 mm, the strongest field was at the mid-section.

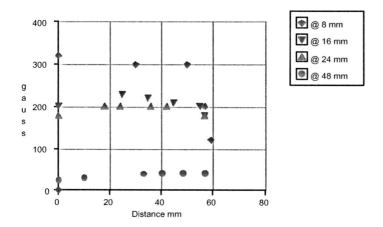

Figure 35: Field Strength at Magnet

The field strength readings were taken at the face of the disc nearer to the magnet. As an indication of the difference across the disc, the readings at the face further from the magnet were about 75% of those at the nearer face when the disc was 8 mm from the magnet. (The detailed readings at distances of zero, 27 mm and 49 mm in from the rim were 73%, 75% and 81% respectively.)

These results indicate the rapid falloff of the magnetic field with distance from the magnet, including across the disc itself. From the pattern, it is clear why the voltages on the spinning disc (figure 34) were almost the same at distances of 16 mm and 24 mm. The field results for the 16 mm distance are only slightly greater than those at 24 mm. The difference is greater between the results at the 8 mm and 16 mm distances and between the 24 mm and 48 mm distances. The field strength figures conform to the voltages produced when the distances between magnet and disc are varied.

The strength of the permanent magnet can be appreciated from the pattern of the field measured at the face of the magnet nearer to the disc. At distances of zero, 15 mm, 25 mm, 50.75 mm (at the brass bushing, figure 30), and 59.25 mm (at the shaft) from the outer rim, the field readings were 1,200, 500, 350, 600 and −30 gausses respectively. These readings are not shown in figure 35 because they would expand the scale inordinately.

Figure 36 shows a similar set of readings for the solenoid. This time, the disc is at a fixed distance. Field strength readings are given at the end-plate of the solenoid at a distance of 13 mm where there was no disc and at 57 mm where the disc was fixed.

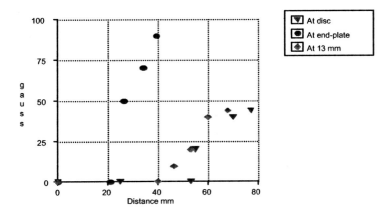

Figure 36: Field Strength at Solenoid

The field at the disc was much less strong than in the case of the magnet tests. The distance on the *x* axis was measured from the outer rim of the disc inwards towards the shaft; 78 mm is at the shaft. The field was concentrated near the shaft, and there was no measurable field at the outer 55 mm of the disc. Even at the end-plate of the solenoid, the field was not measurable for the outer 20 mm. The field could not be measured all the way to the shaft at the end-plate because the slip ring for delivering the current to the solenoid was situated there.

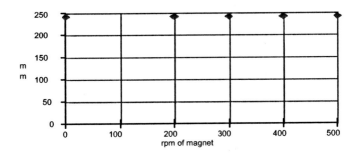

Figure 37: Rotating Disc and Solenoid

Figure 37 shows the results of another test. Here the disc was rotated at a steady speed of 500 rpm. The solenoid was then rotated in the opposite direction in increments of 100 rpm. The addition of the rotation of the solenoid made no difference to the reading recorded when the disc alone was rotating at 500 rpm. I will name this the Kissane test after my late friend Brian Kissane, who suggested it while witnessing the experiments.

189

Faraday Generator

A rotating magnet of conducting material (such as the two side portions of the magnet in figure 30) on which a voltage is produced between the rim and the axis is known as a 'Faraday generator'. In effect, the Faraday generator dispenses with the spinning disc and uses instead the conducting body of the magnet. Faraday discovered this phenomenon, and the device was subsequently named after him. His statement that the rotation of a magnet about its north-south axis had no inductive effect did not refer to the Faraday generator but solely to circuits that were totally exterior to the magnet. Faraday was very clear in what he wrote.

Faraday investigated this phenomenon thoroughly. He never returned to the peculiar behaviour of a rotating magnet in relation to a nearby exterior circuit – something that is now explained in this book. Luckily for this author, Faraday left behind one remaining aspect as he moved on to make many more important discoveries.

The ceramic non-conducting central portion of the permanent magnet in figure 30 is a non-performing Faraday generator in so far as there is no voltage generated between the rim and the axis of the magnet. The performance of the conducting and non-conducting portions of the magnet was confirmed in the series of experiments currently being described. The voltages generated on the side portion of the magnet between the rim and the shaft are shown as the 'zero' distance results in figure 34.

It was a stroke of luck that the magnet used in the current tests happened to be one that was salvaged from an old loudspeaker – none of such a size was located in the brochures of magnet makers and so the old magnet was employed. Modern magnets are mainly ceramic because they are better and stronger. The non-conducting ceramic central portion and the ferrous-conducting side portions made it possible to distinguish between a genuine Faraday generator and a non-performing one, where no voltage was generated. Had the conducting portions been removed, the tests on the Faraday generator, which proved to be crucial in the series of experiments, would not have been possible.

Vigier (1997) described the separate character of the 'field' and the source of that field. In the case of a Faraday generator, he concluded that *"a magnet moving in free space is really influenced by its own self-B field"* and that *"Faraday's one-piece generator is an absolute space-time detector"*. This reflects the currently accepted interpretation that the magnet cuts its own field and in this way generates the effect. This idea will later be shown to be incorrect.

Laws of Electromagnetic Induction

Faraday's Law of electromagnetic induction is commonly written as $\varepsilon = -d\Theta_B/dt$ (see Young), where ε is the electromotive force (emf), $d\Theta_B$ is the magnetic flux in a magnetic field B and t is time. The law means that the induced emf in a circuit equals the negative of the time rate of change of magnetic flux through the circuit. However, it is accepted that there are two forms of electromagnetic induction, a 'transformer' form (given by Faraday's Law) and a 'motional' form (see Cohn, Moon & Spencer, Vigier, and Young).

The motional electromagnetic force is $\varepsilon = v\text{BL}$, where B is a uniform magnetic field, v the velocity of a moving portion of conductor with respect to the laboratory in which the experiment is taking place and L the length of the conductor. A straight piece of conductor of length L moving across a magnetic field of strength B at a speed of v yields the motional electromagnetic force above. A disc rotating on the axis of a magnet, such as utilised in the experiments described earlier, is a case of pure motional induction because there is no alteration during the experiment in the magnetic flux over the area of the disc. There is also no alteration in the area concerned. In this case, the transformer form (Faraday's Law) is not applicable because there is no change in flux.

In some cases, the two forms are equivalent. An example of this is illustrated in figure 38, where a rectangle is formed by three fixed sides and one moving side; the moving side slides along while keeping contact with the two adjacent sides, thereby altering the area over which a constant magnetic field operates. The field is perpendicular to the page of this book. It can be claimed that the change in area causes a change in total flux through the circuit and that the motional formula also applies.

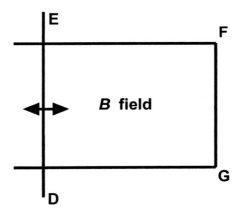

Figure 38: Both Formulae Apply

Cohn (1977) complained that *"the two formulas are presented as two different ways of expressing the same thing. This implication is usually substantiated by deriving one from the other and by solving problems which give the same result from both formulas."* He adds:

> *It is unfortunate that the equivalence of these two formulas is stressed because it leads to the formation of two schools of thought (both wrong). One group believes that all induction phenomena can be handled with the flux-cutting law, while another believes that the flux-linking law is all-inclusive. Adherents of these two schools go to extremes in the invention of ad hoc explanations to bring all inductive phenomena within the scope of their equation.*

Cohn concludes that *"only the combined use of both motional and transformer induction will guarantee validity of results in all cases of induction"*. It will later be shown that this does not give the correct result in all circumstances.

Cramp and Norgrove (1936) said that:

> *The question is whether a variation of flux enclosed by, or linked with, an electric circuit creates an emf or whether the emf requires an actual cutting of magnetic lines or tubes of induction. The view is widely held that the two are practically identical, but that the former covers the latter case.*

Howe (1935) refers to a usual derivation for the spinning disc problem, which assumes that the area concerned is altering because the radius under the brush that rubs on the rim of the disc is moving due to the spin of the disc. This is used in many texts (see Young) as a method of claiming that the area has altered in order to get a resulting alteration in total flux. Howe describes this as *"a very dubious and unconvincing argument and involves a far fetched interpretation of the word 'circuit'"*. This confused situation persisted for over 170 years until the current tests were undertaken.

Further Experiments

Further novel experiments will now be described. These were done to test the postulate proposed here that, in contradiction to previous evidence, the 'lines of force' rotate with a magnet about its north-south axis. In considering the results of the following experiments, the reader should bear in mind that the lines are assumed to rotate with the magnet when the magnet rotates about its north-south axis. In this way, it can be decided whether or not the proposed theory fits the experimental evidence observed. As far as can be determined, the following analysis of the problem has never before been proposed.

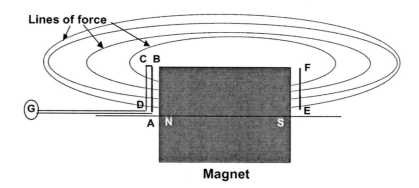

Figure 39: Voltages Produced at Magnet

In figure 39, lines of force are depicted in the usual fashion. G depicts the measuring galvanometer, which records the voltage generated. The circuit G–A–B–C–D–G has opposing effects generated in the parts A–B and C–D when that conductor moves near the magnet. In the usual manner, we shall refer to the voltage that results from that effect. The lines that cross A–B from right to left then cross C–D from left to right as we follow the circuit around from A to B to C to D. The voltage on C–D is in the opposite direction to that generated on A–B. There should therefore be no resulting voltage in the circuit.

Conductor E–F has a voltage generated when moved near the magnet. However, to measure the result, we need to connect E and F to a galvanometer. In doing so, if the leads to the galvanometer are arranged as in the former case, an opposing voltage will be generated.

A simple test with a magnet from a reject loudspeaker, a piece of conductor and a voltmeter (a multimeter from your local electrical store, with a resolution of 100 microvolts on a scale of 200 millivolts) can reproduce these results. If the conductor is doubled back tightly upon itself and moved near the pole of the magnet, no voltage results.

Two different arrangements of a circuit that is totally external to the magnet and that is cut twice (net) by the lines are shown in figure 40. The apparatus is constructed so that the complete circuit back to the galvanometer (but not the galvanometer itself, which is situated on the axis of the magnet and at a distance of 1 m) can be rotated. The connections to and from the galvanometer are via two brushes rubbing (where the arrowheads are shown) on two slip rings that rotate with the shaft. In this way, connections to the disc rim (at B) and to the shaft can be brought out to the galvanometer as the apparatus is rotated.

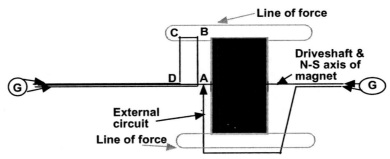

Figure 40: Circuits near Magnet

First consider only circuits that are not touching the magnet body and are external to the magnet. Table 3 shows the test results. For the first three tests, (a), (b) and (c), figure 40 shows diagrammatically the experimental setup on the left side of figure 39. A–B depicts the disc radius and B–C–D–G the return circuit to the galvanometer. The brush in this case rubs on the disc at B on the rim of the disc.

The 'circuit' is the total circuit comprising the disc and the leads to and from the galvanometer. This is different from the earlier experiments where rotation of the disc alone yielded a voltage; this difference will be explained later. Previous experimenters thought that the connecting leads B–C–D–G–A–B to and from the galvanometer played no part in the matter.

Table 3: Résumé of test results

Arrangement	Galvanometer Reading	Comments
Circuit external to magnet		
(a) Whole circuit spins	0	Lines cut circuit twice
(b) Magnet only spins	0	Lines cut circuit twice
(c) Magnet and whole circuit spin	0	No relative motion
Faraday generator		
(d) Magnet spins	Yes	Lines cut leads once
(e) Leads spin	Yes	Lines cut leads once
(f) Magnet and leads spin	0 or yes	
(i) in unison	0	No relative motion
(ii) in opposing directions	Yes	Result is twice that of test (e)
Disc tests		
(g) Disc only spins	Yes	Some lines cut disc once
(h) Disc and magnet spin ±	Yes	Lines cut leads once
(i) Magnet only spins	0	Lines cut circuit twice
(j) Disc and leads spin	0	Lines cut circuit twice
(k) Disc, magnet, and leads spin	0	No relative motion
(l) Leads (not disc) spin	Yes	Lines cut leads once
(m) Magnet and leads spin	Yes	Lines cut disc mainly once

Note: Voltages in cases (g) and (h) and cases (l) and (m) are not necessarily equal.

In cases (a) and (b), the circuit is cut twice by the lines and therefore there is no effect. In case (c), there in no relative motion between the magnet and the circuit so there should be, and is, no effect. This latter test does not seem to have been repeated since done by Faraday, who missed the significance of the result. These results conform to the proposal that the lines rotate with the magnet.

Figure 41 shows the experimental setup for the Faraday generator and pertains to experiments (d), (e) and (f). In these tests, the circuit goes through the body of the magnet, whereas in the first three tests, the circuit does not touch the magnet. The circuit comprises a magnet (of conducting material) and leads that go to and from the galvanometer. In the arrangement shown in figure 41, the lines cut the circuit once only (net). The body of the magnet forms part of the conducting circuit. The circuit is G–B–A–G (through the body of the conducting magnet at B–A). The spinning disc used in the earlier experiments is, in effect, replaced by the spinning conducting magnet body. The same effect could be got by attaching the disc to the face of the magnet and rotating the two together; the voltage would be measured from the rim of the disc to the axle. For the Faraday generator to be effective, the magnet must be of conductive material.

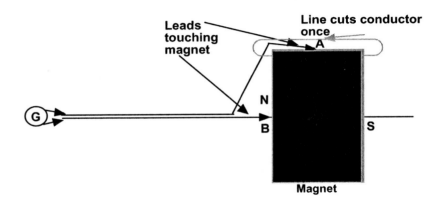

Figure 41: Faraday Generator: Circuit Partially Internal to Magnet

In figure 41, the nearer the connection A is to the midpoint of the magnet, the greater the effect. Connections can be brought out from the rim of the magnet via the brushes rubbing on the two slip rings on the end of the shaft. This enables us to carry out more detailed experiments on the Faraday generator. Rotation of the magnet alone in the Faraday generator setup – case (d) – gives a result. The standard explanation of this phenomenon has been that the magnet cuts its own lines as it rotates. The following explanation is now proposed. In case (d), spinning the magnet generates a voltage in the lead from the rim of the magnet to the galvanometer (A–G) because the rotating lines cut that lead mainly once, as in figure 41. The test results are shown in figure 42. While Faraday commented that the conductor crossed the lines once in case (d), he did not consider this important distinction in his other tests.

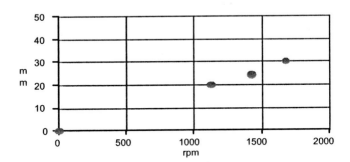

Galvanometer scale: 0.001 sensitivity

Figure 42: Faraday Generator: Magnet Rotating, Conductor Fixed

In case (e), spinning the leads alone produces a similar result because the circuit cuts the magnetic lines, which in this case are stationary. The test results for (e) are shown in figure 43 and conform to the proposal that the lines rotate with the magnet. The scale used in figure 43 is the direct scale whereas in figure 42, it is 0.001 sensitivity.

195

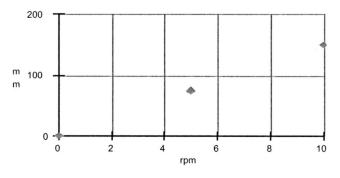

Galvanometer on direct scale

Figure 43: Faraday Generator: Conductor Rotating, Magnet Fixed

Rotating both the magnet and the connections to and from the galvanometer in unison and in the same direction – case (f, i) – gives a zero result because there is no relative motion between the magnet and the circuit. This test does not seem to have been done before, even by Faraday. The zero result is explained by the fact that there is no relative motion between the lines and the magnet-cum-circuit because they all rotate in unison. Rotating the magnet and the leads at equal speeds in opposing directions – case (f, ii) – gives a result that is double the result of rotating the magnet alone – case (d) – or the leads alone – case (e).

Now let us consider the 'disc' tests in table 3. Some of these are a repeat of the first three tests, (a), (b) and (c), and are shown here for comparison with the other disc tests.

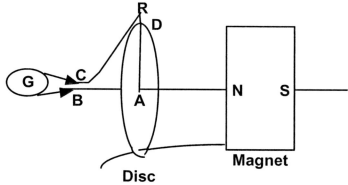

Figure 44: Disc as Part of Circuit

A disc comprises only a part of the circuit that is subject to the effect of the movements (see figure 44). In this arrangement, the disc and the circuit C–R–D–A–B can be rotated as a unit. Alternatively, the disc alone can be rotated, leaving the conducting leads stationary. To facilitate this, we need a carbon brush contact on the rim of the disc at D

196

and another brush at B on the axle at the axis of the shaft. A third brush makes contact on a slip ring at C through which the generated voltage was brought out. The whole circuit includes the disc, the leads to and from the galvanometer and the galvanometer itself, which is on the axis, 1 m from the magnet. Leaving the galvanometer stationary does not affect the results. A test that proves this is mentioned later.

The mystery was caused by ignoring the part of the circuit that was outside the disc. Previous experimenters all concentrated on the disc and did not even show the leads to and from the galvanometer. They assumed that these leads could have no function other than conducting the resulting voltages to the galvanometer. That simple oversight caused all the confusion since the time of Faraday.

As shown in figure 44, many of the lines cut the disc only once when the disc alone rotates. In case (g) (table 3), there is an effect. Because the magnet is stationary, there are no lines rotating and there is a minimum cancelling effect by the lines cutting a circuit twice.

When the disc and the magnet rotate together in the same direction (clockwise or counter-clockwise), there is a result – case (h) – because many of the lines cut the leads to the galvanometer once. There is no relative motion between the disc and the magnetic lines because the magnet is also rotating in unison with the disc. Therefore, there is no effect in this part of the circuit from the rotation of the disc-cum-magnet. The radius D–A (figure 44) does not generate any voltage. The effect is solely in the lead R–C to the galvanometer. This is somewhat like case (d) for the Faraday generator (the magnet incorporating the disc in that case).

In case (h), where the disc and magnet rotate together in the same direction, a voltage is generated on the leads (which are stationary). Call this result v–. Now consider the case (not shown in table 3) where the magnet rotates in one direction (clockwise) and the disc in the opposite direction. This case requires a detailed explanation. Here the relative motion of the lines (which we assume are rotating with the magnet) and the disc (which is rotating in the opposite direction) is about twice that in case (h) (where the effect is caused in the stationary leads). In this case – let's call it case (n) – the voltages generated are 2v+ across the disc radius (because of the double relative motion of disc and magnet) and v– in the leads, as in case (h) (caused by the magnet rotation in relation to the stationary leads). Consequently there is a resulting net voltage of v+.

A second case worth considering (also not in table 3) is where the direction of rotation of the magnet is changed but the disc direction of rotation is unchanged. In this case – let's call it case (o) – we get a voltage of v+ on the leads to the galvanometer because the direction of spin is the opposite to that in case (n). On the disc radius, we get 2v– because of the double relative speed of motion of the disc and the magnet. The net result is v–.

In case (i), where the magnet alone rotates, the lines cut the stationary circuit B–A–D–R–C–G–B twice, with zero result. This test is the one that deceived experimenters (including this author initially) into concluding that the lines did not rotate with the magnet. Case (i) is the exact same as case (b) and is being repeated here for completeness. None of the previous experimenters, including Faraday, depicted the leads to or the

197

position of the galvanometer, presumably in the belief that the leads could have no effect on the experimental results. However, as already highlighted, the leads play a critical role in the formation of the resulting voltages.

When the disc and the leads to and from the galvanometer spin in unison – case (j) – there is a zero result because the circuit is cut twice by the lines. The remainder of the disc does not come into play because the voltage generated on any radius is the same as that on A–D, which is being cancelled. This is the very same as test (a).

When the magnet, disc and leads all rotate together in the same direction, there is no relative motion and therefore no effect – case (k). This is the same test as case (c). Of course, if the magnet and the disc spin in one direction and the leads in the opposite, the result is about the same as in case (f, ii). As far as could be ascertained, tests (j) and (k) had never before been carried out.

In case (l), rotation of the circuit between the galvanometer and the disc (but not the disc or the magnet) generates a voltage because the circuit is cutting the stationary lines once. In case (m), when the magnet and the circuit (from the disc to the galvanometers), but not the disc, rotate in unison, a voltage is generated across the disc because the lines cut the stationary disc mostly once. There is no relative motion between the magnet and the portion of the circuit that rotates, and therefore there is no effect in that portion of the circuit.

If 'magnet' is replaced by 'magnet plus disc' in the tests on the Faraday generator where only the disc is considered, we get the very same results. For example, in table 3, case (d) reads 'Magnet spins', and we get the same result in case (h), which reads 'Disc and magnet spin ±', where the disc and magnet are not stuck together. Case (e) gives the same result as case (l).

There are many combinations not included in table 3, such as alternatives to cases (j) and (k). In case (j), where the disc and leads rotate in the same direction, there is no result. However, if the disc and the leads rotate in opposite directions, there is a result. Case (k) assumes the disc, magnet and leads all rotate in the same direction. Again, if the leads rotate in the opposite direction to the disc and magnet, there is a result. All these combinations will be obvious to the reader when the lines of magnetic force are taken as rotating with the magnet.

It is significant that, as mentioned previously (see figures 32 and 33), the voltage generated when the disc alone rotates is different from that generated when the disc and magnet rotate in unison. In several of the current series of tests, the distinction between the two cases was not great and was initially thought to be due to the experimental spread of the results. The variation from one experiment to another was often greater than the difference between the results. As an experiment proceeded, factors such as the alteration of bearing friction, the heating of the coils in the solenoid and the contact resistance of the brushes rubbing on the rotating disc and shaft tended to occlude this important difference. However, when such variations were suspected, the experiment was set up more carefully and a sizeable and consistent difference was found, as depicted in figures 32 and 33.

The cause is different in the two cases (disc alone spinning versus disc and magnet spinning in unison). When the disc alone is spinning, the voltage is generated across the radii of the disc. However, when the disc and magnet rotate in unison, the cause is the cutting of the lead to the galvanometer by the rotating lines of the magnet. As the profile offered to the lines can be greater for the lead (R–C in figure 44) than that offered by the radius of the disc (A–D), the voltage can be greater; this will be explained in further detail below. The two cases can substantially yield the same voltage when the lead to the galvanometer does not emerge radially from the point of contact on the disc but runs from point D down towards the galvanometer.

A test in which the disc and magnet were rotated in unison while the orientation of the leads was altered had not been done previously. Tests were done by others where the disc and magnet were rotated in unison but where the leads were not moved. It can now be appreciated why the voltages in figures 32 and 33 are greater when both the disc and solenoid/magnet rotate than when the disc alone rotates. By varying the route taken by the small section of conductor between the rim of the disc D and point R, it was shown that:

- when R–D is radially out to the maximum distance (figure 44) and the subsequent path of R towards C is not such that it cancels out the extra voltage in D–R, the voltage generated is at a maximum.
- when the conductor is aligned to run to the galvanometer without any radial component, the voltage is at a minimum.

Kennard and Das Gupta commented that the two tests (disc alone rotating and disc and magnet rotating in unison) gave about the same result. They assumed that any difference was due to experimental variances.

Then recorded a 20% difference in 1960 but no difference in 1962. He amended his 1960 statement that the combined rotation of the disc and magnet gave the larger result (which was found in the current tests) to the following: *"an emf is developed that is as large as that when the field is stationary and the conductor rotates"*. This was an ambiguous statement that seemed to allow for the possibility that the rotation of the two might have the larger voltage, but he did not say that. How often is a strange experimental result brushed aside, only to be shown later to be of great importance? When using a stationary solenoid with a ferrous core that could rotate, Then proposed that *"since the solenoid did not rotate, it is conceivable that even though the magnetized core was rotated the external magnetic field did not rotate."* He said, *"it is impossible to measure or detect the rotation of a uniform or symmetrical magnetic field"*. The current tests positively identify the rotation of such a magnetic field.

Then also maintained that *"the stationary parts of the circuit develop no emf,"* when the magnet was rotated. It is shown in the current experiments that, when both the disc and magnet rotate, an emf is generated in the stationary leads. The magnet used by Then was totally of ceramic material, so he could not have carried out tests (e) and (f).

Then, like Faraday, appreciated that the cutting of a circuit in two opposing directions gave a zero result, but neither of them proceeded to draw the conclusions in this book. He said, *"if one could go to the microstructure of the discrete magnetized particles in the ceramic magnet, surely it would seem reasonable that a microscopic conductor would experience the same effect as one visualizes."* This was in an experiment where

Then had the poles of a horseshoe permanent magnet moving in a circle around the circumference of a conductor; the poles chased each other around the conductor. This arrangement is quite different from the cases where the magnet rotates about its north-south axis near a conductor. This test by Then was, in effect, a lateral movement of the magnet poles in relation to the conductor. Then suggested that, at the macroscopic level, one cannot discern the rotation of the field, even though he suspected that it existed.

However, Then, like all the earlier experimenters, did not allude to the position of the galvanometer or to the routing of the connecting leads between the galvanometer and the disc. He concluded (in relation to the case where a disc and magnet rotate in unison), *"even though there is no relative motion between the conductor and the magnet the induced electric field is developed and it is proportional to the speed of rotation of the combination"*. Here, Then was assuming that the rotating disc was the only 'conductor' that mattered, whereas the rest of the circuit to and from the galvanometer was also of critical importance.

Cramp and Norgrove (1936) said that their test

> *. . . disproves the statement often made in physics textbooks, that a magnet is made up of a large number of small magnets, each being the origin of an associated bundle of tubes of induction. A cylindrical magnet spins as freely about its tubes as does a solenoid.*

It is true that a permanent magnet behaves somewhat like a solenoid, but it does not follow that either of them spins about the 'tubes' of the field. Others who published ideas on the subject are Blondel, Hering, Cohn, Moon & Spencer, Webster, Tilley, Crooks, Muller and Scanlon & Hendriksen.

Faraday did not do test (j), where the disc and the leads to the galvanometer rotate in unison. He did not notice any difference between cases (g) and (h). In 1832, Faraday said:

> *Taking, then, a mass of metal or an endless wire, and referring to the pole as a centre of action, if all parts move in the same direction, and with the same angular velocity, and through magnetic curves of constant intensity, then no electric currents are produced.*

So, Faraday was aware of the effect of rotating all parts of a closed circuit in unison but did not draw the same conclusions given in this book.

Assis and Thober (1994) gave a theoretical analysis of the behaviour of a magnet, disc and galvanometer spinning in various combinations. Their paper was uncovered after the current series of tests was done. They utilised Weber's electromagnetic theory in their analysis. Their predictions agree with the results of the current tests, which was a great surprise to this author because no previous publication had correctly forecast the experimental results achieved in the tests. This is surely a strong vindication of the ideas of Assis and Thober. I had the pleasure of meeting Assis on several occasions and of discussing these matters with him. Assis and Thober's paper should be read by those interested in their analysis.

The external circuit has to be compact to achieve the above effects. The return portion (C–D in figure 39) has to be near the portion of the circuit that is near the magnet (A–B). The distances between C and B and between A and D have to be short. As those are lengthened, the cancelling of the effect gradually disappears because at the further distance, the magnetic field is weaker. With the permanent magnet used in the current tests, the distance C–B has to be 100 mm or less to have full cancellation; with a longer spacing, the cancellation gradually decreases.

Another test was done to test the veracity of the proposal that the lines rotate with the magnet. If this proposal is correct, there should be a variation in the voltage produced with both magnet and disc rotating if the route taken by the connecting leads between the galvanometer and the disc is altered. In fact, rerouting the lead from the rim of the disc to the galvanometer on a zig-zag route (A–C–D–G), somewhat as shown in figure 45, causes a significant reduction in the galvanometer reading. By experimenting with the routing of the leads, the recorded voltage could be varied downwards significantly on the galvanometer. This test was done with the solenoid and also with the magnet.

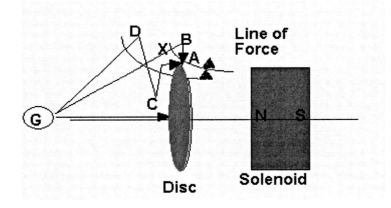

Figure 45: Effect of Altering Route of Connections

The reason for the variation in the net voltage that is generated can be appreciated by considering the net number of times that a line of force is intersected by the connecting lead to the galvanometer. With the magnet and leads rotating, the lines cut the lead A–B–G once only (except for a small portion enclosed by A–B–X, figure 45). This single cutting gives a voltage, as discussed earlier. The two magnetic lines of force depicted in figure 45 cut the lead B–G once only. If the lead is changed to take a zig-zag route, somewhat like A–C–D–G, any part that is cut twice will reduce the voltage that is produced. The lower of the two lines depicted cuts the lead A–C–D–G three times; there is a portion from A to C and back level with A where the voltage will be cancelled out, giving a smaller net result. There is also a small triangle near the apex of C–D–G where lines that will not have previously crossed the conductor will cut the conductor twice and cancel out.

When the lead A–B is routed vertically, as depicted in figure 45, as opposed to

201

horizontally from point A, the voltage will be at a maximum because a greater length of the lead is cut once only (portion X–G). The lead portion X–G offers a greater radius to the magnetic lines than does the radius of the disc; therefore, the greater voltages in the former case can be appreciated. These experiments are to be contrasted with the case where the disc alone is rotated, and no difference occurs in the voltage produced, no matter what the configuration of the leads. In that case, the voltage is being generated across the unchanging radius of the disc; no effect occurs in the lead, which has no motion in relation to the magnet. Changing the disposition of the lead can therefore have no effect.

Experimenting with alternative routing of the leads with both disc and magnet rotating was not carried out by previous experimenters, who all tested with the disc alone rotating. Consider the difference between two tests, one where the disc alone rotates and one where the disc-cum-magnet rotates in unison. In the case where the disc alone rotates, there is no alteration in the result when the leads are moved around. In the second case, an alteration of the route taken by the leads causes a change in the result. The only difference between the two cases is that, in the second case, the rotation of the magnet is added to the rotation of the disc. In both cases, the disc is rotating. Therefore, any alteration in the result must be due to the rotation of the magnet. The added rotation of the magnet from the first case (and that alone) causes the change in the result. No other explanation is possible. If the lines did not rotate with the magnet, there would be no such alteration in the result because there would be no relative motion between the lead to the galvanometer and the lines to add this new phenomenon to the case where the disc alone rotates. This calls for an important change in current thinking concerning the behaviour of magnetic fields.

Consequently, there can be no doubt but that the so-called lines must rotate with the magnet on its north-south axis. Q.E.D. The current theory that holds that the lines do not rotate with a magnet turning about its north-south axis can no longer be justified.

Consider a small, very thin wedge of north-south material (say 0.001 mm in thickness) cut out from near the perimeter of a circular annular magnet such as used in these tests. (The magnet has a large hole in the centre – see figure 30, which shows the brass bushing fitted in the hole.) Movement of such an isolated wedge (or lozenge) near a conductor will cause a voltage on that conductor. When the magnet is rotated, the small wedge (replaced in its original position but insulated from the rest of the magnet) passing by a nearby stationary conductor would behave just like the lozenge-shaped piece of magnet passing laterally by such a conductor as described above. Because the lines must move and therefore rotate with that small thin wedge, all other lines will similarly rotate with all of the remaining portions of the circular magnet.

When a complete circular magnet is rotated, each tiny wedge passing by a nearby stationary conductor would also behave just like a bar magnet passing laterally by such a conductor. A very large annular-shaped magnet would approach the case of a bar magnet passing laterally by a conductor. This effect was reproduced in the current tests by having a very small length of conductor near the periphery of a large (200 mm diameter) annular magnet – a motion of the magnet or of the conductor each caused a voltage on the conductor. This goes to show that the lines of a bar magnet rotate on the magnet's north-south axis.

The last word has not been said on this matter. There is an anomaly. The Faraday generator results are different from those of the spinning disc-cum-magnet; the rerouting of the leads in the case of the Faraday generator does not alter the voltage, while it does so in the case where the disc is separate. This is left for posterity to explain. There is still an unsolved problem here. Surprise, surprise! For some reason a magnet alone does not behave in this particular instance like a magnet with a disc attached to one of its poles.

Flux-Cutting or Flux-Linking?

Cohn (1949) described the difficulty of forecasting a correct result if either a 'flux-cutting' or a 'flux-linking' theory is used. In 1915, Blondel had shown that a circuit could be altered by winding on or off coils from a spool without altering the voltage produced. Bewley (1929) had shown a similar effect, stating that *"the turns linking the flux may be changed in such a way as not to cut through the flux, as by winding on turns or substitution of circuits, thus effecting a change in interlinkages without introducing a voltage."*

A test was carried out to confirm this conclusion. A circuit was formed to and from the galvanometer with a continuous double conductor (figure 46). The insulated conductors coming from and returning to the galvanometer were kept close together. The circuit from the galvanometer is G–A–B–C, which doubles back underneath the outgoing conductor and returns as D–E–F–G. The out and back parts of the circuit were one over the other. The leads to and from the galvanometer, G–A and F–G, were also one over the other. When the magnet was moved towards (into the page) or away from the circuit, no deflection occurred on the galvanometer. When the circuit was moved to and from the pole of the magnet, no deflection occurred.

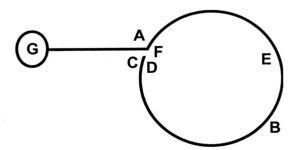

Figure 46: Circuit with No Effect

In this test, the lines are cutting the circuit in opposing directions and the effect is cancelling out. There is a large alteration here in the flux through the circuit, but no voltage is being generated. This proves that changes in flux do not necessarily produce a voltage, which contradicts Faraday's Law (see earlier in this chapter). Using a single conductor from the galvanometer on the route G–A–B–C and directly back to the galvanometer gave an appreciable reading with the slightest movement of the circuit or the magnet.

This experiment confirms that in the case of double cutting of the conductor by the lines, there will be no effect. This is similar to the test described earlier with the circuit that doubles back on itself, as depicted in figures 39 and 40.

It is well known that no voltage occurs in a rectangular circuit crossing a uniform magnetic field with two opposite sides each cutting the lines at right angles. Opposing voltages are generated in two sides that are cutting the lines; these voltages cancel out. Consider a rectangle as in figure 38 (but with no sliding side) and moving sideways through a magnetic field of limited extent corresponding to about half the width of the page. On entering or leaving the field, a voltage is produced only in the side that is alone in cutting the lines. This effect is easily reproduced in the laboratory using a magnet and a rectangular circuit in which a measuring metre is inserted.

All these experimental results conform to the assumption that the lines rotate with the magnet.

Tilley (1968) describes as follows an experiment (figure 47) similar to that of Blondel and of Bewley: *"When the switch on the left is closed and that on the right is opened, the galvanometer circuit experiences a large flux change but there is no induced electromagnetic force."* Tilley commented that *"Faraday's 'flux rule' the statement that the electromotive force induced in a circuit is proportional to the rate of change of magnetic flux through the circuit, cannot be applied indiscriminately."* There was, Tilley says, *"a large rate of change of flux but no induced electromagnetic force"*. He describes this test as *"a gross violation of the 'flux law'"* but offers no alternative explanation. Neither Tilley nor Bewley referenced Blondel's work. Tilley's result was reproduced in the current series.

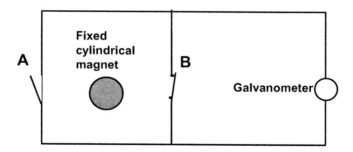

Figure 47: Tilley Test

This enigma can be explained by assuming that the basic cause of the effect is not due to the rate of change in 'flux' but to the actual cutting of the conductor circuit by the lines of force. In Tilley's test, where there is no alteration in the position or direction of the lines in relation to the stationary but altering circuit, there is no effect.

Faraday was very close to carrying out all of the tests performed here. In one setup, he used the arrangement shown in figure 48. He rotated the circuit and kept the magnet stationary (case (e) in table 3). He also rotated the magnet with the circuit stationary – case (d). However, he did not rotate the magnet and the circuit in unison – case (f, i).

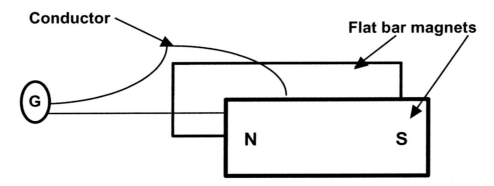

Figure 48: Internal Conductor Test by Faraday

As far as could be ascertained, Faraday never wrote down what is known as 'Faraday's Law'. The law was the idea of those who studied Faraday's experimental results and put a mathematical representation on them. In the same way, the theoretical implications of the experiments described here are not addressed in this book but instead are left for others to do. Such mathematical representation will have to describe accurately the movement of the lines of force in space in relation to the conductor – a 'rate of change of flux' or a 'movement of a conductor' is not sufficient. The old laws ('Faraday's Law' and the 'motional law of induction') are not sufficient either because they represent particular cases, not the general rule.

There are cases where there is no change in flux or area but there is an effect – case (g), for example. Faraday's Law applies to cases where a change in flux is taking place. In the experiments carried out here where the disc or the magnet-cum-disc was at a steady rotational speed, there was no alternation with time in the magnetic field or of the area concerned. In such cases, the voltage produced has nothing to do with a changing magnetic field or flux. This fact reinforces the proposal that it is the cutting of the conductor by the lines that is the critical factor. There are also cases where there is a change in flux or area but where no effect is generated (the Tilley test).

The traditional 'Faraday's Law' is a particular case that applies only when the flux change through a circuit is simultaneously associated with either (i) a locational change of a nearby circuit or magnet/solenoid or (ii) a change in the strength of the field of a solenoid, such as is caused when the current through the coils of a solenoid is altered, which causes a change in the strength of the associated magnetic field. In these circumstances, the changing of flux through a circuit will be proportional to the cutting of the conductor by the lines. Any alteration in the flux intensity from altering the current through the coils of the solenoid must also cause a cutting of the circuit by the lines because of the altered positioning of the lines in space.

It is not any cutting by the lines of force that causes a result. The cutting must be in one direction (net) or, if cut in opposing directions, the cutting must be by unequal force lines to yield a result.

It has been suggested that Faraday's Law is not a general law and that it is not the rate of change of flux that is the basic cause of the emf. In 1963, Feynman (a Nobel Laureate), when referring to the transformer effect (Faraday's Law) and the motional effect (as in a spinning disc test), says:

> We know of no other place in physics where such a simple and accurate general principle requires for its real understanding an analysis in terms of two different phenomena. Usually such a beautiful generalisation is found to stem from a single deep underlying principle. Nevertheless in this case there does not appear to be any such profound implication.

It is proposed here that the single underlying principle is the requirement that the circuit must be cut by the lines of force. This can be caused either by a movement of the circuit or magnet with respect to each other or by an alteration in the position of the lines of force in space (by a change in the current through the coils of the solenoid).

The simple adding together of the two phenomena – 'rate of change of flux' and 'physical movement' – cannot give the correct answer in all cases because the flux rule is incorrect in some situations (such as in the Tilley test – figure 47). Some authors add the two to get a composite result.

Railgun Experiment

In 1996, Graneau and Graneau describe their 'railgun' experiment, which is the reverse of the Tilley experiment. Referring back to figure 38, a rectangular area is formed by two fixed 'rails', E–F and D–G (half-inch diameter copper tubes) plus two other sides. E–D is another copper tube, free to roll on the rails. If the side F–G is removed and a battery connected across between F and G, the copper tube will roll away from F–G to the left along the rails. This is a simple experiment that can be done in the laboratory using a 12-volt car battery. It also works with an alternating current supply. Graneau and Graneau say that these results are not in accordance with Maxwell's equations. This idea has been developed into a 'railgun' whereby a gun is made to move rapidly along rails by the introduction of a current.

Graneau and Graneau also report the following strange phenomenon. When the rolling copper tube is replaced by aluminium or stainless steel, the effect is the same, but if the rolling tube is of carbon steel, the tube rolls in the opposite direction! Neal Graneau (1997) challenges someone to explain this. I have had the undoubted pleasure of meeting Neal Graneau and discussing with him several of the topics in this book.

Hooper-Monstein Experiment

Support for the proposal that Faraday's Law is not a general rule is provided by the Hooper-Monstein experiment (figure 49). This is a simple experiment to reproduce.

As we saw already, if a permanent magnet is moved towards a conductor, a current in caused in the conductor. Now, place two identical permanent magnets on opposite sides of a conductor, with the north pole of one magnet opposite the south pole of the other (figure 49). The magnets are at right angles to the conductor so that they affect just a short part of it. When these two magnets are moved simultaneously with the same speed towards the conductor, the fields from the magnets cancel each other out, as would be expected. This is confirmed by placing a Hall detector at the conductor.

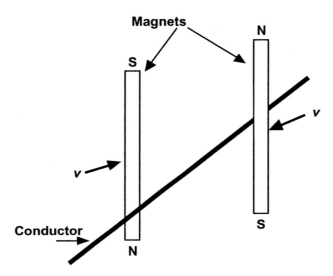

Figure 49: Hooper-Monstein Experiment

However, the current in the conductor has doubled compared to the previous case where just one magnet and the conductor are involved. We would have expected a zero result because the magnetic fields have cancelled out. How can this occur? This experiment seems to confirm that it is not the magnetic field that induces the current in the conductor.

If we now fix one of the magnets and move the other at twice the former speed towards the conductor while the conductor is moved towards the fixed magnet at half the speed of the moving magnet, the same double current is caused in the conductor. This proves that it is the relative movement of the magnet and conductor that is the deciding factor in this experiment. The Hooper-Monstein experiment confirms the findings discussed earlier.

Assis and Graneau & Graneau

An important discussion on related matters is in the work of Assis and of Graneau & Graneau. The latter have shown by many experiments that there is a force, never mentioned in textbooks, that operates along the direction of a flowing current in a conductor. It was discovered by Ampere over 170 years ago and is buried in the archives because it does not conform to the currently accepted theories that rely on Maxwell's equations, which in turn accept Faraday's Law as correct. Heresy is not allowed in the accepted religion. Interested readers can read the work of those authors to learn more. This book is primarily concerned with relativity theory and will not divert into other paradoxes in physics, such as Maxwell's equations and their veracity. There are serious problems with Maxwell's 'field' interaction idea, which was also adopted by Einstein.

Where Is the Seat of the Emf?

A debate has also raged over the years as to where the 'seat' of the electromagnetic force (emf) was situated – was it in the magnet, the disc or the conductor? Müller (1990) described how measurements *"cannot discriminate between one theory or the other"*. Barnett, Pegram and Kennard said that the seat of the force was not in the magnet. No publication has been located that proved, or indeed even claimed, that the seat of the emf was in the magnet. In a chapter entitled *Seat of Unipolar Induction* by Wesley (1991), it is stated that the seat of the emf remains in the disc when the disc and the magnet are rotated together. This will now be shown to be incorrect.

A voltage is generated between two points on the periphery of the magnet, one of which is closer to the midpoint of the magnet. In figure 30, a voltage is measured between points a and b when the magnet is rotated. Because we record a voltage here, how can the seat of the emf be in the disc (which does not exist in this case)? Müller used magnets of ceramic material, which could not show the above effect because the magnets used were non-conductive.

If the disc and magnet are separated by ever-smaller distances, the emf gets larger, as depicted in figure 34. Eventually the disc is tight up against the magnet and the voltage is at a maximum for a separate disc. We can then discard the disc altogether and use the outside part of the magnet instead. Measurement of the volts from this outer part of the magnet gives a slightly larger voltage. As we move the measurement of the voltage along the surface of the magnet towards the midpoint, the voltage rises still further.

The age-old problem as to the position of the 'seat' of the emf is now solved – it is shown to be in the magnet. This is contrary to previous authors' conclusions (e.g. Kennard and Pegram). It is also shown that the field rotates with the magnet. Furthermore, we now have an answer to the problem of what causes the emf. The emf is produced by the magnet through the cutting of the circuit by the magnet's so-called 'lines of force'. The emf is not produced unless there is such cutting, and, additionally, the cutting must either be in one direction (net) or by unequal force lines if in two directions (net). We should remember that 'lines of force' have never been located; they are a convenient concept devised by Faraday and useful to this day.

When either an electric or a magnetic field is changing with time, a field of the other kind is induced in nearby regions of space. Such an electromagnetic disturbance results in the generation of an electromagnetic wave. The emission of such a wave at the speed of light in relation to surrounding space is independent of any motion of the source of that wave. Because of this fact, it has been assumed that the idea that a magnetic field does not rotate with a magnet on its north-south axis conforms to the behaviour of electromagnetic waves. However, the proposal that the magnetic field rotates with the physical material of the magnet in no way clashes with the theory of electromagnetic radiation. When a magnet is moved laterally from one place to another, the field of that magnet moves with the magnet at the speed at which the magnet is moved (v). This movement of the field at velocity v does not conflict with the behaviour of electromagnetic waves. There is no reason to suppose that a rotary motion of the magnet would behave in a different manner from a lateral motion as far as the movement of the lines at the speed of v is concerned.

It is possible to explain almost all the experimental results by assuming that the lines do not rotate with the magnet. Assuming that any cutting of the conductor twice by the lines produces a zero result and that cutting once produces a result will satisfy almost all the results. The only phenomena that the assumption does not satisfy are:

1. The fact that moving the connecting leads while both the disc and magnet are rotating changes the result.
2. The fact that moving the connecting leads while both the disc and magnet are rotating changes the result whereas moving the connecting leads while the disc alone is rotating does not change the result.
3. In the case where there is no resulting voltage, moving the connecting leads out to a position far from the magnet before turning them towards the axis of rotation, and thus to the galvanometer, affects the result.

Galvanometer Rotated

Despite what has been described above, there may be some people who will maintain that the results would be different if the galvanometer were to be rotated with the disc. Well, there is bad news for such doubters. Valone (1994) actually succeeded in carrying out a very ingenious test of this possibility. He measured the voltage as recorded on a small device that rotated with the rotating disc. He had a connection from the rim to the axle of the disc, and the whole device rotated with the disc. He showed that when the device rotated with the disc, there was no voltage recorded. However, as we know, when the galvanometer was stationary in the laboratory while the disc rotated, a voltage is detected. Does this then mean that measurement in the 'rotating' frame gives a different result from measurement in the 'stationary' frame?

Valone presumed he was measuring the voltage in the 'rotating frame of reference'. There is a simpler explanation. The voltage generated in the connection in which the measuring device was situated cancels the voltage generated across the radius of the disc. Consequently, there could not be a reading on the small device that he used. This is confirmation that rotation of the magnet, disc and leads, as well as the galvanometer, produces no voltage.

General Comments

While the above description of the experiments on magnets and conductors reads as if everything fell into place easily, this was not the case. The project was carried out over a three-year period, with two months of each summer being spent working with sequential teams of three apprentice fitters per team. The expertise and creativity of the manager, supervisors and apprentices were a crucial part of the success of the experiments. The author gave only a general idea of what was required, and the apprentices designed and built the apparatus accordingly. I owe a great debt of gratitude to these people. The fact that one of the apprentices was on the Irish team that won the world apprentice championships that year is a good indication of their level of expertise.

A difficulty arose when carrying out the experiments with the solenoid. There were magnetisable trace elements in the material of the solenoid coils. The residual readings on the galvanometer had to be subtracted from the readings to get the real effect. It was eventually found that by reversing the polarity of the battery supply to the coils, the effect disappeared and a 'clean' set of readings could be achieved. In the case of the experiments with the permanent magnet, no such problem occurred.

A sting in the tail is as follows. In mechanics, all states of uniform motion (including that of rest) are equivalent. For any one body, it is equally true to say it is at rest or moving at any uniform velocity we choose to assume; this indifference is expressed in Newton's first law of motion. However, in electromagnetism, it is quite another story. An electric charge at rest is said to be surrounded by only an electric field, but an electric charge in motion is equivalent to an electric current and is surrounded by a magnetic field.

From this, the motion in electromagnetism is not merely relative but absolute. Einstein's theory was aimed at reconciling these two systems of kinematics and electromagnetism. Assis et al. (1999) show that there is another complication – there is an electric field outside a stationary conductor carrying a constant current. This causes a problem for relativity theory because, as they say, *"As regards those who consider magnets as a relativistic effect, we have shown that a resistive current carrying wire generates not only an electric field but also a magnetic field."* Where will it all end?

Effect of Magnet on Light

In another test (No. 2159, 1846), Faraday showed the effect of a bar magnet on light that passed by the end of the magnet (see figure 50). This was discussed earlier in the section on the behaviour of light. The magnet had no effect on a beam of polarised light that passed through a piece of heavy glass that was exactly opposite a pole of the magnet. However, if the polarised light were made to pass through the heavy glass before it reached the end (pole) of the magnet (at A), a change in the polarisation of the light occurred. If the glass plate was transferred to where the light travelled after passing by the end of the magnet (at B), the change in polarisation was in the opposite sense to the former case. If the light passed over (at D) or under (at C) the end of the magnet, no change in polarisation occurred.

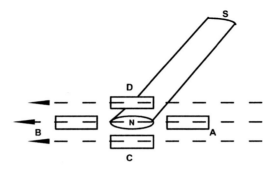

Figure 50: Faraday Experiment

Faraday did not draw the conclusion that is now proposed. The opposing magnetic lines of force, i.e. those (not shown) that would go to the right and left as viewed from the end-on position in figure 50, are postulated as having opposing effects and cancel each other out at the end of a bar magnet. This is because there are equal amounts going left and right and passing through the heavy glass plate when that is placed against the flat end of the bar. As stated above, when light is sent through the plate of glass across the end of the bar magnet, there is no change in the polarisation of the light. We appear to have an east-west as well as a north-south effect from the poles of the magnet, although the east-west effect is quite unlike the north-south effect.

The balancing of the opposing effects of the magnetic lines of force would explain this. On the other hand, when the glass is moved away from the end of the bar and is to one side, the lines of force are all of one type and have an effect. It is significant that the effect on the polarisation of the light is in the opposite sense when the glass is placed on the near side of the end of the bar (in relation to the direction of travel of the light) than when placed on the far side.

An analogous phenomenon is described by Aharonov and Bohm (1959). They sent a split electron beam across a charged solenoid magnet. They sent one part of the beam over and the other part under the solenoid. The beams went from one side to the other, not at the poles but across the midriff of the solenoid. They reported a similar phenomenon to that discovered by Faraday. The two beams had a different influence from the solenoid, and the difference showed up as an interference. The body of the solenoid was shielded from the direct beams by a plate, and the beams passed over and under the solenoid and avoided hitting it.

This experiment has had several exotic attempted explanations, but no reference to the simple Faraday experiment was located in any discussion on what is nowadays called the Aharonov-Bohm effect. It is proposed here that the explanation could very well be a simple east-west effect on the solenoid, just like the effect found by Faraday over 100 years earlier. An 'east-west' effect refers to the effect of the opposing field on opposing sides of the magnet; no geographical orientation is implied.

211

Résumé of Magnet Experiments

1. The lines of force rotate with a magnet on its north-south axis.

2. Earlier attempts to explain away the apparent non-reciprocity of the effect when rotating a magnet and a conductor about the north-south axis of the magnet are now seen to be futile attempts to justify the non-reciprocity on spurious grounds.

3. The emf produced by a magnet in a nearby circuit is caused by the cutting of the circuit by the lines of force of the magnet. The emf is not produced unless there is such a cutting. Additionally, the cutting must be in one direction (net) or, if cut in two directions (net), the cutting must be by unequal force lines.

4. The Faraday generator phenomenon is caused by the cutting of the stationary circuit by the rotating lines of force of the magnet as the magnet rotates. It had previously been supposed that the magnet was cutting its own lines of force.

5. When a magnet rotates near a stationary concentric disc, the results are anomalous. The results are now fully explained. Heretofore, experimenters considered only a portion of the whole circuit instead of considering the complete circuit, as has been done in this book.

6. The apparent non-reciprocity of the voltage produced when rotating the magnet or the nearby conductor (or disc) is now explained as being due to the different parts of the circuit that comprise the 'conductor' in those particular tests. There is no longer a problem in relation to reciprocal relative motions of magnet and conductor.

7. Faraday's Law of electromagnetic induction is true only in particular circumstances. The law of motional electromotive force is also true only in particular circumstances. One single general rule is missing. A physical description of the rule is given here.

8. Unipolar induction tests do not conflict with relativity theory, as claimed by several authors. It was this claim that prompted this author to ascertain the truth of the matter through the current series of experiments.

It might be fitting to end this section with a word of warning. If ever someone tries to explain the result of an experiment in your laboratory by bringing in such things as the distant masses in the universe, would you ever tell them to get lost! If anyone uses obtuse words like 'cybernetic', tell them they are not fooling you. If you want to find an explanation for some simple laboratory experiment (like one using a 100-mm-diameter magnet and a 1-mm-diameter conductor, or the Sagnac experiment on a 1-m-diameter disc with a rim velocity of less than 10 m/s), watch out for such nonsense talk. Figure out for yourself the cause of the results, which must be glaringly simple for such a simple experiment. Think of Ockham's razor – the simplest or most obvious explanation of several competing ones is the one that should be preferred until it is proven wrong.

The ideas recorded here were first recorded in Monograph No. 6 (1998) in the Institution of Engineers of Ireland and later in *Physics Essays* (1999) and *Annales de la Foundation Louis de Broglie* (2004).

Chapter 10

Whither Galaxies?

Hubble's Law

There are four independent topics in this chapter.

1. A novel alternative interpretation of the evidence for Hubble's Law is proposed. It could be called 'Hubble's Law reversed'. The consequences of this on the origin of the universe are discussed.

2. A potential source of much of the so-called mysterious missing 'dark matter' in the universe is given. This could explain where most of the missing matter in the universe resides.

3. A potential explanation of the shapes of some galaxies is proffered.

4. Finally, yet another interpretation of Hubble's Law is introduced. This was given by Hubble as a viable alternative but was largely ignored ever since. It is called the 'tired light' phenomenon.

Firstly, because everyone is familiar with 'Hubble's Law', we will temporarily accept it.

We hear the siren of an ambulance change tone as it approaches and then recedes. This is called the Doppler effect and is due to an alteration in the wavelengths of sound arriving at our ears caused by the motion of the ambulance. When the ambulance approaches, the wavelengths are shortened; when it recedes, the wavelengths are lengthened.

In the same way, we can tell from the wavelength of light whether its source is approaching or receding. The wavelength of the light coming from almost all galaxies is lengthened, which indicates that the galaxies are receding from earth. The longer wavelengths of light are towards the red end of the light spectrum. The speed of recession of a galaxy is computed from the redshift of the known spectrum lines of elements.

The distance to galaxies has been computed from their relative brightness and by other methods. The dimmer the galaxy, the further away it resides. When a plot of the distances versus the speeds of recession was graphed, it was found to lie very close to a straight line. This is shown in figure 51. The vertical axis shows the recession velocities of galaxies in km/s and the horizontal axis the distance of the galaxies from earth in light-years. One light-year (l-y) is the distance travelled by light in one year and is immense. Light travels 300,000 km in one second. One light-year is 9,500,000,000,000 km. To write the distance in km would be very clumsy, and so the term 'light-year' is used.

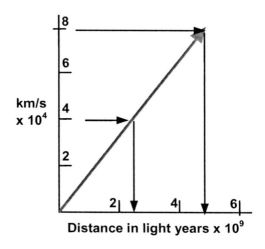

Figure 51: Distance Versus Speed of Recession

The computation of distance versus speed of recession of galaxies led to the rule that 'the further away the galaxy, the faster it is receding from earth'. This is called Hubble's Law (after the discoverer). The relationship between the distance and the speed of recession is called the Hubble constant H_0. Recession speed = H_0 times distance to the galaxy, or put more simply, $v = H_0R$, where v is the recession speed, H_0 is Hubble's constant and R the distance to the galaxy from earth. Hubble's constant is usually measured in a mixture of units, i.e. in metres per second for the recession speed and in light-years for the distance. The value of H_0 is (Young) as follows:

$H_0 = 17 \times 10^{-3}$ (m/s)/l-y
Time 't' is distance (R) divided by speed (v)
Hubble's constant = [speed (v)]/[distance (R)], i.e. $H_0 = v/R$.
Therefore $t = 1/H_0$.

If we make the units compatible, $H_0 = 1.8 \times 10^{-18}\text{s}^{-1}$. Due to the scatter of the readings, the value has an uncertainty of 25% or so.

The inverse of Hubble's constant gives a time of 18 billion years, and this is proposed as the approximate age of the universe (Young).

The age of the universe and its extent are yet to be determined (Cowen, 1998); the jury is out on these matters. Recent observations suggest a much lesser age of 11,500 million years (Willick and Batra, 2001). In this book, a round value of 15,000 million years will be used. What is a few thousand million years between friends!

In Hubble's Law it is assumed that the galaxies are still all behaving as they used to when the light left them to travel to earth. The earth only came into existence about 4,000 million years ago. The solar system was formed about 4,600 million years ago (Van Flandern, 1993). It is not reasonable to assume that our galaxy was behaving as it was 5,000 million years ago because it was not there at all! To assume that a galaxy from which light has taken 10,000 million years to get here is still at the same place and behaving in the same way is unreasonable.

Hubble's Law Reversed

An alternative interpretation of the above facts will now be proposed. While we on earth observe today the light that left faraway galaxies a long time ago, the light did not leave the different galaxies at the same time. The light from the farthest-away galaxies took the longest time to get here. When the light left the galaxies many millions of years ago, we know they were receding at a certain speed relative to the spot in the universe that the earth now occupies.

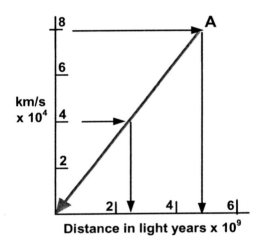

Figure 52: Slowdown of Recession

As depicted in figure 52, a galaxy at a distance from earth of 5,000 million l-y was receding at a speed of 80,000 km/s when the light signal left it; the signal took 5,000 million years to get here. A galaxy at a distance of 2,500 million l-y was receding at a speed of 40,000 km/s when the light signal left it; the signal took 2,500 million years to get to here. A galaxy at a distance of 500 million l-y was receding at 8,000 km/s when the light signal left it to travel to earth. Our latest news comes from the nearest objects, which were receding at a much slower rate when the light signal left them than objects that sent us information from an earlier time.

A slowdown has occurred along the line A–O, with all galaxies now stationary with respect to each other (apart from their current orbits and other random movements). The furthest away galaxies observed are at a distance of about 15,000 million l-y. Figure 52 shows the more recent part of the slowing process from 5,000 million years ago.

From this we conclude that the more recent the time, the slower the recession speed of a galaxy. Currently, all galaxies are in a steady state with respect to our galaxy. To change from a recession speed of 80,000 km/s to a lower speed of 8,000 km/s in a time of 4,500 million years required a deceleration of about 5×10^{-10} m/s^2. This is the reverse of the acceleration assumed under the Hubble postulate. We could claim that there has been a decrease in the recession speed of galaxies over the past 15,000 million years. This decrease seems to have been at a constant rate.

We cannot be sure that the deceleration was constant – there could have been acceleration and deceleration periods. We have no idea what has happened to the faraway galaxy (at A in figure 52) since it sent its signal from where it existed 5,000 million years ago at a distance of 47,500,000,000,000,000,000,000 km away. Because the light has travelled a distance of 5,000 million l-y in the intervening 5,000 million years, the galaxy must have been at the place 5,000 million years ago that we now observe. Maybe the galaxy no longer exists. Information concerning the current status of that galaxy cannot reach the earth for a further 5,000 million years. Will the earth still exist then?

An observer on a star at a distance of 10,000 million l-y could conclude that the earth is not here now because no such planet could be discerned at the spot where the earth exists right now. Our galaxy was not formed when a light signal left the spot in space now occupied by earth to travel to that star (assuming a light signal could be emitted from that place 10,000 million years ago).

Hoyle (1980) and Bondi (1964) had theories on a steady-state universe. They imagined a universe that exists for an infinite time and is of infinite extent and did not have any major changes in its general behaviour. The theory put forward here is quite different. It proposes that the universe developed from a non-steady state to a universe that is in a generally steady state. It proposes that galaxies had immense recession speeds in the distant past and that these recession speeds are not current.

The speed of light (c) is 300,000 km/s. In figure 52, 80,000 km/s was the recession speed at a distance of 5,000 million l-y. The speed of recession is proportional to the distance; the speed of c would have occurred (assuming for the moment that this is possible) at a distance of $300/80 \times 5,000 = 18,750$ million l-y. The fastest identified recession was about 0.96c in 1999. It is said to be impossible for a galaxy to attain the speed of light – it would require an infinite amount of energy. As the speed approaches c, the increment of speed achieved should be less and less with each increment in distance. This seemed to be confirmed in some observations. An example is Kristian et al. (1978), who state that the Hubble line has a *"persistent positive curvature"* for the furthest away galaxies.

A few galaxies are observed as approaching the earth (Morris, 1992), although the vast majority are observed as receding. It is noteworthy that no recession is observed for anything within a 10^6 l-y distance from earth. This is the most recent information we have. The objects that are approaching earth are among the nearest (Eddington, 1929). The few that are approaching are perfectly acceptable in a steady-state theory, which claims that some galaxies approach earth and some recede in the normal course of their random behaviour in space. The few that are approaching are a nuisance in the Hubble postulate.

It is proposed that all galaxies are now approximately in a steady state in relation to each other.

216

The Standard Model

The standard model of the Big Bang cosmological model of the universe states that the universe is expanding according to Hubble's Law, i.e. $v = H_0R$, where v is the recession velocity of a galaxy at distance R and H_0 is the Hubble constant (Peebles et al., 1991).

If the gravitational attractions of all the masses in the universe are strong enough, the universe should expand more and more slowly and then stop and begin to contract and eventually collapse into a Big Crunch. If those gravitational forces are too weak, the expansion of the universe continues forever. There is a critical figure for the average mass density (ρc) of the universe where the expansion eventually slows down and is in balance. This idea is attractive as it says that our universe will not expand forever nor contract back into a Big Crunch. We would not like to be caught in such a massive squash.

Invisible Galaxies; Dark Matter

We are invited (Young) to consider a large sphere (figure 53) containing many galaxies.

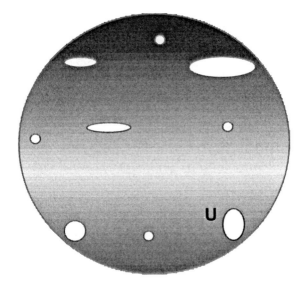

Figure 53: Spherical Space

On the surface of the sphere is our galaxy (U). The total gravitational force on our galaxy is caused by all of the masses inside the sphere. The idea that the universe is like a big sphere (similar to but much larger than figure 53), with all the mass of the universe inside that sphere, has led to the requirement that mass inside the supposed sphere pulls everything in towards a 'centre'. That theory relies on a 'Big Bang' having started the whole process at a single 'point', thereby creating the expanding sphere inside which everything resides.

If the force is less than required to balance the assumed recession of the galaxies,

217

then the sphere will expand further. However, the gravitational effect required to match the recession speeds that exist is far greater than that expected from the amount of matter detected. 'Dark matter' is the name given to the supposed missing mass whose gravitational effect would balance the recession speeds of the galaxies.

As derived by Young, the total mass inside a sphere of radius R is the density (ρ) times the volume ($4/3\pi R^3$); kinetic energy is $1/2mv^2$ and the gravitational potential between two masses m and M is $(GmM)/R$, where R is the distance between the masses and G is the universal constant of gravitation. When in balance, these two equate and $1/2mv^2 = (GmM)/R$. Substituting $(4/3\pi R^3)\rho$ for M and H_0R for v, we get the critical density $\rho c = (3H_0^2)/8\pi G$.

The value of the critical density is given as 9.2×10^{-27} kg/m³ by Freedman and Kaufmann (2002). To give an idea of the magnitude of that density, the mass of a hydrogen atom is 1.67×10^{-27} kg/m³.

To avoid it expanding indefinitely, the critical density of the universe would require about 100 times the mass so far located, including the mass equivalent of the total radiation in the universe (Young). However, although there is evidence of the existence of dark matter, the nature and source of it in the universe have yet to be determined. As Freedman and Kaufmann say, *"To date the true nature of dark matter remains unknown."* Hawking (2001) says:

> *Missing mass could also be evidence of the existence of a shadow world with matter in it. Maybe it contains shallow* (sic) *human beings wondering about the mass that seems to be missing from their world to account for the orbits of shadow stars around the centre of the shadow galaxy.*

Stars and galaxies are often shown to be pulled together by the gravity of material that is invisible. Some 80% to 90% of the mass and clusters of galaxies is estimated to exist in this dark form. Other evidence of invisible matter is in the behaviour of the arms of spiral galaxies, which would fly off were there not some invisible matter to hold them towards the centre of the galaxy. The nature of such dark matter is a mystery but it is suspected that it may consist of elementary particles left over from the Big Bang (Young).

These two features would account for about 10% of the total missing matter required to achieve the critical density for the universe. We are not concerned here with that 10% but with identifying a potential source of some of the remaining 90%, which forms the bulk of the missing dark matter.

The evidence that will now be put forward finds a sizable proportion of the 90% of matter that remains to be identified. In this way, it contributes significantly to the average density of the matter in the universe.

Dark Energy

Recently, two independent teams, Riess et al. (1998) and Perlmutter et al. (1998), showed that dozens of supernovae recess at a slower rate than expected from the straight Hubble line. This indicates a slower expansion of the universe at an earlier time, which is a surprising result and which will require some explanation. It shows that the Hubble line is not yet determined accurately over its complete range. The observations of Riess et al. and Perlmutter et al. support the notion that the expansion of the universe is accelerating! Indeed, they proposed that a new kind of energy (dark energy) is required to explain this. There is even a name for it – 'quintessence' (Cowen, 1998). This energy would need to have strange qualities; it would need to decrease in density as the universe expanded but at a lower rate than the decrease in the density of matter.

This question grabbed the headlines around the globe when published. Riess et al. state that *"further studies are needed to determine the possible influence of any remaining systematic uncertainties"*. The consequences of this research are discussed by Freedman and Kaufmann (2002). In analysing the existence of dark energy and dark matter, Riess et al. conclude, *"Future observations including space-based high-precision measurements of the cosmic background radiation and supernovae may help resolve the nature of dark energy."* They say this helps to *"pin down the value of the Hubble constant, thus giving us a better understanding of our curious universe"*.

Hot on the heels of similar claims by Riess et al. and Perlmutter et al. comes a paper by Blanchard et al. (2003), which says that this is not necessarily correct and that the universe is likely to be at the critical density. Blanchard et al. say that the visible matter plus the missing dark matter are sufficient without adding any dark energy.

We locate most of the missing dark matter in this book, so maybe with an extension of the proposals made here, there will be little need for any further search for anything 'dark'.

There will be many more exciting as well as useless 'hares' raised in this field over the years. However, in the long term (1 billion years?), the matter will become clear.

'Big Bang' or 'Full Stop'?

The Big Bang theory proposes that the beginning of the universe occurred with an immense explosion with all matter concentrated at one small place (Young). Thereafter, rapid expansion formed the universe and resulted in galaxies having velocities close to those we observe today. Others (*Scientific American Editors 2002* book) describe it as follows:

> *At a particular instant roughly 12 to 15 billion years ago all the matter and energy we can observe, concentrated in a region smaller than a dime, began to expand. Subatomic particles brewed in a microscopic energy cauldron. In it, all energy and all matter that would become the universe waits in potential. Then in a hyper-instant gravity waves and space-time inflate, and the pent up universe expands out into the budding matrix, and fills it.*

Could Shakespeare have described this more eloquently when writing about Macbeth's witches and their cauldron? Other authors in the *Scientific American Editors 2002* book say that the Big Bang started from an object *"smaller than a turnip"* or *"the size of a grapefruit"*. Why not a pinhead? The article is peppered with such questions as *"what was before the Big Bang?"*

It is calculated that the gravitational pull of objects in our universe acts against the dispersion in such a way that the objects are being pulled back towards a 'point' where the Big Bang took place. Assuming a universe has a 'centre' is a rather parochial view. The ancients thought that the sky (and visible stars) was the cover of our universe. We have a similarly limited vision of what exists. We are transfixed with the idea of a sphere of space. An infinite universe has no 'inside' or 'outside' and no requirement of pulling matter towards any particular place.

The detected galaxies that are furthest away are at a distance of 15,000 million l-y. The life of the universe is said to be about the same figure (15,000 million years). This lifetime agrees with that deduced from radioactive decay that occurs from the naturally occurring radioactive materials on earth. The universe is said to be expanding at a rate of 7.5% every 1,000 million years (Hawking).

We can observe things at a distance of about 15,000 million l-y. This means that we can see a total, in opposite directions, of twice that distance, i.e. 30,000 million l-y. We can see two places in diametrically opposite directions, each at a distance from us of 15,000 million l-y. At each of these places, an observer would need to see as far as 30,000 million l-y to see the other place that is visible to us on earth, which is not possible because the light signal would take longer than the age of the universe (15,000 million years) to travel such a distance! As we are not at any magical place in the universe, there must be similar observations from everywhere else. Every place of observation can therefore observe two other places in diametrically opposite directions in the universe where an observer at one of those places could not possibly see an observer at the other place. There is something wrong here (Morris). This is a difficulty with the Big Bang theory and one that remains even if the universe is found to be of a greater or lesser extent or of a different age than currently assumed.

We have not succeeded in seeing further than a distance of 15,000 million l-y. There could be objects galore at greater distances out there from which light has not been recorded on earth. If a star existed 100,000 million years ago at a distance of 100,000 million l-y from earth, we cannot know about it because as yet we do not have the capacity to detect it.

Light that left an object 15,000 million years ago and arrived just now on earth would also have travelled in the opposite direction from its source and directly away from earth. That light should by now be at a distance of 30,000 million l-y from earth. Suppose that a second object was also 15,000 million l-y from earth in the opposite direction to the first object. Light from the second object would also have travelled a distance of 30,000 million l-y from earth. So, the light from these two objects should now be 60,000 million l-y apart – a far greater distance than the supposed size of the universe! The mind boggles.

It is proposed here that the galaxies *were* separating at the speeds shown in figure 51 at the time when they emitted the light signal but have by now come to a halt as shown in figure 52. The earliest situation we can deduce is when everything was flying around at the speed of light. From this stage onwards there has been a slowdown, and everything is now approximately at the 'steady-state' phase, which could be referred to as the 'Full

Stop'. There would be a huge release of energy associated with the slowing from the speed of light, which could explain all the rest energy and kinetic energy of all the matter in our universe.

According to the proposal in this book, about (300,000/80,000)(5,000) million years ago, all those faraway objects were travelling at the speed of light. This is because the speed of light is 300,000 km/s and the speed of recession of objects 5,000 million years ago was 80,000 km/s; the slowdown to zero has been along a straight line (figure 52). There is no problem with things that were travelling at the speed of light slowing down to zero. The reverse seems impossible because the amount of energy required to accelerate matter to the speed of light is calculated as infinite.

We could claim that the universe was entirely made up of 'energy' flying around at the speed of light roughly 15,000 million years ago. The cosmic background radiation (Penzias and Wilson, 1965), which is coming from every direction, could be evidence of that original state. Such radiation travels at the speed of light. The background radiation, *"very massive ... the mass density in radiation,"* is one thousandth of the total mass density of the universe (Longair, 1976).

Assuming a universe that is infinite in extent and in a steady state conforms to the fact that the universe looks pretty much the same in every direction. We could assume a different type of Big Bang whereby the 'bang' created light that was everywhere to infinity and travelling at the speed of light. This light then slowed down and released all the energy needed to form stars and galaxies.

Now that we realise that galaxies are not currently receding at the speeds derived from the Hubble line in figure 51, there is no need for such dark matter to balance the so-called but non-existent recessions of the galaxies. Ironically, we shall later see that there is plenty of dark matter out there!

GR gives a different version of events. It proposes that what appears as a Doppler effect is really the expansion of 'space'. We are invited to picture the continuous expansion as somewhat like all the galaxies being on the surface of an expanding balloon, where each galaxy gets further from all the others as time passes (Young). This theory says that galaxies do not recede from earth at the speeds indicated by the redshift of the light coming from them but that 'space itself' is what expands. This idea was proposed by Schrödinger in 1928. He proposed that the apparent redshift was really the consequence of dilatation of expanding space during the time of travel of the light from the distant galaxy to earth. While he said it would be difficult to prove, this interpretation is now generally accepted by cosmologists.

It is proposed here that such a 'balloon' would have deflated steadily from 15,000 million years ago to the present time. This is because the recession of galaxies from each other (or the expansion of space) has been shown above to have decreased steadily over the aeons.

Forbidden Questions

Here are a few obvious, if uncomfortable, questions. If the universe is expanding, to where is it expanding? It has to expand somewhere. A decade ago, the fastest recession speed detected was 0.8c. Now it is 0.96c. If this expansion eventually comes to a halt and the universe reverses and starts to contract, what will happen? From where will it contract and what will be left behind?

Assuming a universe of 'infinite' extent is just as credible or incredible as assuming a Big Bang. Maybe it is easier to imagine the universe as beginning from one tiny spot in a Big Bang rather than beginning from an infinite size. If there was ever a creation of the universe, then it is surely just as likely that it began with everything flying around at the speed of light as with one concentration of everything at one magic spot. Such a 'spot' could hardly exist in isolation from the supposed 'nothingness' all around it. A 'spot' is a more comfortable idea to us because it is smaller and allows us to imagine 'observing' a place where it all began! However, if we try to explain what lies outside the boundaries of space or what was there before the Big Bang, we arrive at an infinite universe. We are not allowed to ask what happened five minutes before the Big Bang. What caused the Big Bang? Furthermore, what caused the event that caused the Big Band? And so ad infinitum.

Galaxies have been formed gradually over the aeons. This being so, how do they acquire the vast recession speeds associated with their distances from earth? Where does the massive energy come from that gives them this movement? This energy cannot have come from the Big Bang – that is supposed to have given the energy required for the universe to expand very rapidly in its early seconds.

Our understanding of light is imperfect. As Freedman and Kaufmann put it, *"The best answer to the question 'Is light a wave or a stream of particles?' is 'Yes'."* As was discussed in an earlier chapter, our understanding of gravity is minimal – we know the effects but not the 'why'.

It seems almost churlish to throw doubts upon such a neat and seemingly satisfactory theory of the beginning of the universe as the Big Bang. According to Hawking, at a meeting with some of the world's top scientists, Pope John Paul II said that *"it was all right to study the evolution of the universe after the Big Bang, but we should not inquire into the Big Bang itself because that was the moment of Creation and therefore the work of God."* I had this confirmed by the secretary to that meeting (Dr. Maura Brück of the Royal Observatory, Edinburgh).

Locating the Dark Matter

Sound travels at a speed of 344 m/s in still air at 20° C. Consider the emission of a number of split-second bangs one second ago from sources that are situated at the following distances from you in still air. You are situated at O (figure 54).

A	344 m
B	688 m
C	1,032 m
D	1,376 m
E	172 m

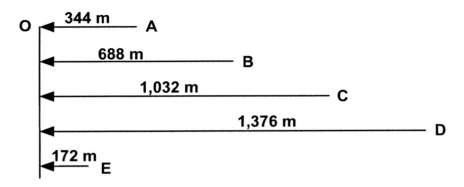

Figure 54: Sound Signals

At this precise instant, you will only detect the bang emanating from A. In the case of B, C and D, the noise will reach you later. In the case of E, the noise has already passed you by and you cannot hear it right now. At this moment, your observation is that there is just one bang; all the others are unknown to you.

If you were to listen after three seconds instead of one, you would hear only the bang from C. The noise from A, B and E would already have passed by while that from D would not yet have arrived.

Similarly, with light signals, if a number of instantaneous light flashes were emitted exactly 1,000 years ago at the following distances (in light-years) from earth, what would you see? (Remember that light travels a distance of one light-year (l-y) in one year of time.)

F	1,000 l-y
G	2,000 l-y
H	3,000 l-y
I	4,000 l-y
J	500 l-y

The only flash you will see right now is that from F. Flashes G, H and I will not have reached you yet. The flash from J has already passed earth and will never be seen again. Earth in the year 3005 will see the flash arriving from G because it needs another 1,000 years to get here.

All stars are presumably moving in some direction or other. The following requirement must be satisfied if a star is to be observed in any particular position of its trajectory: the position that was occupied by a moving star must have been such that the distance from that place to earth (in light-years) must be equal to the years of time elapsed since the light left the place to travel to earth. This single simple fact is the basis of the following discussion on the location of much dark matter.

The definition of distance in light-years is the source of some confusion. A star that was at a distance of 10,000 million l-y from earth 6,000 million years ago cannot be observed at that position. The information will not reach the earth for a further 4,000 million years. The distance from earth to the star in light-years and the time elapsed in years since the light left the star at that particular position do not match; therefore the star cannot be observed in that position.

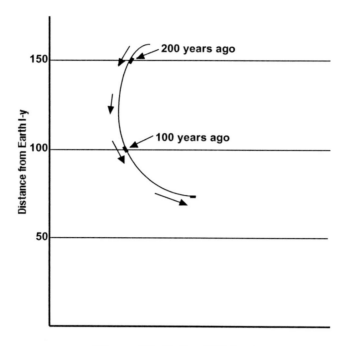

Figure 55: Path of Object

Consider the path of an object as depicted in figure 55. Suppose that the object emits an instantaneous flash of light every 25 years but nothing in the intervening period. Two hundred years ago the object was at a distance from earth of 150 l-y. It cannot be seen at that particular position because the signal from 200 years ago has already passed by the earth 50 years ago. One hundred years ago it was at a distance of 100 l-y and could be seen at that position. On its subsequent travels, the object is not seen. Today, it is at a distance of 75 l-y and the signal cannot be seen at that position. In 75 years' time, the information that the object *was* there at that time will arrive here on earth. For the signals emitted to continue to be detected on earth as coming from the object at its position on the path depicted from the time when it was visible 100 years ago, the object would have to travel towards earth at the speed of light; it would have to come a distance of 25 l-y nearer to earth in 25 years' time from a distance of 100 l-y to a distance of 75 l-y.

This is a simple example of the general behaviour and visibility of stars in the universe in relation to the earth. A star is visible only at a particular point in its movement relative to the earth. This applies to all stars (which must be the vast majority) that are not at a fixed distance from earth. It is therefore impossible to map all the stars in the universe because we cannot see them all at the same time; most remain invisible at their current locations for most of their history. Many stars will grow, live and die without ever being

224

seen on earth. Take, for example, a star that was formed 6,000 million years ago at a distance of 9,000 million l-y from the earth, lived for 1,000 million years and then died at a distance of 9,500 million l-y. During its entire existence, the star could not be seen on earth.

However, stars send out light continuously. The sun sends out light that arrives here on earth about 500 seconds after the time of its emission. We never see the sun in its current position but see it where it was 500 seconds previously. Luckily, the sun is at a fairly constant distance from earth; the distance varies by as little as 3% over the year because its orbit is almost a perfect circle. Because the sun is always a distance of 500 light-seconds from the earth, light is supplied continuously from the sun to the earth. The sun does not move away on a trajectory (as does the object in figure 55) that would take it to a different distance from the earth. This is lucky for the human population!

A continuous supply of light also comes to us from other stars like the sun that are at a fairly constant distance from the earth. Such stars are permanently visible to us – we see them as they were at a given time in the past.

Invisible Galaxies and Stars

A galaxy that was at a distance of 15,000 million l-y from earth 15,000 million years ago is seen now at the precise location that it occupied 15,000 million years ago.

We see every galaxy as it was at a particular stage of its development long, long ago; any previous or subsequent alterations are unknown to us. In the following discussion, whatever applies to a galaxy also applies to an individual star and vice versa. What we see is the view of a galaxy at a specific time. A galaxy may, at a later time, have acquired or lost stars of newer or older origin than the bulk of the galaxy, but we cannot observe this. We have a snapshot of the galaxy as it was at a particular time. Once a galaxy becomes visible on earth, it will remain visible forever (until it or the earth dies) because it cannot move away from earth at a speed greater than the speed of light.

Any coincidence of the light-year distance from a star to earth and the years of time for the light signal to arrive on earth right now will result in a sighting on earth right now of that star in its then position. However, any such coincidence that is scheduled to occur in the future will not result is a sighting right now.

If a galaxy was formed 5,000 million years ago (about the same time that our galaxy was formed) and at a distance of 6,000 million l-y from earth, then what? We cannot view that galaxy now because the first light from it will take another 1,000 million years to get here. If the galaxy and the earth maintained their same relative positions, then anyone on earth in 1,000 million years' time could view it because the signal coming from it would then have arrived at earth. If, however, the galaxy moved relative to earth, as seems more likely, then what would happen? It would have to approach earth faster than the speed of light to have been seen at any time in the past 5,000 million years. This is a highly unlikely occurrence! If the galaxy moved over the following 2,000 million years (starting 5,000 million years ago) to a position where it is at a distance of 4,500 million l-y from earth, it still cannot be seen on earth.

If a cluster formed at a particular location 10,000 million years ago at a distance of 10,000 million l-y from earth, it will be visible now at that place. If the cluster added stars to form a spiral galaxy 6,000 million years ago at a distance of 7,000 million l-y from earth, all we see is the original cluster – the rest of the additional stars will be invisible. Much depends on when the various galaxies were formed. We cannot see the galaxies that were formed at times and places in the universe from where the light could not yet have reached earth. So, improvements in observation techniques cannot solve this problem.

We could call it 'dark matter'. Perhaps a better name would be 'Yet-to-be-seen matter'? It is not really 'dark' because it could be clearly seen if the signal showing its existence had arrived here. It is a perfectly normal galaxy, just like any other. The fact that we cannot see it is our problem; it is visible from many other places in the universe.

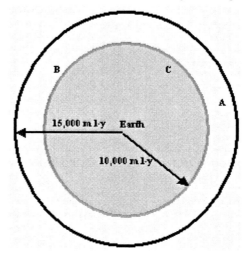

Figure 56: Invisible Galaxies

Consider a very simple model of the universe (figure 56). Suppose all galaxies were formed uniformly throughout the whole of the universe 10,000 million years ago. Considering the volume of the complete universe (of radius 15,000 million l-y) versus the smaller volume of a globular space centred on the earth with a radius of 10,000 million l-y, we find that the space where galaxies formed 10,000 million years ago would be invisible.

The shaded area denotes where the galaxies are visible. It is only those galaxies that were formed within a distance of 10,000 million l-y that can be seen on the earth. Galaxy C will be visible whereas galaxies A and B will not. Any galaxy formed 10,000 million years ago at a distance further than 10,000 million l-y from earth would not be visible on earth now because only 10,000 million years have elapsed since its formation. The total volume of the universe is $4/3\pi r^3$, where r is the radius of the universe. The volume of the invisible space, $4/3\pi 10^{27}(15^3 - 10^3)$, is 70% of the total volume.

Figure 56 is in two dimensions and does not properly depict the situation; the unshaded area is but 56% of the area in two dimensions while it comprises 70% of the volume. The assumption of 10 billion years ago as an average date for the formation of galaxies does not preclude individual stars or galaxies from being formed as far back as 15 billion years ago or being formed much more recently than 10 billion years ago.

If, on the other hand, the galaxies were formed 12 billion years ago, then the volume of space where galaxies could have been formed but cannot yet be seen comprises 50% of the total. If all the galaxies were formed on average 12 billion years ago, then over 50% of them are invisible.

The following list shows the percentage of galaxies that are invisible under assumptions relating to their time of formation and assuming they were formed uniformly throughout the universe.

Time of Formation	% Invisible
15,000 million years ago	0
12,000 million years ago	49
10,000 million years ago	70
5,000 million years ago	96
1,000 million years ago	99.97

Stars formed uniformly throughout the universe 1 billion years ago are 99.97% invisible. Galaxies formed at about the same time as our galaxy (5,000 million years ago) are 96% invisible.

Van Flandern, Freedman and Kaufmann and also the *Sunday Times* supplement *The A-Z of the Universe* (2002), compiled by experts, say that our galaxy was formed 4,600 million years ago. There are some stars in our galaxy that were formed much earlier and many that joined later, but the whole galaxy as observed by us right now is what interests us.

In the case of a galaxy formed 15 billion years ago at a distance of 10 billion l-y from earth, it will have reached a place where its distance from the earth (in l-y) will be equal to the time elapsed since the light signal left the galaxy at that position to travel to earth. It will have become visible to us on earth at that location in space. Because nothing can travel faster than the speed of light, that galaxy will remain visible on earth thereafter.

Such invisible matter clearly contributes to the gravitational attraction of the total mass in the universe and should be included when computing the average density of matter in the whole universe. To date, these invisible galaxies have not been computed because they have not been, and cannot have been, detected. In this respect, they can be termed 'dark matter'. Adding in the mass of these invisible galaxies would considerably bridge the gap between the matter detected to date and the critical density of the universe.

Light-Cones

Einstein (1922) defined the lower half of the light-cone (figure 57) as the cone containing points from which a light signal could have been sent to reach a point P. The *x* and *y* dimensions are shown with the passage of time in the vertical direction. Consider the earth to be at P. The cone is the envelope containing points that can send information at the speed of light to the point P. To the observer at P, nothing other than that inside or on the surface of the lower cone can be observed. To observe anything outside the cone, light would have to travel faster than c, which is impossible. Such light-cones are missing one dimension – the 4th dimension (z), which one must imagine.

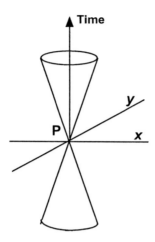

Figure 57: Light-Cone

The top part of the cone is what we shall see in the future. Galaxies that are so far away that light from them cannot yet have reached earth are not contained in the cone. Such a light-cone assumes that the light-years distance is equal to the years elapsed since the light left the object. However, as we have seen, that is not always the case. If the distance (in l-y) from the apex of the cone to the place where a galaxy was created is greater than the time elapsed since the formation of the galaxy, the cone of light does not apply.

This explanation of the visibility of objects in the universe is to be compared to the definition of 'contemporaneous' given by Russell (chapter 2). The explanation given here does away with the necessity for the description of 'space-like' given by Russell for objects lying outside the cone.

As shown above, if all stars and galaxies were formed uniformly throughout the universe at an average time of 10 billion years ago, then 70% of them are still invisible to any one particular 'observer' situated at a particular place in the universe. It is not the same 70% that is invisible to every such observer; for each, a different 70% is invisible.

We are unable to add all the visible objects in all the innumerable individual light-cones of all possible observers to get the total matter in the universe. We can reasonably assume that what is visible in our light-cone is typical and that all other light-cones have a similar amount of visible matter. Some matter that is visible in our light-cone on earth will not be visible in many other light-cones. This occurs where the distance (in l-y) from such matter to another observer somewhere in the universe at the apex of another such cone is greater than the time in years elapsed since the formation of the object.

To get a sum of the total matter in the universe, we would need to add all matter that is visible in the innumerable possible light-cones (and that was not recorded in any other light-cone) for all observation points in the universe. We should therefore count any one piece of matter only once. That would be some task!

Age of Galaxies

From the above discussion, we could reasonably conclude that about 60% to 70% of galaxies are invisible. This then explains most of the mysterious dark matter said to be in the universe but not yet located (Freedman and Kaufmann).

Ironically, even though this book postulates that all galaxies are now in a 'steady state' and no extra unseen matter is required, in the Big Bang theory, extra mass is required to explain that model; such extra mass is now located in plenty. Adherents of the Big Bang theory can latch onto this explanation of dark matter – they may adopt the idea free of charge. In the steady-state model, the extra mass is not needed but still exists.

We might also deduce the presence of other invisible matter from the gravitational effect of an invisible galaxy on a visible one. A combination of circumstances is required, which an example will now illustrate. Suppose a galaxy A was situated near another galaxy B 5,000 million years ago. These two galaxies will have a gravitational effect on each other. If galaxy A was at a distance from earth of exactly 5,000 million l-y, it is visible on earth today. If galaxy B was at a distance from earth of 5,000.1 million l-y at that time, it is not visible on earth at that place now. The gravitational effect of galaxy B on galaxy A will be noticed, but galaxy B will not be observed.

Gravity acts at an enormous speed – maybe up to 10^{10} the speed of light (see Van Flandern), and its effect would not have to wait for transmission at the speed of light. That question of the speed of gravity is discussed in detail in a later chapter on the subject of gravity. The effect of gravity of galaxy B on galaxy A would be apparent as acting 5,000 million years ago and at a distance of 5,000 million l-y. Such a coincidence of events could explain the presence of some so-called dark matter. This fact could show the presence of small amounts of dark matter by inference but not by observation. However, would gravity work with sufficient strength at the distances required to cause this phenomenon?

The idea that there must be a huge amount of dark matter to explain a movement of our own and nearby galaxies led to the proposal that there was a 'Great Attractor' somewhere out there nearby. Could this be a huge number of stars or galaxies formed at a place where the light cannot yet have reached earth? Could this be the explanation? It is unlikely.

There is considerable speculation on the timing and method of formation of galaxies. Ellis et al. (2000) suggest that ellipticals (elliptically shaped galaxies) may have formed from the merging of spiral galaxies. They say, *"close examination of some (but not all) ellipticals reveal tell-tale remnants of recent merging"*. On the other hand, Freedman and Kaufmann (2002) say, *"ellipticals were already well developed 4 billion years ago. . . . In contrast, spiral galaxies have been forming continuously over the past*

10 to 15 billion years." This says that spiral galaxies are forming even today. Longair (2000) describes the considerable uncertainty concerning the sequence of events and their timing. He stresses that the global average of the history of galaxies does not necessarily reflect the history of any particular galaxy. Sandage and Sandage (1975) say that some steady-state models of the universe predict that 10% of galaxies are less than 1,000 million years old.

There is evidence that there was an era of very active star formation in the early history of the universe. Edmunds (1982), in an article entitled *The Age of Galaxies*, says that there was such a period at one-third to one-fifth the age of the universe. The formation rate of galaxies was then approximately 1,000 times the formation rate at more recent times. This is supported by a European Space Agency report (1999).

More precise assumptions than the simple global assumptions in this paper as to the age of particular categories of galaxies will yield more precise totals for the invisible matter in the universe. However, the total amount of such invisible matter in the universe is considerable and should be taken into account in the calculation of the average density. As better data becomes available concerning the age of galaxies in general and of each category of galaxy in particular, the percentage of matter that is invisible can be refined.

Galaxy Shapes

Hubble classified galaxies into different categories: elliptical, spiral and irregular. He split the spiral ones into 'normal spirals', which have vast globular clusters at their centres, and 'barred clusters', which have vast bar-shaped formations of stars at their centres. Astronomers calculated the rotational speed of spiral galaxies; the calculations showed that the spirals would break up due to centrifugal forces unless they were held together by the gravity of more matter than they appeared to contain. Massive amounts of 'dark matter' were assumed to make them stable. The first observation of the famous whirlpool galaxy was by the Earl of Rosse in Ireland at Birr, Co Offaly in 1845; see Garret Scaife's book *From Galaxies to Turbines* (2000).

Why do the spiral arms of a spiral galaxy not go right around the core cluster? The galaxy should have been spinning for aeons and shown many such complete circuits. This is a mystery. If we could explain the shape of a few typical galaxies, perhaps we would have a clue how to analyse many of them.

The shape and behaviour of galaxies varies from those that are furthest from us to those that are nearest. At the greatest distances, there are just tiny slivers but no galaxies to be seen (Freedman and Kaufmann). This was confirmed by the observations from the Hubble telescope that was recently launched outside the earth's atmosphere. This supports the notion proposed in this book that, over 15,000 million years ago, everything was flying around at the speed of light and galaxies were formed later.

The speed of light is not infinite and takes a long, long time to get from a galaxy to earth. Because the light takes time to get from the far side to the near side of any galaxy and because galaxies move in various directions, we can rarely observe their true shape – we see a distorted view. The magnitude of the distortion depends on the movements of the galaxy. For small groups of stars in random formation, the distortion will not be identifiable. For symmetrical formations containing millions of stars, the distortion will be observed.

A typical galaxy is 100,000 l-y in diameter. It takes light 100,000 years to get from the back to the front. During that time, the whole galaxy may have moved an appreciable distance in space. If a galaxy is moving directly towards or away from earth, we will see no distortion of note. If a galaxy is moving sideways to our line of sight, there will be an observed distortion – every star except the very nearest will be seen in a position that it occupied at an earlier time in the life of the galaxy. The simplest case is that of a spherical galaxy moving sideways to our line of sight (figure 58). This comprises millions of stars closely packed into a sphere. Consider yourself (left-hand diagram) situated at the bottom of the diagram looking up at the galaxy. Point O is right in front of you and point B is very far away. If the galaxy is 100,000 l-y from front to back and is moving from left to right at a speed of 0.25c (75,000 km/s), then its appearance is as shown in the right-hand diagram.

Figure 58: Elliptical Galaxy

All stars except the nearest star at O will appear where they were at an earlier time. Because the galaxy is moving from left to right, point B (left-hand diagram) will appear at B' (right-hand diagram) where it was 100,000 years earlier. The galaxy appears to have a shape like a rugby football, which merely indicates that it is moving at a considerable speed sideways to our line of sight. The time taken for the image to reach our eyes from the front of the galaxy will not alter the shape that eventually arrives at our eyes. The image that we see is what reaches the front (level with point O in the left-hand diagram) at the same instant. This simple analysis could explain the peculiar shapes of about 30% of all galaxies that are elliptical in shape. Many of the so-called elliptical galaxies would then be no more than spherical galaxies that are moving across our line of vision.

Compared to figure 58, there would be slight distortion of the viewing of stars at the sides of the galaxy from earth because the lines of travel of the light from the sides are not parallel to the line of travel from O – such lack of parallelism is insignificant for the faraway galaxies and is ignored here. To explain their elliptical shape, elliptical galaxies are said to contain stars that have different speeds in different directions (Freedman and

Kaufmann). This bizarre assumption is not now required – why would different stars assume different speeds just because they happen to be travelling in a particular direction? How could these stars 'know' or be attuned to do that? There has to be a better, more sensible, reason.

Evidence to date shows that the lateral movement of galaxies is limited to about 2,000 to 3,000 km/s. Such speeds would cause only a tiny ellipticity in the appearance of a spherical galaxy. However, if it were ever determined that the lateral movement of galaxies is some 20 to 30 times greater than hitherto determined, the shape of elliptical galaxies could be explained as above. In the meantime, these proposals are hypothetical.

Lensing could possibly explain a few examples but not the large percentage of galaxies that depict an elliptical shape.

A referee who assessed a paper (by this author) on the appearance of a spherical galaxy moving rapidly sideways claimed that the appearance would not be as Terrell (1959) (or I) said. The referee claimed that all spheres appeared as spheres (to the observer on earth) regardless of the sideways speed of the galaxy. On this basis, the article was rejected. Terrell's paper explained the matter with great clarity. The referee thought that we were contradicting SR by saying that the galaxy would be observed as other than a sphere. However, this sideways movement has naught whatever to do with SR; it is merely concerned with the speed of light and the sideways movement of the galaxy. Indeed, no less a person than Einstein stated that a sphere moving sideways at very high speed would appear as an ellipsoid as viewed from the stationary system, and he worked out the equations to show it. In his first 1905 paper on relativity, he said, *"A rigid body which, measured in a state of rest, has the form of a sphere, therefore has in a state of motion – viewed from the stationary system – the form of an ellipsoid of revolution."*

The idea for the above analysis of elliptical galaxies came from Ann Ferguson, whose late husband had the idea but failed to get it published. Ann Ferguson attended the first launch of the idea in a paper by this author in November 2001. She had read about some of my other publications in the press and wrote to me in the hope that her husband's idea could be brought into the public domain. Ferguson's idea spurred me to investigate further possibilities, as outlined below.

Transverse Movement of Galaxies

GR claims that 'space itself' expands and that galaxies do not have the high velocities implied by Hubble's Law. This is based on the idea that the redshift of light coming from galaxies is not an indication of the recession of the galaxies away from earth but of an expansion of space itself. The recession of a galaxy is said to be limited to about 2,000 to 3,000 km/s. However, even accepting that theory (for readers not yet convinced that SR is disproven), a sideways movement of what is thought allowable under GR would show an elliptical shape, though not at all to the same extent as surmised above.

If space is expanding, does the space within a galaxy not also expand? Why should that particular space within the boundaries of the galaxy be exempt from expansion? There is no evidence that faraway galaxies are more spread out than nearer ones, and neither does there seem to be evidence that galactic clusters have expanded.

Because we have shown SR to be incorrect, we can dismiss the idea that 'space' is expanding as claimed by GR. It can therefore be argued that what we see in the redshift of galaxies is their actual recession speeds and not the expansion of space. Perhaps it may be shown in the future that the shape of elliptical galaxies is proof that they are moving sideways to our line of sight at speeds that are a sizable percentage of the speed of light. Large sideways movements would cut across the Big Bang theory whereby everything came from the one spot and expanded outwards thereafter.

Quasars and Radio Galaxies

While quasar jets appear to move laterally at speeds that exceed the speed of light, the distance from earth of those quasars is the subject of much debate.

There is an ongoing debate about whether or not the redshift of the light coming from these sources can be interpreted as indicating such great speeds; some claim their distances from earth are miscalculated. Arp and also Van Flandern have published papers and books on this topic, claiming to have irrefutable evidence that such objects are far nearer to earth than astronomers calculate – this would mean that their sideways movements are not at such high speeds. These authors claim that there is compelling evidence that shows that the redshift of the light arriving at earth from these objects does not follow the Hubble line rule.

Freedman and Kaufmann say that a debate fuelled by Arp in the 1970s ended in favour of the view that the quasars' redshift indicates their distance from earth, just as in the case of normal galaxies. However, Arp has published a later book, *Quasars, Redshifts and Controversies* (1987), which consolidates his earlier work. This was also discussed by Van Flandern (1992).

Galaxy Turning on an Axis

The following analysis arrives at a potential reason for the shapes of spiral galaxies. However, this section is purely speculative and has no experimental observations to back it up. Until astronomers identify galaxies that move in the manner assumed below, the following deductions are merely guesses of an interesting nature.

We have examined elliptical galaxies that comprise some 30% of all galaxies. The remaining 70% have more complicated shapes. Consider a galaxy that has an idealised shape as shown in figure 59. There is a core of stars forming a cluster at the centre and a rim of stars around that at a distance from the core. The light from point O arrives at our eyes x years later – this will be an immense time (thousands of millions of years). Light from any other part of the galaxy takes even longer than x years to arrive at our eyes. Light takes 100,000 years to traverse the diameter from back (point P) to front (point O) and x + 100,000 years to reach our eyes. The light will take x + 50,000 l-y to reach our eyes from the points marked Q. We have to add various times to the time x, depending on the time for an image of an individual star in the galaxy to reach the front of the galaxy in line with the point O at the 'starting line' Z–Z. The image from each individual star that

233

reaches this starting line at exactly the same instant will be the precise image that will be seen much later by the observer on earth. In all cases, we assume that the galaxy met the criterion that the distance to the galaxy from earth equals the time taken by a light signal to traverse that distance. Otherwise, the galaxy will not be visible at that particular place.

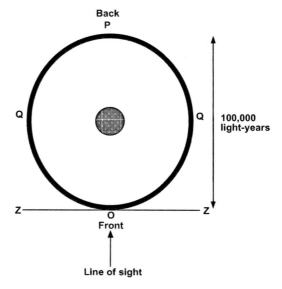

Figure 59: Actual Shape of Galaxy

A galaxy that is spinning about an axis is shown in figure 60.

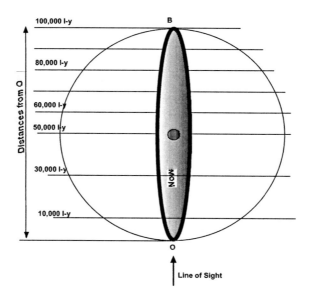

Figure 60: Current Position

234

Consider the galaxy to behave like the blades of a wide circular propeller spinning about the hub (central cluster hub shown in figure 59). The galaxy comprises an outer circular ring of millions of stars and a separate central cluster at the hub. In figure 60, the galaxy has depth; the circular outer ring is shown almost edge-on to the viewer. (The galaxy is the shaded item in the figure; the large circle with diameter OB merely indicates the orbit of the points O and B as they swing around.) The galaxy is shown in two dimensions only. It is an idealised perfect galaxy where all stars are in the one plane. The line of sight is shown looking towards the galaxy from earth.

The image that arrives simultaneously at the starting line in figure 60 is the image that will eventually be seen on earth. The distance from that starting line to earth is ignored in the diagrams because it does not alter in any way the image that will be seen later. The left side of figure 60 shows the distances from O that the light from a star has to travel to get to the starting line. In each case, the extra distances are what are shown in the diagrams.

In figure 60, we can see the nearest part of the galaxy at O in its position at the starting line. We cannot observe in this diagram any other part of the galaxy in the position it occupied some time previously and which will be the image that will reach the starting line to travel onwards to the earth together with the image of point O. To deduce the image that will simultaneously arrive at the starting line, we have to consider the movement of the galaxy in the past. This galaxy is assumed to be turning like a propeller. We cannot ever see the galaxy as it really existed x years ago unless all of it is lying in a plane with each part being exactly the same distance from us and at such a distance that the light gets here in exactly x light-years.

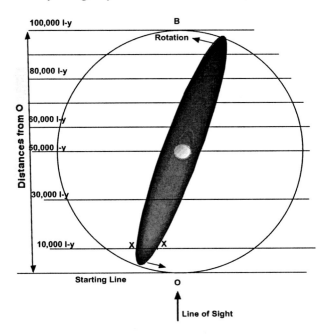

Figure 61: Position 10,000 Years Ago

235

10,000 years ago, the galaxy was at the position shown in figure 61. We cannot observe parts of the galaxy in the position depicted in the diagram except those marked X. This is because those parts happened to be at the precise distance of 10,000 l-y exactly 10,000 years ago. The distance from X–X to the starting line is 10,000 l-y. Consequently, the points X will reach the starting line in 10,000 l-y and travel onwards towards the earth in tandem with the image of point O. We can therefore analyse what arrives at the starting line at the same instant, which will give us the complete image of the galaxy that will eventually arrive at earth.

In the same way, figure 62 shows the position (chosen arbitrarily) of the galaxy 50,000 years ago. In this position, a considerable amount of the galaxy is to be seen, including the hub of the 'propeller' and the points marked Y on the outer rim of stars. Light from any other point of the galaxy will not be seen because light from such points has either not yet arrived on earth or has already passed by.

Figure 63 shows some of the successive positions of the 'propeller galaxy' as it turned on its axis. The positions of the galaxy 80,000 years ago and 60,000 years ago are shown, as is its position 'now' from figure 60 (the vertical position of the 'propeller'). We are able to see only specific parts of a galaxy. From figure 61 we see parts marked X; from figure 62 we see parts marked Y.

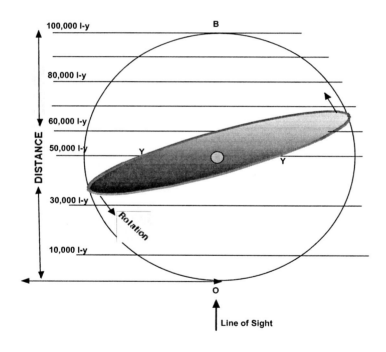

Figure 62: Position 50,000 Years Ago

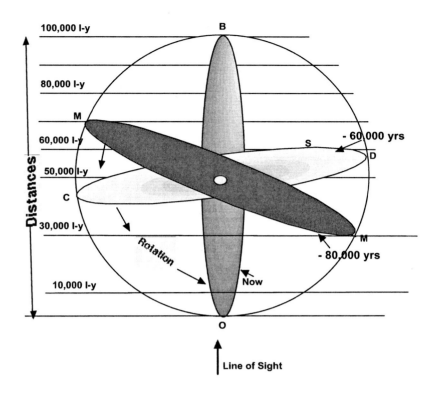

Figure 63: Galaxy Turning on Axis

From figure 63 we can appreciate that the part marked S can be seen currently because that part of the galaxy was a distance of 60,000 l-y away 60,000 years ago. Where the galaxy was 60,000 years ago is the oldest position that is visible. No part of the galaxy was at a distance of 80,000 l-y from earth 80,000 years ago so nothing can be seen from the position occupied by the galaxy then. M–M is the axis of the galaxy 80,000 years ago. It is clear that no light from any star in the galaxy at that position could possibly be seen on earth now because the light from any part of the galaxy would take less than 80,000 years to get here and would have passed by the earth long ago. The greatest time that would be taken by the light from any star in the galaxy to come here (from its position at M (top-left) 80,000 years ago) is 70,000 years. All sightings of the galaxy at this position passed the earth 10,000 years ago.

Figure 59 showed the cluster of stars at the centre, or 'hub', of the galaxy. Figure 63 also shows that the hub area (the small white circle at the centre of rotation of the propeller) will have been seen from approximately the positions it occupied 48,000 to 52,000 years ago; these positions intersect the required distances from earth at the correct times. The hub is in the same position all the while so it will be seen wherever it intersects the distance lines, which it does at distances of about 48,000 to 52,000 l-y. This hub area will be observed as a somewhat enlarged cluster.

Consider next the case of a galaxy that is rotating about an axis at right angles to our line of sight, as shown in figure 64. Successive positions are shown at a, b and c,

237

which depict the galaxy at the reversing point on a huge orbit. The galaxy is shown as it turns around the corner and reverses such that the portion B that was in the front left position (a) is now seen at the front right position (c).

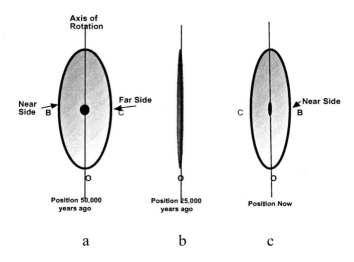

a   b   c

Figure 64: Galaxy at End of Orbit

In figure 64a, assume the near side was on the left and the far side was on the right 50,000 years ago. After 25,000 years, the galaxy is exactly edge-on to our line of sight (64b). At the present time (64c), the galaxy is tilted the other way around – what was the near side is now on the right and what was the far side is now on the left. We cannot see the galaxy in any of these positions because, as explained above, during the time taken by light to traverse the distance to the front of the galaxy at O, it will have changed its position. What we observe is a combination of positions of portions of the galaxy at different times on its orbital path.

Figure 65: Appearance of Galaxy in Figure 64

The resulting shape that we see is somewhat similar to that shown in figure 65 – closed loops emanating from a large cluster. While these positions are in three dimensions, our eyes observe them in two dimensions, as shown in figure 65. The derivation of these shapes required a three-dimensional exercise, which was carried out by rotating and viewing from a fixed position an inflated balloon with the galaxy drawn on its surface.

Many galaxies are spiral. These have truncated arms, a feature that has puzzled astronomers. The fact that the arms are curtailed and do not continue to closure is explained here by the requirement that distance in light-years must equal the time in years for a light signal to traverse the same distance. As explained above, this requirement is not necessarily met for all parts of a galaxy, which is rotating. Consequently, there is a cut-off point beyond which we will not observe anything. In the example in figure 63, the cut-off point is at a distance of 60,000 l-y; beyond that we see nothing.

Figure 66: Spiral Galaxy

If we now combine the two movements shown in figures 63 and 64, we have a spiral galaxy as shown in figure 66. The movement shown in figure 63 yields the appearance of symmetrical arms that radiate out from the cluster at the core of the galaxy in a curved shape, as depicted in figure 65. The additional movement about an axis as shown in figure 64 also introduces a cut-off of the arms, as depicted in figure 66. The 'hub' will appear larger because point O in figure 63 will merge with the appearance of the hub. The galaxy Messier 100 is of this appearance.

The arms of spiral galaxies do not continue right around the core. They are truncated. This has been a mystery because many of these galaxies exist for aeons. In that time, the arms should have shown up as continuous circuits right around the core. The proposal made here explains that enigma.

The arms of a spiral galaxy are measured as having different speeds, which has been interpreted as a rotational velocity. In figure 66, however, the outer tips are going in opposing directions caused by the orbital turn; this could explain the differing ± speeds. Also, the speeds of the arms are reckoned to be fairly constant no matter how far the part of the arm is from the centre of the galaxy. The proposal made here explains this on the basis that the arm as seen is really an optical illusion of a disc shape, which would have about the same speed at any point on its rim.

This explanation does away with the requirement for extra mass to provide the gravitational inward pull that would prevent the so-called 'arms' of spiral galaxies from flying away from the cluster at the core. The arms are no more than an optical illusion. The actual shape of the galaxy is that of a disc-shaped ring of stars with a core of a cluster. If this analysis proves to be correct, the search for this particular dark matter can cease.

These are a few preliminary attempts to replicate the shapes of some galaxies by assuming their movements. With different combinations of spin and velocity, a wonderful variety of shapes emerges. Some show just curved and truncated arcs, more show L-shaped arms while others look like the number 3.

All the shapes derived here assume that instead of space expanding, galaxies actually travel at immense speeds. The recession speeds of galaxies are so immense (up to 0.96c) that rotational and sideways movements could possibly also be so immense as to facilitate the generation of a multitude of different galaxy shapes. The basic idea is proven correct to some extent in the very simple case of galaxies that appear to have an elliptical shape. The idea is launched here for others to investigate further.

Astronomers Block and Wainscoat (1991) have lately observed different galaxy shapes when viewing the infrared radiation or the optical blue light appearance. They say this indicates that the categorisation of 'Hubble' types is not a good indicator of the distribution of mass in such galaxies.

The above analysis does not upset all the wonderful work done by astronomers over the centuries. There are convincing theories on the formation and death of stars. This book merely proposes some additions to the fountain of knowledge.

Tired Light Phenomenon

Another proposed explanation of the redshift of the light coming from faraway stars will now be discussed. This plausible explanation would mean that the galaxies are not at all as far away as deduced from Hubble's Law and would simplify considerably the whole of the universe. Furthermore, there is no Big Bang requirement with this explanation and no evidence of an ever-expanding universe.

The idea of galaxies receding at ever-increasing velocities with increased distance from the earth brings in the awful possibility that we are right in the centre of the universe. This embarrassment is now removed. The shapes of galaxies, as discussed above, are tenable without the restriction of a limit on their lateral movement. The universe is stationary. There is dark matter out there, but its presence is not required to explain any expanding universe.

Despite having proposed an alternative explanation of Hubble's Law above, this tired light idea is more attractive than either the conventional interpretation of Hubble's Law or the alternative proposed earlier in this chapter. In short, the tired light is the preferred solution, with the current interpretation of Hubble's Law in third place. It would seem natural to expect that light would lose some energy while travelling 140,000,000,000,000,000,000,000 km through space from the furthest galaxy to earth.

Let us go back to what Hubble said. His name has been given to the law that states that the further an object is from us, the faster it is said to recede. Hubble was not adamant about such an idea. Assis and Neves (1995) give an excellent history of the redshift phenomenon, and it is not what is assumed in Hubble's Law. They quote Hubble as follows:

Light may lose energy during its journey through space, but if so, we do not yet know how the energy loss is explained. . . . If the recession factor is dropped, if redshifts are not primarily velocity-shifts, the picture is simple and plausible. There is no evidence of expansion and no restriction of the time-scale, no trace of spatial curvature and no limitations of spatial dimensions.

In 1953, Hubble said, *"When no recession factors are included, the law will represent approximately a linear relation between redshifts and distance."* This statement will surprise many readers. Sometimes a law is named after a person who was not all that enamoured by what is given in the law. This was seen earlier in the case of Faraday's Law.

Assis and Neves also discuss a paper by Finlay-Freundlich (1954), where some difficulties with the current theory are given. Finlay-Freundlich says:

The B-stars in Orion nebula show a systematic redshift relative to the lines in the nebula amounting to at least +10 Km/s. This value is, by a factor of the order of ten, larger than the redshift predicted by the theory of relativity.

Assis and Neves also give several other examples from that paper of where the redshifts are not explicable by relativity theory. More from Finlay-Freundlich:

We see thus that the large redshifts reveal a physical effect which cannot be interpreted either as a gravitational displacement or as a true recession effect. . . . I propose to introduce an additional hypothesis that light passing through deep layers of intense radiation field loses energy – perhaps due to photon-photon interaction – and that the energy loss is proportional both to the density of the radiation field and to the length of the path of the light through the radiation field.

Finlay-Freundlich concluded by saying:

We may have, therefore, to envisage that the cosmological redshift is not due to an expanding universe, but to the loss of energy which light suffers in the immense lengths of space it has to traverse coming from the most distant star systems. That intergalactic space is not completely empty is indicated by Stebbins and Whitford's discovery (1947) that the cosmological redshift is accompanied by a parallel unaccountable excess reddening. Thus the light must be exposed to some kind of interaction with matter and radiation in intergalactic space.

Finlay-Freundlich proposed a formula for this effect and showed that it applies to all sorts of redshift phenomena with, as they say, *"great success"*.

Max Born (1954), a Nobel Laureate, showed that the theory of Finlay-Freundlich (photon-photon collisions as the cause of redshift) was scientifically sound. Louis de Broglie (also a Nobel Laureate) stated that 'photon ageing' was due to a continuous loss of energy by the photon. All of the above is freely quoted from Assis's papers.

All the photons of light that are passing in all directions from all sources throughout the universe must have an effect on each other. Consider the light from every source spreading out in trillions upon trillions of spheres that criss-cross each other's paths. They simply *must* affect each other to some extent.

Repeated here is something said earlier. Do you remember? Just think about this. A blink of light that emanated 7,000 million years ago would by now be a sphere with a radius of 7,000 million l-y. At what speed is the surface of that sphere expanding? The expansion is about $8\pi rc$, and r is by now 7,000 million l-y. The light travels at a speed of c in a straight line from the point of generation to us. However, the speed of expansion (and the light is expanding to cover the whole surface of the sphere) is 12.5×10^{34} m/s. This is no less than 4×10^{26} times the speed of light. Try to explain that while holding the view that nothing can move faster than the speed of light! The light itself is moving transversely across our eyes at that immense speed. It is generally supposed that no information can be transferred at a speed greater than c, yet here we have a practical example of where the information on the faraway galaxy is being transferred laterally at a far, far greater speed than the speed of light.

How does this all come from one spot where the flash of light occurred? What magical properties does the light have? How could light possibly have the power (or energy) to expand so much? If there are 'photons', how can they continue to divide (seemingly unendingly) to allow for this expansion? If photons do not divide, how can the light fill such an immense volume of space? It simply does not make sense. There has to be a more logical explanation.

In another paper in the same year (1995), Assis and Neves show that the authors who took the universe to be stationary came up with far better predictions of the cosmic background radiation temperature. It was in 1965 that the background radiation was eventually measured by Penzias and Wilson. They got a figure of $3.5° \pm 1.0°$. This discovery was interpreted as proof of the Big Bang theory and was based on a prediction by Gamow (1961) that the temperature should be a certain figure. However, Assis and Neves show that the prediction by Gamow was far from the actual temperature that was measured; they also show that much earlier predictions of the temperature, all based on a static universe, were much closer to the actual figure. Other predicted figures were 3.2° by Eddington in 1925, 2.8° by Regener in 1933 and 2.8° by Nernst in 1937, while Gamow, whose figure was supposed to support the Big Bang idea, predicted 7.0° in 1953 and 50° in 1961. Assis and Neves show that Gamow later tried to say that his 1961 prediction was a maximum of 50°K but that this was not what he published. So much for the supposed confirmation of the Big Bang theory. Eddington, who originally did his calculation on the temperature that would balance emission and absorption of heat by a body in outer space, later altered his view to accept the expanding universe theory.

The recent book *Understanding Cosmology* (2002) by the editors of *Scientific American* states that *"the steady state model of the universe could not plausibly account for"* the background radiation.

This tired light proposal is supported by another publication. La Violette (1986) shows that an assumption that light gets 'tired' as it travels through space, i.e. that it loses about 6% of its energy every billion light-years of travel, fits the observational results better than the expanding universe model under four separate criteria. The Hubble diagram in that paper has a better fit from the tired light model than from the expanding universe model. The paper concludes:

The relatively poor performance of the Friedmann expanding universe model on these tests calls into question the Doppler shift interpretation of the cosmological redshift and thus weakens one of the prime supports of the big bang hypothesis; ... there are other sets of observational data (e.g. the 3° K background) which have traditionally been cited in support of the big bang theory and which are not addressed in this paper in particular detail.

As discussed above, the 3° K background is shown by Assis to have been better explained by conventional methods than by a Big Bang assumption.

It would be fine if science had reached the end of discovery and everything was fully explained. What a hope! The human race will always strive and new discoveries will continue. Someone is just now experimenting in a garage somewhere and getting astounding results that will upend some sections of the textbooks. Feel sorry for those who have learned what they believe to be the truth and who are now teaching that to students around the world. They are in for a great shock.

I had the pleasure of meeting Professor André Koch Assis from Brazil on a few occasions and discussing some of these problems with him – he looks for the truth in such matters. It is interesting to note that he is a descendent of Einstein's maternal uncle (Koch).

Synopsis

These conclusions are independent of each other and stand on their own merits.

1. It is proposed that the galaxies in the universe are now approximately in a steady state with respect to each other.
2. Most galaxies are invisible. At the time they were formed, they were too far away for light to have had time to arrive on earth. Most 'dark matter' is simply invisible normal matter.
3. A possible explanation of the curious shapes of some galaxies was given.
4. Tired light is the preferred explanation of the redshift phenomenon.

The practice so popular in discussions on relativity is that of propounding an imaginary experiment and of stating the result obtained. It is useless because an imaginary experiment cannot yield any information, and misleading because it appears to provide experimental support for what are mere assumptions. In imaginary experiments there are neither observers nor observations and the use of such expressions is simply a misuse of language. Scientific theories, if they are to be of value, must be based on the results of actual experiments.

Louis Essen (1964)

Chapter 11

Gravitation and General Relativity

Gravity

In 1935, Einstein wrote:

> . . . *the theory of relativity resembles a building consisting of two separate storeys, the special theory and the general theory. The special theory, on which the general theory rests, applies to all physical phenomena with the exception of gravitation.*

Therefore, if Special Relativity (SR) loses its basis, general relativity (GR) is also without foundation. Einstein says, *"the elements which form their basis and starting-point are not hypothetically constructed but empirically discovered ones,"* which he describes as having *"security of the foundations"*. Einstein also wrote, *"The chief attraction of the theory lies in its logical completeness. If a single one of the conclusions is proven wrong, it must be given up; to modify it without destroying the whole structure appears to be impossible."* This means that, because we have comprehensively disproved SR, GR is also demolished.

Even though that task has been completed, here are a few thoughts on GR. GR is based on the claim that there is no distinction between a uniform gravitational field and uniform acceleration. A person in an accelerating spaceship that is out in space and not under the influence of any planet or sun nearby has the same sensations as a person on earth, where the force of gravity is acting. A person in a free-falling lift does not experience gravity. If an object is dropped in such a lift, it does not fall to the floor of the lift – it just stays where it is let loose.

The force of gravity on earth (or indeed on any planet, star or sun) is directed towards the centre of the mass. The directions of these forces all meet at this centre. This is not an idealised uniform gravitational effect. There is, therefore, a distinct difference between gravity on the earth and idealised straight-line acceleration.

The GR conclusions that space is bent, curved or warped near massive objects and that light is deflected because it travels along space that is bent near massive objects, such as the sun or a star, can be otherwise explained. If light is affected by gravity and can also change speed relative to observers, an alternative explanation is possible. From the analysis earlier in this book where it was shown that light travels with the earth on its orbit around the sun, it is reasonable to assume that gravity has a serious connection with light. Light and energy and mass are all connected, and if gravity attracts mass, then it should also attract light (with its so-called 'momentum').

Light has a 'virtual' momentum (French, 1968), even though this concept is not understood because no measurable mass has yet been detected. In the same way, light has a 'virtual' mass and would be attracted by any gravitational force. Vigier (1990) proposes that the mass of a photon is in the order of 10^{-65} grams (g). This is so tiny that it has not been measured to date. Einstein and Schrödinger also discussed this proposal.

Saying that space is 'curved' is very mysterious. It boggles the imagination and terrifies us into believing it to be so. If we query it, we may be accused of being old-fashioned and of holding on to our limited understanding of the universe. Time is not postulated as being 'bent' under GR, which means that the bending is in three dimensions, not four. Why is that so? It would be more interesting to have 'bent' time!

Newton did not explain gravity – he simply stated what its effects were. He showed that if we assume that the pull between objects was in accordance with his formula, this conformed to experimental evidence. Similarly, Einstein did not explain the curvature of space near massive objects. He showed that if we take his calculations, we get the correct results for the effect of the gravitational pull of massive objects on other objects. Neither Newton nor Einstein had any explanation as to what causes the effect they postulated. Both produced very useful laws for dealing with many problems.

There is confusion concerning the effect of gravity and acceleration on the timekeeping of clocks. To quote Pagels (1984), *"Remember that gravity (because it is the equivalent of acceleration) not only causes rulers to contract, but it also causes clocks to run more slowly."* The basis of the existing theory on gravity and time is described in the 1,200-page, 500,000-word tome *Gravitation* by Misner, Thorne and Wheeler (1973). Einstein's GR is basically a theory of gravitation. Misner, Thorne and Wheeler state as the starting point for the effect of accelerated fields:

An accelerated observer can carry clocks and measuring rods with him, and can use them to set up a reference frame (coordinate system) in his neighbourhood. His clocks, if carefully chosen so their structures are affected negligibly by acceleration (e.g. atomic clocks) will tick at the same rate as unaccelerated clocks moving momentarily along with him.

It is said that there is no suggestion in Einstein's theory that normal acceleration (as distinct from gravitational acceleration) has any effect on the rate of clocks. This is recorded in several publications (e.g. Fock, 1964; Cannon and Jensen, 1975). Fock proposed that:

. . . one can abandon the idea of a universal formula for the reading of a clock moving with an arbitrary acceleration and introduce instead the weaker hypothesis that whenever the acceleration is caused by a gravitational field the reading of a clock in free motion in this field is expressed by . . .

Fock then gives an equation. He continues, *"This hypothesis has in its favour the fact that the gravitational field, and only it, is capable of penetrating into any material body, and of acting on all its parts in proportion to their masses."* That discussion leads to the idea that only gravitational acceleration, and not other accelerations, has the above stated effect. This seems to contradict Einstein's principle of equivalence. Is it reasonable that one type of acceleration will have a different effect from another while they are said to be indistinguishable from each other? Cannon and Jensen discuss the matter as follows:

The special theory of relativity is founded on two hypotheses:
  1. *The laws of physics do not distinguish between coordinate frames moving at constant velocity.*
  2. *The speed of light in free space is the same for all observers.*

Since accelerated observers are not considered by hypotheses 1 and 2, one must ask does the same relationship hold. This question is usually answered in the affirmative by the introduction of a third hypothesis:

  3. *The inertial (non-gravitational) acceleration of a clock relative to an Inertial Frame has no influence on the rate of the clock.*

The use of the word 'inertial' here is confusing; perhaps Cannon and Jensen should have used a word that did not have another connotation.

Møller (1952) and Fock (1964) both maintain that this third hypothesis is a necessary separate assumption if SR is to stand. To quote Møller:

Hence we assume that the acceleration of the clock relative to an inertial system has no influence on the rate of the clock, and that the increase in the proper time of the clock at any time is the same as that of the standard clocks in the rest system S_0 i.e. the system in which the clock is momentarily at rest.

This would seem to lead to the conclusion that clocks run slow when in uniform motion but not to any greater extent when accelerating. If the acceleration has no extra effect, then a clock that moves along with ever-greater velocities would show the same reading as each of a series of clocks that are individually moving at different velocities and with which the clock is sequentially compared.

The fact that acceleration does not affect the time on atomic clocks but gravity does can be considered to be a basic flaw in the idea that acceleration and gravity are equivalent. Cannon and Jensen state:

The effects of gravitational fields on the relative rates of clocks transported along geodesics of space-time can be viewed, even without the assumption of hypothesis 3, as relative differences between the magnitude of the units of measure along their respective paths.

They continue:

It thus is reasonable to extend the principle of equivalence to suggest that it is equally capable of directly altering the units of measure of clocks. Nothing compels us to assume that clocks with identical velocities but different accelerations will be going at the same rate. Although such an assumption is built into relativity theory and constitutes the essence of hypothesis 3, it is equivalent to the assertion that two identical clocks side by side and at relative rest, one in the

247

gravitational field and one not, will also run synchronously. However the physical meaning of the tensor describing gravitational fields would deny the synchronism of such clocks. Clocks can be subjected to different accelerations while having identical velocities. In such instances, the equivalence principle suggests that synchronism between such pairs of clocks must also be denied.

Where an accelerating source is concerned, some physicists accept that the speed of light can be other than c. Bernstein (1991) states, *"An observer accelerated with respect to a light source will measure a speed of light that is smaller than the speed of light measured in the rest frame."* As we saw earlier when discussing the synchronisation of clocks on the earth, a stationary clock at the equator will run slow all the time by a certain amount with respect to the earth's centre. The amount is 1.195×10^{-12} s/s, which is 103.2 ns, or 103×10^{-9} s per day.

Frisch and Smith (1963) said that *"any dependence of the decay probability of radioactive particles on their speed is an example of a general property of clocks in motion relative to the observer"*. Essen (1964) mentions evidence that an atomic absorber at the end of a rotating arm has a frequency that is lower than that of an atomic emitter at the centre of a rotor. The amount by which it is less ties in with the above suggestion. These deductions can apply equally to radioactive decay and explain the results of the varying half-life of moving materials.

The question of the decay rates of cosmic rays as they enter the earth's atmosphere is often quoted in favour of SR. Browne (1958) states that there is indirect evidence that the cosmic rays are travelling at speeds in excess of c. If they did not do so, they would have decayed before they reached the earth.

Perihelion of Mercury

The peculiar movement of the planet Mercury on its orbit around the sun (the precession of the perihelion of Mercury) is taken as a proof of GR. GR is said to have predicted the correct movement. This proof is to be tempered by the fact that, before GR was promulgated, Gerber (1898) had published in Leipzig a calculation giving the exact same result without the use of any relativity theory. When Einstein was confronted at a meeting by Gehrcke (1920) with evidence of the earlier derivation, he did not deny that Gerber had derived the same answer as he had. In relation to the meeting, Einstein said that *"a motley crew has collected whose present purpose seems to be to disparage the theory of relativity and me its originator in the eyes of non-physicists."* Referring to one of the participants, he remarked that he *"does not seem to be any kind of expert (Doctor? Engineer? Politician?). I could not find out what he is."* Clearly the gloves were off! Einstein then said:

Mr. Gehrcke maintains that the relativity theory leads to solecism, a statement that every expert will greet as a joke. He bases this on the known example of two clocks (or twins), one of which makes a round trip with respect to an inertial system while the other does not. He asserts – although he has been refuted by the greatest experts of the theory often both orally and in writing – that the theory leads in this case to the really nonsensical result of two clocks lying side by side each losing time with respect to the other. I can consider this only as an attempt intentionally to mislead the lay public.

The reader can decide from the evidence produced in this book whether or not Einstein or anyone else satisfactorily explained the twin paradox over the past 100 years. It seems that no mere *"doctor, engineer or politician"* should express any opinion on these matters; I wonder would patent clerks be suitably qualified?

Einstein continued:

. . . Gerber, who has given the correct formula for the perihelion of mercury before I did. The experts are not only in agreement that Gerber's derivation is wrong through and through, but the formula cannot be obtained as a consequence of the main assumptions made by Gerber. Mr. Gerber's work is therefore completely useless, an unsuccessful and erroneous attempt. I maintain that the theory of general relativity has provided the first real explanation of the perihelion motion of mercury. I have not mentioned the work by Gerber originally, because I did not know it when I wrote my work on the perihelion motion of Mercury; even if I had been aware of it, I would not have had any reason to mention it.

This riposte by Einstein (1920) was published in a Berlin daily newspaper. Einstein was responding to a lecture delivered in the Berlin Philharmonic by Gehrcke (1920) in which he, Gehrcke, challenged Einstein that Gerber had priority in the matter of the perihelion of Mercury. Gehrcke had stood up at the meeting and declared in reference to Einstein, who was present, that *"the emperor has no clothes"*. Bjerknes (2002) published a book that has a full description of this debate and many other matters that do not reflect well on Einstein; that book was uncovered at the proof-reading stage of this book and is well worth a read.

An English translation of the 1920 response by Einstein to the challenge by Gehrcke is given in the 1979 book edited by Tauber entitled *Albert Einstein's Theory of General Relativity*. This same Gehrcke had published an article in 1913 saying that Einstein's theory of relativity was really the work of Lorentz; there would have been no love lost between Einstein and Gehrcke. Gerber's article was synopsised in the same year (1898) in *Annalen der Physik* and later reproduced in 1902 and 1917 (see references) in German publications, so it was widely publicised. Einstein did not say what was supposed to be wrong with Gerber's analysis but said that *"experts agree"* that Gerber was wrong. Clearly, Einstein did not like Gerber's derivation!

I have read elsewhere a description of Gerber as a mere 'schoolteacher' as a put-down of his work. If you peruse Gerber's publications, you will see that he was a significant contributor to scientific thought.

Brown (1958) shows that the perihelion can be calculated without using GR. In any case, a 'constant' has to be chosen in either theory. Gerber and Einstein used a value of −3. To arrive at his result, Gerber assumed that gravitational potential was retarded

249

with velocity c. As we saw earlier, this is not the correct speed for gravity, which travels at an enormous speed. A major problem with Einstein's derivation is that the perihelion correction is about 50.9" (seconds) of arc per century and not the 43" derived by Einstein (Morgan, 1930). The claim that Einstein's derivation of the perihelion of Mercury is proof of GR is therefore useless. How can Einstein then criticise Gerber?

A Physical Leap

Let us make the leap and simplify the whole of physics. On the one hand, in a field of gravitational acceleration, we can have bent space. Alternatively, light can be attracted by gravity and the speed of light can be altered, and either one of these can conform to observational results. It is postulated in this book that the second alternative applies.

Tests that are quoted as proof that the frequency of light is altered by the effect of gravity are those done by Pound and Snider in 1963. Their work is often quoted as having provided proof that the frequency of light was redshifted by gravity.

Let us begin by quoting from Pound and Snider's paper: *"The present experiment makes no direct determinations of either frequency or wavelength."* So, Pound and Snider did not measure the so-called redshift of the frequency of light caused by gravity. What then did they test? They tested to determine if, by a movement of the apparatus emitting the photon, *"the effect of gravity would be cancelled"*. That is different from proving directly that the light was redshifted by the expected amount.

As discussed earlier, light has an 'apparent' momentum, which implies that it can also presumably have an 'apparent' mass. Pound and Snider actually tested to see if the 'apparent' mass of light would show up in tests and proved that it did. However, as light has also an apparent momentum, this should not be surprising. What we have is confirmation of the accuracy of the factor gh/c^2 on the apparent mass of light under the influence of gravity on earth.

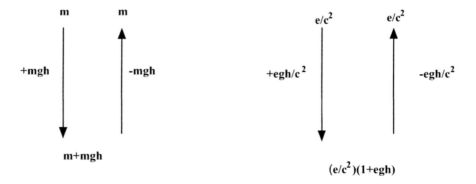

Figure 67: Gravitation and Photons

To discuss this in more detail, let us repeat Einstein's reasoning as set out in Misner et al. (1973). In the left-hand section of figure 67, we see a mass m falling under the force of gravity. As it falls, it gains energy of $+mgh$. At the bottom of its journey, it has a total energy (m being expressed as energy) equal to m + mgh. If the mass then goes back up again against gravity, it loses the same amount of energy (–mgh) and ends up where it started.

Applying this argument to light (see the right-hand section of the figure) was what led Einstein to his famous deduction that light loses energy of –gh/c² when travelling upwards against gravity. The mass has been replaced by its equivalent energy as in Einstein's equation E = mc². Therefore the mass (or photon) starts at the top as e/c²; as it goes down with the direction of gravity, it gains by a multiple of gh, becoming (e/c²)(1 + gh). On the way back up against gravity, it loses by the same gh multiple and ends up as it began. Einstein, by reasoning that if a mass were to fall down, be converted into a photon and go back up, deduced that the photon must lose the same amount of energy or else we would have got energy for nothing.

The energy gained on the way down or lost on the way up is, per unit of energy, equal to gh/c^2. This is Einstein's derivation. Pound and Snider confirmed to a very high degree of accuracy (one part in 100) that this equation was true. However, they just confirmed that it was true for 'masses' and not for any change in the frequency or wavelength of light.

There is a simple derivation of gh/c^2 as follows. Knowing that $E = mc^2$ (as postulated by De Pretto in 1903 before Einstein's papers on relativity) and that the frequency of the photon varies with its energy (as shown by Planck), the higher the frequency of light, the greater its energy. A photon travelling upwards against gravity loses potential energy of mgh, as already shown. Taking the energy of the photon as E to correspond to the mass m in the De Pretto formula, $m = E/c^2$ for the photon. Proceed as follows: $\Delta f/f = \Delta E/E = -mgh/mc^2 = -gh/c^2$. We can therefore conclude that the frequency of light alters with gravity.

To conclude this debate, here is a quotation from the paper by Pound and Snider:

It is to be noted that no strictly relativistic concepts are involved and the description 'apparent weight' of photons is suggestive. The velocity difference predicted is identical to that which a material object would acquire in free fall for a time equal to the time of flight.

In other words, Pound and Snider calculated the time for a photon to traverse the path and then did tests to confirm that the factor gh/c² would apply for a mass that had fallen by that distance. This then appears to confirm the apparent mass of light. Is the existence of the mass of light proven by the Pound and Snider tests?

Universal relativity (UR) proposes that, as light passes near a large mass, its velocity changes relative to that mass. The velocity increases and decreases relative to the mass as light comes under and escapes from the influence of gravity of the mass.

What happens when light (or an electromagnetic signal) passes close to the sun? As mentioned earlier, the Viking craft that landed on Mars gives a clue to this problem. Signals coming from the craft behaved peculiarly when passing very near the sun. Earlier, the fact that light emitted on the earth takes up the orbital speed of the earth around the sun was discussed. The Viking test results are mentioned as being of possible interest in this context. An electromagnetic signal that passes very near the sun (whose gravitational pull is about 300 times that of the earth) may, in some way, be grossly affected. The very peculiar behaviour of the signals sent from Mars to earth as they passed near to the sun was discussed earlier in the book.

Is the change in the speed of light coming from Mars to earth relative to fixed space or relative to the sun? The evidence from Mars shows that the alteration in speed must be relative to fixed space because the signal takes longer and longer to reach earth from Mars as that signal passes nearer to the sun (see Schwinger, 1986).

Shape of the Earth

The earth is shaped like an oblate spheroid (figure 68 – exaggerated for clarity).

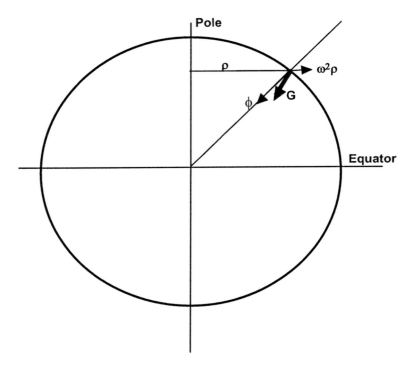

Figure 68: Shape of the Earth

When it was formed approximately 4,000 million years ago, the earth was presumably in a 'fluid' form. Even if it were somewhat solid, the length of the intervening time and the resulting 'creep' of the matter in the earth would cause it to take up a form dictated by the forces acting upon it. There are two distinct forces acting at the surface of the earth – the force of gravity Φ and the centrifugal force $\omega^2\rho$ caused by the spinning of the earth (ρ is the radius of the earth at the particular latitude and ω is the angular velocity of the earth). Both forces are a mystery because we do not know why gravity acts, nor do we know why the earth spins. At the equator, the two forces act directly in opposition; at the poles, the centrifugal force has zero effect and therefore does not affect the shape of the earth. The result is that the earth is flattened at the poles. In figure 68, G is the resultant force of gravity as experienced by us on earth.

Gravity the Magician

Gravity is supposed to have waves. Pagels (1983) says, *"The Theory of General Relativity implies the existence of gravity waves, undulations of the curvature of space that propagate at the speed of light across any distance."* It makes one feel gravity-sick! Gravity is also assumed to act via its gravitons from every particle in the universe upon every other particle. As Pagels puts it:

According to the ideas of modern quantum field theory, which embrace the theoretical physicist's view of reality, every field like the gravity field has an associated quantum particle. For the gravity field these quanta are called gravitons; they are the gluons that bind large masses like stars together. Instead of thinking of the gravity field as some kind of force field that extends between the earth and the moon, modern physicists see that such a gravity field is 'quantized' into countless gravitons. Really the earth and the moon are exchanging gravitons and these exchanges make up what we perceive as the gravitational field between these bodies. This is an unfamiliar, but completely correct way of viewing the effect of gravity and other fields.

This is a huge task for whatever is causing gravity! Furthermore, it is said that there are virtual gravitons that go in the opposite direction to these gravitons and also identify all other particles in the universe. Hawking (1988) puts it as follows: *"The gravitational force between the sun and the earth is ascribed to the exchange of gravitons between the particles that make up these bodies."*

Can gravity operate at any distance? While it gets weaker with the separation of two masses, it still exists. There is another difficulty with the notion of gravitons. How is it that they cause an attraction? Any other particle-like object causes a repulsion. Let us see what all this means. The universe is said to be about 10^{24} kilometres in diameter (Morris, 1992). At the speed of light (300,000 km/s), how long would it take any information or action to get from one side of this assumed universe to the other? According to existing theories, nothing can travel faster than c, and this includes gravitons.

It would take 3×10^9 years to traverse the universe from one side to the other. Therefore, the unfortunate gravitons, or whatever else is causing the gravity, would have to operate at this distance and speed and at this time delay. With this constraint, they would need to be very busy indeed if they had to operate from every single item on every other single item in the universe. Every time I type a character on the keyboard, I move my hands; this movement must then be noticed and acted upon by every piece of matter in the whole universe! Given the size of the universe, a graviton would have to travel, on average, half the universe each time it had to operate on anything. With the assumption of an expanding universe (we debate this concept elsewhere), the graviton is losing ground on each journey that it makes from one side of the universe to the other.

The theory that gravitons operate on every item from every other item in the universe is not likely to be true. In the time it takes to traverse the universe, what changes have occurred? For example, consider a graviton that goes off to interact with another particle that it assumes to be at a particular place. By the time the graviton gets there in the one million, million years that the journey might take, the particle would be somewhere else.

Travelling at what is supposed to be the maximum possible speed for anything (even for an object that has no mass), i.e. the speed of electromagnetic phenomena, there is no possible way for gravity to act from all particles to all other particles in the universe. Even assuming the speed of gravitons to be 10^3 times the speed of light, the action could not be any quicker than three million years! So this idea is wrong. To be in any way credible, the speed of gravitons would surely have to be, let us say, $10^{1,000,000,000,000,000,000,000,000}$ times the speed of light. Some speed!

So, whatever is causing gravity, it is not fast-flying gravitons. Could it be that gravity, spin, mass, energy and electromagnetic phenomena are one and the same elemental thing? Bell's theory (see Index) supposes action at a distance as a way to explain all this. There is as yet no evidence to support the ideas of that Irish scientist. The cause and behaviour of gravity remain a mystery, as do those of light and radioactive decay.

As stated earlier, a book by Van Flandern (1993) gives a totally different proposal for gravity. Van Flandern shows that the line of flight of light from the sun to the earth is not parallel to the line of the effect of gravity. Light, which takes 8.3 minutes to come to earth from the sun, travels along a different line (the apparent line) from the line directly between the sun and the earth. Gravity is shown to act along the actual line from the actual position of the sun rather than along the apparent line. Gravity must travel at a far greater speed than light (at least 20 times) or be caused by some other phenomenon entirely. Van Flandern lists the reasons why he believes the speed of gravity to be extremely high. Here he quotes one simple reason, which was set out by Eddington in 1920, as follows:

If the Sun attracts Jupiter towards its present position S, and Jupiter attracts the Sun towards its present position J, the two forces are in the same line and balance. But if the Sun attracts Jupiter towards its previous position S', and Jupiter attracts the Sun towards its previous position J', when the force of attraction started out to cross the gulf, then the two forces give a couple. This couple will tend to increase the angular momentum of the system and, acting cumulatively, will soon cause an appreciable change of period, disagreeing with observations if the speed is at all comparable with that of light.

Van Flandern says:

The Sun's gravity emanates from its instantaneous true position, as opposed to the direction from which its light seems to come. If gravity propagated at the speed of light, it would act to accelerate the orbital speed of bodies. By observation, no such acceleration exists down to the level of about one arc second per century squared for the Earth's orbit. The absence of the acceleration implies that the gravitational lines of force arriving at the Earth from the Sun are not parallel to the paths of its arriving photons, but rather have directions which differ by about 20 arc seconds. This is true for any model of gravitation.

Van Flandern also gives other reasons why the speed of gravity is greater than the speed of light. However, SR stipulates c as the absolute limit for the speed of anything.

Gravity and Eclipses

In a cover feature in the *New Scientist* of November 27th 2004, Schilling reviews the peculiar behaviour of pendulums during eclipses of the sun. He quotes the 1954 pioneering work of Maurice Allais (Nobel Laureate, mentioned earlier in connection with the Michelson and Morley tests). Allais found that a pendulum's rotation rate increased and decreased during the course of a normal day. He also found that during an eclipse of the sun, the rate altered radically. The phenomenon has no explanation.

During the course of a day, the swing direction of a pendulum appears to rotate slowly clockwise, due to the rotation of the earth. This has been known since 1851, when the French physicist Foucault discovered it. However, at the start of a solar eclipse, the swing direction begins to rotate rapidly counter-clockwise. When the eclipse has passed, the pendulum returns to its normal direction of swing.

Saxl and Allen (1971) found the same phenomenon during an eclipse in 1970 and wrote that *"gravitational theory needs to be modified"*. Tests, which are awaited with interest, are planned to be carried out 2005 and 2006 to repeat the Allais experiments.

Van Flandern and Yang (2003) have proposed a potential explanation in mass air movements during eclipses. However, if a torsion pendulum were used, it should not be subject to influence from air movements. If the pendulum is charged to a few thousand volts, the effect is said to be altered. Further tests are planned for the coming years.

Black Holes?

What of black holes? If there are places with very high gravity that attracts light (via its 'virtual' mass) to a sufficient extent, it is possible that light cannot escape from such places. Black holes are places from where no light can emerge. The behaviour of an electromagnetic signal as it passes very close to the sun shows that gravity has, indeed, a profound effect upon the signal. This was discussed earlier in relation to the Mars-to-earth signals from the Viking craft. The signals went 'crazy' within three suns' radii of the centre of the sun, and the results were discarded in the analysis. The idea of black holes, while plausible, is speculative.

Astronomers have detected invisible objects by studying their influence on other stars. The effect is detected in a binary star system, where one star is visible and the second star is not. In such a twin star system, the stars spin around each other. *"Because the unseen companion does not emit visible light, it cannot be an ordinary star,"* say Freedman and Kaufmann, claiming that it is *"likely to be a black hole"*. It could in fact be a normal star but one that cannot be seen for reasons described above. There may be genuine black holes, but some phenomena indicating their presence may be ascribed to the influence of invisible (not yet visible) normal stars or galaxies.

Some mathematical models of black holes include what are termed 'singularities'; these are none other than 'infinities' such as are found by dividing 6 by zero. Infinite solutions to a mathematical equation mean that the theory behind the mathematics has broken down; we must go back to the drawing board to set a better-defined problem for the mathematics to solve! Are these singularities not just mathematical curiosities with no physical meaning? Remember that the cube root of 8 gives three answers but that two of them are just mathematical curiosities with no physical meaning – do not think that a mathematical solution has necessarily a real meaning.

A practical example of where a theory breaks down is found where the response of a particular material to loads that are applied to the material is being forecast. The theory (elasticity theory) is fairly accurate when applied to metals at moderate loads. The application of elasticity theory to the prediction of what happens when a material contains a fine slit (say, a crack) being pulled open by an applied load leads to anomalous results. The theory predicts that the stresses rise rapidly as the crack tip is approached (as happens in practice). However, an infinite stress is predicted at the tip of the crack. The crack tip is called a 'singularity'. No engineer would ever consider the concept of an infinite stress occurring in a real material. Engineers are realists.

Of course the stress does not in reality become infinite in a real material. What is clear is that the elasticity theory has broken down in the vicinity of the crack. A new theory is needed – such a theory has been developed and is called plasticity theory.

In a similar way, whenever an infinite answer results from some mathematics, this means that the theory being utilised has broken down and there is a need for a better theory. Examples of such a breakdown are in the 'singularity' supposed to have been at the beginning of the Big Bang or in the infinite density supposed to exist at a black hole. It is good fun to pretend that such 'singularities' and 'infinities' are real, but they are science fiction.

Quantum Theory

We cannot leave the pitch without mentioning a further mysterious theory, namely quantum theory. According to Heisenberg's principle of uncertainty, as quoted by Eddington (1929), *"A particle may have a position or it may have velocity but it cannot in any exact sense have both"*. Aspden (1972) asks:

> *Is Eddington really suggesting that a particle cannot have a position and a motion at the same time, or is he saying that our powers of observation are limited and preclude us from determining the exact position and velocity of the particle at any instant?*

Even more scathing is Scott Murray (1983), who penned a series of nine articles on this topic. You had better get those if you want to investigate further the mystery surrounding that *"religion,"* as Murray terms it. In the meantime, just a few brief quotations from his papers will suffice to give a taste of the fog surrounding this area.

> *When an electron is at rest (relative to an observer) the velocity of the matter-wave as formulated in the theory is infinite. Waves of infinite velocity simply cannot be physical waves. Moreover, as soon as the observer starts to move, the wave velocity suddenly becomes finite. There is something very wrong here.*

> *The new wave mechanics actually predicts a finite possibility of finding an electron in a position where, by the law of the conservation of energy, an electron cannot be.*

> *A typical example of this confusion today is the common belief that matter-waves exist, and that they are waves of probability. They don't and they aren't.*

Murray favoured the idea (proposed by Einstein) that light 'waves' consist of periodic variations of photon density.

Feynman (1963) describes the testing of electrons as they are sent through holes in a screen. When sent through only one hole, an electron behaves like a particle. The image projected on a screen looks just like that when particles are shot through such a hole in an intermediate screen. However, the behaviour of the electron when being measured is quixotic. Feynman then describes the results of measuring electrons that are sent through two adjacent holes in a screen (like the two-slit experiment described in chapter 4). He shows that if we try to detect an electron that has come through a particular hole in the screen, it behaves quite differently from an electron that we do not try to detect. From this, it has been concluded that the electron cannot possess both a position and a velocity at the same instant – it is taken as having just a probability of a particular position or velocity. However, Feynman says that *"No one has ever found (or even thought of) a way around the uncertainty principle."*

Let us try. Suppose that the action of detection actually alters the electron in some basic manner that alters its behaviour. That would seem a perfectly reasonable possibility. This would explain why the act of detection would alter the subsequent behaviour of the electron in the above experiment. When we do not carry out any detection, the electrons behave as if they had wave properties when coming through two adjacent holes in the screen. Then, when we introduce detection by having a light source or other particle (or wave) with which the electron can react and scatter some of the light, its subsequent behaviour is altered so that it behaves more like a particle than a wave. The simplest explanation is that there is a physical alteration in the electron that makes it behave like a particle. Feynman describes this as follows: *"We must conclude that when we look at the electron the distribution of them on the screen is different from when we do not look."*

This book does not purport to investigate the problem thoroughly but merely points the reader to another fascinating puzzle in the current theories of physics.

All the other fellows do not look from the facts to the theory, but from the theory to the facts; they cannot extricate themselves from a once accepted conceptual net, but only flop around in it in a grotesque way.

Albert Einstein (1935)

Chapter 12

Comments and Conclusions

In their frustration at being ignored by mainstream scientists, some authors who are convinced that SR is flawed develop a persecution complex; they seem to think there is a conspiracy among the physics fraternity to prevent their ideas from being promulgated. There is no such conspiracy. It is impossible for any scientist to read all the publications on physics that appear nowadays, even on a single topic, such as relativity. The so-called conspiracy is merely the pragmatic time constraint on scientists to study everything that is published on a topic. If a particular investigator (as in my case) gets an idea and looks for a specific piece of information relating to it, that person is very likely to find evidence for and against the idea. A good example is when I looked for a Michelson-Morley experiment of very high accuracy that showed up a difference between the time taken by light signals to traverse distances at right angles to each other. I found it in the 1979 test by Brillet and Hall. Why should I accuse the physics fraternity of hiding it? Indeed, those authors themselves did not appreciate the vital information they had uncovered – it was Aspden who later showed its significance.

Everyone is far too busy doing their own daily work to notice all the new information that might be contained in the thousands of weekly publications in scientific journals. A physics lecturer that happened upon a book such as this would not be too keen to alter lecture notes on relativity, which have stood in good stead for many years. Otherwise, there goes one's summer holidays!

This author was very lucky in that the Institution of Engineers of Ireland had the courage to publish a series of seven monographs by him between 1995 and 2001. Then, by another stroke of luck, a person (the late Pat Fleming) who had read one of these papers happened to spot a man standing alone at a conference in London. Pat engaged the man – the famous Professor J-P. Vigier – in conversation and asked him if he had ever read my paper. This coincidence led to Vigier's ringing me and subsequently publishing an article agreeing with my publication. Had that unlikely coincidence not happened, I would never have got the backing of Vigier.

Some investigators were unlucky in that their work was not recognised until many years after it was carried out. In his 1911 thesis, the young German student Harress described tests on the refraction of light in rotating prisms. His results were later acknowledged as showing the effect worked out by Sagnac. To take another example, why did Poincaré or De Pretto not get the acclaim for publishing the equivalence of mass and energy later attributed to Einstein?

During the course of the investigation for this book, I made many friends, most of whom I never met, such as Galileo, Newton, Fitzgerald, Lorentz, Michelson, De Pretto, Einstein, Sagnac, Dufour and Prunier, O'Rahilly, Brillet and Hall, Dingle, Faraday,

Saburi, Vigier, Essen, Von Mettenheim and all those mentioned and referenced in this book. I did meet Post, Aspden, Assis, Bartocci, Graneau, Wang, Van Flandern, Wesley, Monti, Keswani, Chappell and Spencer. It feels like we are all part of an international team trying to find answers to the great puzzle of nature. I hope this book has provided a tiny push forward with that search. The many correspondents who have contacted me regarding relativity over the past ten years have made life most interesting for me.

Christoph Von Mettenheim penned a book entitled *Popper Versus Einstein* (1998) in which he demolished SR theory from the point of view of logic. He is a German lawyer and wrote the book in English. When he first wrote to me, I was sceptical of his claim that it was possible to disprove relativity using logic. I believe he has done just that. I reviewed the text for him, and he referenced much of my work. He misquoted some of my conclusions towards the end of the book.

I also read much murky and abstruse material – better left uncited – that has the effect of making SR seem even more mysterious. I set out to try to understand relativity theory. Later on, I was looking for something that would explain, and not try to justify with abstruse gobbledygook, anomalies and paradoxes that were thrown up by SR.

I was very lucky to have within a mile of my home an outstanding scientific library at University College Dublin. The library houses all the main scientific journals in English, German and French, going back to the year 1800. The early material was originally from the former Royal College of Science in Dublin, which I had attended as an engineering student.

This book is being released in the interest of getting information on relativity theory into the public domain. It was difficult to call a halt – there are so many tantalising loose threads. We can have a theory that gives acceptable explanations for the majority of all known phenomena, but it is expecting too much to think that a new theory can explain satisfactorily all the known observations and tests that have been done. Anomalies and 'hard to believe' results stay with us until some new theory arrives that tidies up some of the loose ends.

The philosopher Karl Popper had it right when he proposed that discoveries are made by thinking of an idea initially and looking for evidence to support it later. It is not possible, he said, to just read all the literature every day (you would not have the time) and then come up with a new theory on something about which you have not had a previous inspiration. In Popper's book *The Logic of Scientific Discovery*, we read:

Einstein speaks of the 'search for those highly universal laws – from which a picture of the world can be obtained by pure deduction. There is no logical path leading to these laws. They can only be reached by intuition, based upon something like an intellectual love of the objects of experience'.

This is more from Popper:

The empirical basis of objective science has thus nothing 'absolute' about it. Science does not rest upon solid bedrock. The bold structure of its theories rise, as it were, above a swamp. It is like a building erected on piles. The piles are driven down from above into the swamp, but not down to any natural or 'given' base; and if we stop driving the piles deeper, it is not because we have reached firm ground. We simply stop when we are satisfied that the piles are firm enough to carry the structure, at least for the time being.

Einstein wrote, *"In so far as the statements of geometry speak about reality, they are not certain, and in so far as they are certain, they do not speak about reality."* Popper remarked on this by saying that *"in so far as a scientific statement speaks about reality, it must be falsifiable"*. In 1935, Einstein wrote a letter to Popper and said, *"I think (like you, by the way) that theory cannot be fabricated out of the results of observation, but that it can only be invented."*

Feynman wrote:

If it disagrees with experiment it's wrong. In that simple statement is the key to science. It doesn't make any difference how beautiful the guess is, it doesn't make any difference how smart you are - who made the guess, or what his name is, it's wrong. That's all there is to it.

This statement covers the name of Einstein and the beautiful theory of relativity. The experiments discussed in this book disagree with that theory.

The relationship between light, mass, energy and gravity is a great puzzle, which will probably be unravelled in many years to come. I suspect that the key to the puzzle is something remarkably simple and that the ignorance of the human race in the 21st century will be considered as astounding when all becomes clear. In the meantime, here ends this particular detective story of finding the solution to the puzzling behaviour of light. On the way, quite a different problem was solved. Faraday's enigma in relation to the movement of magnets and conductors was unravelled. Some new ideas on the origin of the universe and the reason for dark matter came from considering the behaviour of light as it traverses the universe.

If you are a student, avoid mentioning this book to your lecturers. After all, you want to pass your examinations, and examinations are an exercise in reproducing what you are taught during the year. You most certainly will not be told about much that is described in this book. The Sagnac and Michelson & Gale tests alone send shivers down the spines of many teachers. As for mentioning the name Dingle (or Kelly) – that would be examination suicide.

If you are a lecturer in physics, mathematics or engineering, do not let your colleagues know that you got a copy of this book. Cover it with plain brown paper! After all, you aspire to some higher position. Any discussion on the possibility that relativity theory might be deficient is forbidden. Professors and lecturers have been pushed out of their positions because they became sceptical and critical of the 'sacred' theory. Many are genuinely scared that they might be branded as mavericks.

I have met people who dared to question some aspect of relativity theory. They were ostracised, their telephones were disconnected and they were put in a closet under the main stairs in the building. In short, they were frozen out. You could see the immense hurt in their faces. One person who questioned matters but did not have that hurt look puzzled me. When I asked him about it, he said he had become very rich after being frozen out of a very senior position and was now laughing at the petty minds of those who did the dirty work. I have quoted much of his work here.

Keep your big mouth shut. You have been warned! Luckily for this author, he could not be silenced or fired because he was not a member of a faculty involved in teaching or part of an organisation doing research on the matter. He was employed in a firm that encouraged new ideas and experimental research.

If someone brands this author a 'crank', 'maverick', 'dissident' or 'iconoclast', that would be a great tribute because it would mean that no major flaw was found in the conclusions of this book. No doubt some unimportant errors have been made.

Random Thoughts

Reflect for a moment on the fact that the earth spins on its axis. Why? The moon, the sun and other heavenly bodies also spin on their axes. There must be a very good reason for this. What is it? Is it in any way allied to the spin of the electron? Is the spin of the electron some sort of 'perpetual motion'? From where does the continuous supply of new energy come to keep all the electrons in the universe in never-ending motion? This problem may have been solved by De Pretto, as described in chapter 2. Will someone find a way to tap into the infinite energy source that exists there? There are already rumblings of such a possibility. If it is achieved, we can stop worrying about the finite extent of oil and coal resources for supplying our energy needs.

What new horrors lie in store for the unfortunate physics fraternity? Did you know that a 12-volt battery, a pair of carbon rods and a glass plate are all that are needed to prove that carbon plus oxygen produce iron? Strike an arc between the two carbon rods through a small heap of carbon dust scraped off the rods. As proved by testing with a strong magnet, there is no ferrous material present before the test. After a minute or two, the magnet shows slivers moving on the plate. Before going to print on the matter, we tried this at the workshops of HDS Energy Ltd. to see if the claim was correct. It was, and the outcome was not due to impurities in the carbon rods. Imagine what this will do to the current theory on the stability of elements. This is the simplest example of an emerging and startling technology that will revolutionise ideas on the immutability of elements (including the heavier unstable ones) under low-energy attack.

A more advanced application of the scheme could potentially do away with the radioactivity in at least the low-level nuclear waste. Five years ago this author visited a nuclear waste treatment facility in the U.K. with the Italian inventor Roberto Monti. Unfortunately, the people at the facility did not get back to us *in a few weeks*, as promised. The president of one U.S. power company that owns nuclear power stations was certain he would try the new discovery until his lawyers pointed out that he had no licence to do so – the company only had a licence to operate the stations and store the waste. Would such an interesting development not immediately attract attention? Not at all. The discoverer is trying strenuously to get some government to try it.

Remember that expensive nuclear storage and treatment facilities would be put out of business if this new invention were developed; commercial considerations come before health and safety ones. Everyone seems more interested in finding out the secret composition of the mixture that caused the reduction in radioactivity. The petroleum industry may soon embrace the new discovery to remove radioactivity from oil filters.

For those interested in further reading, I recommend the following books:

1. *Newton versus Einstein* by Graneau and Graneau. This book shows that there is a force acting on the elements of a current-carrying conductor in the direction of the current flow that tends to break the conductor. Graneau and Graneau have shown this through many experiments. It conforms to Ampere's original experiments but not to accepted electromagnetic theory.

2. *Popper versus Einstein* by Von Mettenheim, as discussed a few pages back.

3. *Dialogues on Modern Physics* by Sachs. This is an intriguing book that describes debates between people who take opposing views on topics. Sachs gives arguments for and against such things as relativity and quantum theory and leaves the reader to decide which is right.

4. *Weber's Electrodynamics* and also *Relational Mechanics* by Assis. These two books discuss Weber's work on topics such as unipolar induction, an alternative to Maxwell's theory. The conclusions conform to much of what is claimed in this book.

5. *Albert Einstein the Incorrigible Plagiarist* by Bjerknes. This book has 200 pages of detailed references to back up the claims in the text.

Conclusions

1. Einstein did not develop the famous equation $E = mc^2$. It had already been derived two years prior to Einstein's derivation and in that exact form by the Italian engineer De Pretto. There was a family connection between Einstein and De Pretto.

2. In free space, light has a constant speed (c), which is independent of any observer or any motion (steady or erratic) of any such observer. Light spreads out in expanding spheres at that constant speed of c from the spot in space where it is generated.

3. An observer travelling at steady speed relative to a source of light can record the light as travelling faster or slower than c in relation to oneself. The maximum (unattainable) speed of light relative to an observer is 2c. Light from distant stars is expanding across our eyes at many orders of magnitude greater than c.

4. Time does not run slow aboard a moving object. A twin sent on a long journey at high speed does not age slower than the twin who remains stationary. Time is not relative; it is absolute.

5. The dimensions of objects are not measured as less aboard an object that is moving at constant speed relative to an observer.

6. Light does not adapt to the spin of the earth on its axis. Light signals sent around the globe eastward and westward do not return at the same time. When going westward,

light travels faster than c in relation to an observer on earth. When going eastward, it travels slower. This has been proven by experimentation.

7. Light adapts to the orbital movement of the earth around the sun. A possible explanation for this is that light moves with the gravitational attraction between the earth and sun.

8. Atomic clocks run slow with increased 'absolute' speed with respect to the earth's centre. This has been proven by experimentation. This is the same place – the centre of the earth – with respect to which light is postulated as travelling on the orbital path of the earth around the sun. Do such clocks run slow with the earth's orbital movement around the sun? The evidence says they do not.

9. The lines of force of a magnet rotate with the magnet when the magnet is rotated on its north-south axis. This is shown by experimentation and contradicts what Faraday concluded concerning this matter. Faraday's Law does not represent the general law concerning the generation of a voltage caused by the relative motion of a magnet and a conductor. A general rule is postulated, which subsumes Faraday's Law plus the 'motional induction' phenomenon. This solves a puzzle posed by Feynman.

10. Galaxies are probably not receding from each other at ever-increasing speeds. Indeed, galaxies appear to be in a static (or close to static) state relative to each other.

11. It is unlikely that there was a Big Bang at the formation of the universe. There is evidence to the contrary. Even accepting the Doppler redshift idea, the universe could just as well have slowed down to a Full Stop from vastly higher speeds.

12. A plausible theory is that the redshift of light coming from faraway galaxies is not a Doppler shift caused by a rapid recession of those galaxies but is caused by the 'tired-light' factor.

13. Much dark matter is normal matter that has been formed so recently that it has not had time to send a light signal to earth. Over 50% of matter in the universe is in this category.

14. The transverse motion of galaxies at right angles to our direct line of sight to those galaxies could possibly explain the shape of elliptical galaxies. An explanation that is independent of dark matter is proposed to account for the shape of spiral galaxies. Furthermore, a tentative explanation for the shape of other galaxies is given.

Appendix 1

The Hafele and Keating Saga

Tests on Travelling Clocks

In 1972, Hafele and Keating carried out tests that claimed to prove that moving macroscopic clocks run slow. The evidence for this claim was derived from the differences between times recorded by atomic clocks transported in aeroplanes eastward and westward around the earth and time recorded by a standard clock station fixed to the earth at Washington, D.C., U.S.A. The time changes predicted and the reasoning given by Hafele and Keating are outlined in this appendix.

Their reasoning was as follows. The time recorded by a clock at the earth's equator may be compared with the time recorded by *"hypothetical coordinate clocks of an underlying nonrotating (inertial) space"*. For this purpose, *"a view of the (rotating) earth as it would be perceived by an inertial observer looking down on the North Pole from a great distance"* is considered. The time recorded by a transported clock (carried in an aeroplane) relative to clocks in the non-rotating space is then considered. Subtracting these two times (eliminating the hypothetical clocks) yields a time difference between the transported clock and the clock fixed to the earth.

The speed of a flying clock is added to or subtracted from the rotational speed of the earth, depending on the direction of circumnavigation. This then yields different differences between the times recorded by the east-flying and west-flying clocks and a fixed clock station.

Hafele and Keating say that according to Special Relativity (SR), a clock rotating with the earth should run slow *"relative to hypothetical coordinate clocks of this space in the ratio 1 - [(RΩ)²/(2c²)],"* where R is the earth's radius, Ω its angular speed and c the speed of light. (Note: Hafele and Keating use the binomial theorem to get the factor $1 - v^2/2c^2$ for the effect of γ; the derivation is given elsewhere. A flying clock has $R\Omega + v$ substituted for $R\Omega$, where v is the ground speed of the aeroplane. The time difference between the flying clock and the ground-reference clock is then obtained from these two ratios and, *"to a first approximation, is given by -[2RΩv + v²][t₀]/[2c²],"* where t_0 is the time recorded by the ground station. Because the aeroplane velocity (v) is positive going eastward and negative going westward, the difference gives a time loss going eastward and a time gain going westward. The reader will appreciate from chapter 5 that the clocks are all running slow with respect to their speeds relative to the centre of the earth or nearby space. That is why Hafele and Keating chose that reference point. However, this has nothing to do with SR; they slipped that in to the reasoning because, as we already discussed, that was what happened in practice.

265

A further calculation is carried out for the effect on the timekeeping of the flying clocks due to their being above ground level; this effect predicts time gains in both directions.

To minimise the effect of the variations in the earth's magnetic field, the clocks were triple shielded. Four clocks were employed, and the average of their times was used to lessen the effect of changes in individual drift patterns relative to the standard clock station. The clocks used had serial numbers 120, 361, 408 and 447.

Figure 69 shows a sketch of the overall test results published as figure 1 by Hafele and Keating in their 1972 paper. The total test period was 26.5 days. The clocks remained on the ground for ten days before any flight commenced. The eastward flight test was undertaken first; its circumnavigation time was 65.42 hours. There was then a pause of nine days, after which the westward test was undertaken. The duration of this test was 80.33 hours.

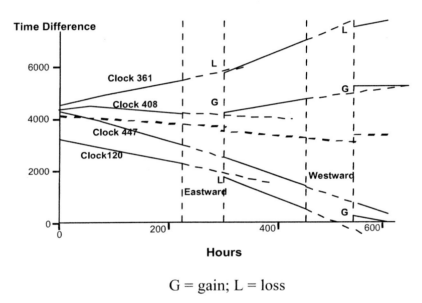

G = gain; L = loss

Figure 69: Tests on Travelling Clocks

The vertical axis in figure 69 shows the difference in time in nanoseconds (1 ns = 10^{-9} s) as read at hourly intervals between each of the four clocks and that recorded by the standard station at Washington. The difference between the average of the times recorded by the four clocks and the time recorded by the standard station was used in the final result. This average is shown as the heavy dotted line running across the middle of figure 69. The aeroplanes had a cruising speed of 230 metres per second (m/s); the difference due to the relativistic velocity effect was calculated to show up as a time loss (−184 ns) going eastward and a time gain (+96 ns) going westward. The effect of height over sea level was calculated to yield time gains going eastward (+144 ns) and westward (+179 ns). The composite forecast effect of these two calculations was that the clocks would lose

266

−40 ns on the eastward journey and gain +275 on the westward journey relative to the standard station.

No two atomic clocks keep exactly the same time. The times recorded by individual small portable clocks, such as those used on these tests, diverge or converge when measured against each other. They also vary against the more accurate time recorded as the average of several larger clocks at a standard earth-fixed clock station. This, in turn, has some drift relative to other standard clock stations elsewhere on the earth.

Hafele and Keating referred to the fact that portable clocks exhibited small but more or less well-defined quasi-permanent changes in rate. The times at which these rate changes occurred were said to be typically separated by at least two or three days for *"good"* clocks. Some of the larger stationary clocks had been observed as having no rate change over several months.

Winkler et al. (1970) reported that the extremely uniform timescale recorded by the clock station at Washington was obtained by averaging about 16 selected beam clocks. Clocks were replaced if their performance deteriorated. They reported that, in a sample of 45 such clocks used at several standard stations around the globe, one failure per six clocks was experienced over two years; design improvements were being implemented as type faults were identified, and this would improve reliability.

During January 1970, three individual clocks at Washington had changed their drift rate by +16 ns, +18 ns and −68 ns per day. Two others were listed as having *"poor performance"* (presumably worse than those three) and were removed due to poor timekeeping, while nine had shown no appreciable change in drift rate in the month. Prior to 1968, a procedure had been adopted whereby the more stable clocks were given more weighting in the calculation of the standard time. Thereafter, the simple average of the time recorded on all clocks was adopted.

Winkler et al. gave the standard deviation of the mean of the Washington assembly as 2 ns to 4 ns when tested every three hours over several five-day periods. In that station, the clocks were housed in six vaults with careful control of temperature and humidity, elaborate power supplies, vacuum systems, signal sources and a fixed magnetic field.

Beehler et al. (1965) record that the accuracy of individual smaller portable clocks (such as used by Hafele and Keating) is worse by a factor of two than individual large stationary clocks. They include variations in the magnetic field among the influences that contribute to the inaccuracy of clocks.

To give results from which reliable conclusions could be drawn, the individual portable clocks used by Hafele and Keating should have displayed a steady drift rate relative to the average time of the standard clock station throughout the tests. It will now be seen that the portable clocks were so poor in this regard as to render them useless. It will also be shown that:

- the atomic clocks used were not of sufficient stability to support the conclusions drawn

- the clocks suffered considerable alterations in performance during the transportation
- these alterations were greater than the net effect forecast by Hafele and Keating
- undisclosed corrections made by Hafele and Keating to the raw data are unjustified and absurd

The Published Results: A Critique

The 'drift rate' of a clock is measured from its change, in ns/hr, relative to the average of the clocks in the standard station. During the 10 days (240 hours) before the eastward flight began, gradual and sudden changes in the drift rate of all four clocks occurred; it is difficult to observe a period when all four maintain a steady drift rate with respect to each other. Had the eastward test begun after 80 hours instead of after ten days, the average trend for all four clocks would have been quite different from that assumed at the start of the test. Taking a period equal to the test duration of 65.4 hours following that 80 hours, the average graph for the four clocks (without ever leaving the laboratory) shows a time loss of the same order as the eastward flight test result found by Hafele and Keating. This fact alone makes a nonsense of the eastward test. Figure 69 does not show the short-term fluctuations; such wiggles in the graphs are to be seen in the original 1972 paper.

It is possible to estimate the drift rates from figure 1 of the 1972 Hafele and Keating paper (figure 69 above). However, the accurate drift rates given in table 4 below are those given in a Department of Defence USNO (United States Naval Observatory) report written by Hafele (1971) three months before the Hafele and Keating papers were submitted for publication. This report supplies data that makes it possible to analyse in detail the performance of the four clocks. When the current investigation was underway, a paper was published by this author based on estimates of the drift rate changes taken from an examination of the graphs in the Hafele and Keating 1972 paper (Kelly, 1995). Critics complained, with some justification, that the original data should surely show that Hafele and Keating were right. Luckily for this author, the original test data was available and was obtained following a phone call to the USNO in late 1995. This led to other papers on the subject being published (Kelly, Monograph No. 3 1996; *Physics Essays* 2000). These give the full details, which are repeated here.

All four clocks showed significant alterations in drift rate during both the eastward and westward flights. To give results that would be of any value, there would have to be a complete absence of an alteration of drift rate. Take a look at table 4, where the drift rates are seen to change radically throughout the tests. The drift rates before and after a test can be compared to determine the change during a test.

It is not possible to determine when such alterations occurred – an alteration in drift rate could be gradual or the result of a series of sudden changes. Three of the clocks altered drift rate between the two tests while they were on the ground.

Table 4: Drift rates of clocks (in ns/hr) before, between and after the tests

Clock no.	120	361	408	447
Before the eastward test	−4.50	+2.66	−1.78	−7.16
After the eastward test	−8.89	+4.38	+3.22	−8.41
Before the westward test	−8.88	+6.89	+4.84	−7.17
After the westward test	−4.56	+3.97	+2.16	−9.42

The alterations in drift rates that occurred during a circumnavigation may also be derived from table 4 and are shown in table 5. The eastward circumnavigation time of 65.4 hours would accumulate the forecast theoretical alteration of −40 ns at a change in drift rate of 0.6 ns/hr. Ideally, the figures in table 5 should all read zero, but any change that was not smaller than 0.6 ns/hr by a factor of at least 5 would obfuscate any result. This means that no clock was of value in reaching any conclusion on the eastward test. The accuracy of the clocks would need to be two orders of magnitude better before the results could be used to draw any conclusions. On the westward test, the forecast change of +275 ns would be accumulated in the trip time of 80.3 hours at a change in drift rate of 3.4 ns/hr. Again, no result can be used with any confidence.

Table 5: Alteration in drift rates (in ns/hr) during the tests

Clock no.	120	361	408	447
Eastward test	−4.39	+1.72	+5.00	−1.25
Westward test	+4.32	−2.92	−2.68	−2.25

It is important to note that none of the alterations in drift rate could be attributed to a relativistic effect because that would affect all four clocks similarly without altering the before-and-after drift rate.

Figure 2 of the 1972 paper by Hafele and Keating gave an enlarged view of the period immediately before and after the tests. A sketch of that figure is shown in figure 70; this sketch does not show all the wiggles in the original and is illustrative of the trends that emerge. As required by relativity theory, the trend lines before and after the tests are shown by Hafele and Keating to be parallel but with an incremental step change downwards and upwards for the westward and eastward tests respectively. This change would, of course, occur gradually during a flight due to any relativistic effect but can only be determined as the resulting step change that emerges following the test.

The trend shown in their figure 2 was derived from the average of the four clocks. However, this trend was sensitive to the number of hours over which it was derived. For example, had the westward test (figure 70a) begun some 12 hours earlier, the trend before that test would be very different. Had the eastward test (figure 70b) begun after 12 hours or 35 hours, the trend would be different from the 25-hour trend used by Hafele and Keating.

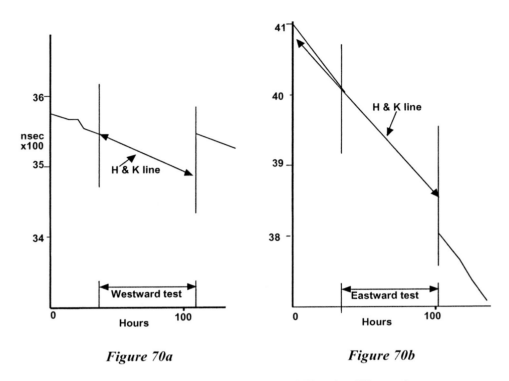

Figure 70a   *Figure 70b*

Figure 70: Sketch of Hafele and Keating Figure 2

We can see that the drift rate before the westward test is open to several interpretations, depending on which period between the zero time and the start of the test is considered – Hafele and Keating took a 25-hour period to determine the supposed drift rate because the line of the drift was in a favourable direction for the period chosen. The arrowed line chosen by Hafele and Keating is seen to be rather arbitrary; it served their purpose by being parallel to the trend taken up by the clocks after the test and showing a gain in time by the clocks during the test.

The starting time for the flights was arbitrary in that it was determined by the time of departure of the designated commercial passenger aeroplane. Using the complete 140-hour period for the eastward test (figure 70b), a time shift of approximately zero could have been reasonably deduced for that test because, if the slope of the line before the test is continued, it coincides with the slope of the line that occurred after the test. This line is the thin line beginning at the zero time on figure 70b at the top of the y axis at the number 41. Hafele and Keating used a trend line that was derived from using a shorter period before the actual flights to calculate the trend line (thick line).

The USNO 1971 report described that eastward result as *"consistently negative or near zero"*. No such comment was repeated in the 1972 Hafele and Keating prescriptive paper. Similarly, the shift caused by the westward flight could have been derived as about 75% of that shown by Hafele and Keating.

This analysis illustrates the lack of stability in the performance of the clocks and the unreliability of such results.

Drift rate changes are random and could have occurred in either a plus or minus direction. It is a coincidence that the four results did not all change in one direction or the other. In such a case, the average drift rate after a test would be very different from that beforehand. Clock 120 altered in drift rate by –4.39 ns/hr on the eastward test and by +4.32 ns/hr on the westward test; it should not be concluded that this clock had an average drift rate change of –0.035 ns/hr. Indeed, this was the clock with the worst in-flight performance. Had the changes in drift rate of this clock been the other way, the results would have been in the opposite direction to the theory, which highlights the danger of drawing any conclusion from such data.

By using trend periods of 100 hours prior to the start of the test to determine the drift rate (from Hafele and Keating's figure 1, reproduced in figure 69 above), clock 447 can be interpreted as having virtually no change in drift to the end of the westward test. Had the clock with the steadiest performance alone been used – clock 447 – the overall result of the tests would again have shown a zero time change. Without giving any explanation, Hafele and Keating used only 25 hours before the test start to determine the drift rate. This illustrates the sensitivity of the results to the assumptions made on the drift rate prior to the start of a test. Surely Hafele and Keating should have shown the sensitivity of the results to the period over which the pre-test drift rate was determined.

Actual Versus 'Massaged' Test Results

No actual raw test result data was supplied in the 1972 Hafele and Keating papers. However, these results were given in the 1971 USNO report and are reproduced in table 6. Looking at the second and fifth columns (eastward and westward test results respectively), it can be seen that the results were scattered plus and minus, which shows the total failure of the tests. The second column should have been all minus, giving an average of about –40; the fifth column should have been all plus, giving an average of about +275. The actual results are far removed from that and wildly scattered.

Table 6: Original test results and Hafele and Keating alterations (in ns)

Clock no.	Eastward			Westward		
	Actual test results	First method	Second method	Actual test results	First method	Second method
120	–196	–52	–57	+413	+240	+277
361	–54	–110	–74	–44	+74	+284
408	+166	+3	–55	+101	+209	+266
447	–97	–56	–51	+26	+116	+266
Average		–54	–59		+160	+273

Notes: (1) The –59 ns and +273 ns averages derived by Hafele and Keating are to be compared with the –40 ns and +275 ns predicted by the theory. (2) Standard deviations were shown for the mean of the second method results as 10 and 7 respectively; the 7 should have read 9.

Hafele and Keating then set about altering the results to get them to line up with the forecast results. This needed some ingenuity and considerable secrecy. They did it by publishing a radically altered version of the results instead of publishing the actual results. The first alterations that Hafele and Keating made to the test results prior to publication of their 1972 papers are seen in columns 3 and 6 and are to be contrasted with the actual test figures shown in columns 2 and 5. The method used by Hafele and Keating to try to bring the results closer to the theoretical forecasts was to take the average of the drift rates before and after a flight and assume that this average applied throughout the flight. Such an assumption would have some credence had the alteration in drift rate been very small, e.g. a change from +3.34 to +3.35 ns/hr, which would not significantly affect the end result. With the changes that actually took place, such an assumption cannot be justified. The actual drift rates doubled (one clock from –4.5 to –8.9 ns/hr), halved (+4.8 to +2.2 ns/hr; –8.9 to –4.6 ns/hr) or reversed (–1.8 to +3.2 ns/hr).

Having made and illustrated those changes in figure 2 (figure 70 here), Hafele and Keating correctly dismissed that approach on the basis that it depended *"on the unlikely chance that only one rate change occurred during each trip and that it occurred at the midpoints"* of those trips. They added that there was *"no obvious method for estimating the experimental error"* of such an assumption. They had actually identified more than one alteration in drift rate on four of the six flights. Indeed, one clock had three identified sudden changes going eastward and four going westward. However, having dismissed this spurious method, they still published the figure and described the method as producing *"convincing qualitative results"*.

It appears that Hafele and Keating's figure 2 was published because it looked convincing and not because it gave a legitimate picture of the test results. While it looks great, it obscures the wide scatter of the data from individual clocks. As Hafele and Keating acknowledge in their 1972 paper, that first method used to amend the extrapolated drift rate cannot be justified. No reference has been located in the literature to the fact that Hafele and Keating had actually discounted figure 2 as useless in the text of their own 1972 paper. It is amazing to read a paper where a central figure is described as misleading and useless by the authors and is still printed as if it were scientific evidence. On the basis that a picture is said to be worth a thousand words, the reader would have accepted Hafele and Keating's figure 2 at face value. After all, this publication was peer-reviewed and published in the reputable journal *Science*.

Having discounted that first attempt, Hafele and Keating used a second, quite different, method to amend the test data (columns 4 and 7 of table 6). It was not possible to check the behaviour of the clocks relative to the standard station during a flight test. However, comparisons that were made between the four clocks during flights were used to decide if one clock had undergone what was deemed to have been a sudden change in pattern. In such a case, it was assumed that the behaviour of the other three clocks was correct. The rationale was that the chance that *"two or more clocks would change rate by the same amount in the same direction at the same time was extremely remote"*. On this basis, Hafele and Keating proceeded to make changes to the test results. There was no definition as to what precisely constituted an in-flight rate-change that warranted correction. Amendments were made on the basis of fourteen such changes: three eastward and one westward for clock 120, three eastward and four westward for clock 361, two eastward for clock 408 and one eastward for clock 447.

These corrections were made after the USNO 1971 report was produced. It is proposed here that the corrections cannot be applied to clocks that exhibit such erratic patterns of changes in relative drift rate. Some years previously, the USNO had adopted a practice of replacing at intervals whichever clock was performing worst in its multi-clock standard station. On a similar basis, the results of clock 120 should, in retrospect, have been disregarded. By discounting this very erratic clock, the resulting uncorrected averages would have been within 3 ns and 28 ns of zero on the eastward and westward tests respectively, a result that could not be interpreted as showing any difference for the two directions of flight.

A sensible conclusion from these tests is that, to the accuracy of the clocks used, there was no measurable difference in the timekeeping of the clocks.

The original raw test results are published here for the first time in columns 2 and 5 of table 6. The actual test results (columns 2 and 5) are very different from the results of the second method (columns 4 and 7). The latter give the impression that the results were compatible, being all of the forecast sign and within a narrow band. The original results were occluded and had to be derived by simple computation from the tables given in the 1971 report – it appeared that the authors did not want anyone to uncover the awful truth.

Just compare the second and fourth columns of table 6 for the eastward trip. Compare also the fifth and the seventh columns. Examples of how great the corrections were can be seen as follows: clock 408 (eastward) was altered from +166 ns (column 2) to –55 ns (column 4), and clock 361 (westward) was altered from –44 ns (column 5) to +284 ns (column 7). A further puzzling example is clock 447, to which Hafele and Keating applied no in-flight correction going westward. (Indeed, the 1971 report stated that no alteration occurred in either direction, while the 1972 paper quoted one correction in the eastward test and none at all in the westward direction.) Nevertheless, the result was radically amended westward from +26 ns to +266 ns without any explanation.

On the eastward test, corrections of +3.5 and –5.5 times the forecast theoretical –40 ns result were applied to two of the clocks. On the westward test, where the forecast was +275 ns, corrections of 0.5 to 1.2 times that amount were applied to three of the clocks. As seen in table 6, there are two instances when a clock altered during the flight in the opposite direction to the theory – clock 408 on the eastward test (which shows a gain of no less than four times the loss that was supposed to occur) and clock 361 on the westward test (which shows a loss of 44 ns instead of a gain of 273 ns). The final answer that was deduced as being the time difference on the eastward test (–59 ns) was less by a factor of 2.8 than and opposite in sign to the time shift of one clock (408) on that test. No averages are shown here for the original test results in columns 2 and 5 because they would be meaningless due to the ± scatter of the four results.

Leaving the actual test result columns aside, a consideration of table 6 would certainly convince one that Hafele and Keating had found a genuine method for correcting the times on the clocks. Outlining one method and then discounting it gave the impression that the second method they applied in their final analysis was acceptable. This tactic put readers off the scent.

It might be justifiable to ignore a single isolated sudden change on one clock during the complete 26.5-day period, but to correct for fourteen such changes in six days of flights and by amounts that exceed the forecast results by multiples of up to 5.5 is totally unacceptable. Hafele and Keating had the nerve to make corrections to the clocks while they were in flight, at which time there was no way to compare their performance with the standard clock station on the ground.

Hafele and Keating stated that the number of measured values was too small for a proper statistical analysis. Nonetheless, they gave a standard deviation of 10 for the four results from the eastward test and of 7 from the westward test – a meaningless exercise. The number 7 was calculated incorrectly and should have read 9. Providing such figures gives the misleading impression that the results are grouped reliably closely.

There is no record of corrections by the authors for any sudden changes in drift rate during the periods when the clocks were on the ground – the USNO 1971 report confirms that such alterations occurred. Such corrections would have affected the drift rates and thus the results. This indicates that either the behaviour of the clocks was adversely and seriously affected by the transportation or similar corrections should have been made and documented for the results over the whole 26.5-day period. In the former case, the results should not have been used; the latter case would have given a different result.

The publication in 1972 by Hafele and Keating of their 'corrected' results only (given here in columns 4 and 7) without any qualification whatever was very misleading. The wild swings in the drift rates of the portable clocks that were used were not mentioned. Indeed, it was not possible to suspect this from the meagre data given.

The whole story describes a shameful episode. It would be amusing as an example of how to cook test results and fool the public were it not for the serious effect those results have had on the physics community over the past 33 years. Having said that, we must admire the nerve of Hafele and Keating in perpetrating the scam.

Hafele and Keating did one thing that was very useful. They seem to be the first authors to have published the fact that atomic clocks run slow with respect to the earth's centre (or, as they put it, the non-rotating space over the pole). This may not be surprising given that the USNO, where Hafele and Keating worked, had, in 1973, planned the Global Positioning System (GPS) – they (the USNO) had (presumably undisclosed) evidence that the clocks would behave in this fashion. Hafele and Keating would have been privy to such classified information and, knowing the expected outcome, proceeded to forecast what the clocks would show on such a test. I wonder if there was a clock in space before 1973 that showed the expected result.

Bodily and Hyatt (1967) stated that 2.5 ns/hr was somewhat less than could be caused by changes in drift rate and random errors in mobile clocks. The average change in drift rate on the four clocks used in the Hafele and Keating tests (table 4) was about 3 ns/hr, which conforms to that statement. Alterations less than 200 ns eastward (3.07 x 65.4 hrs) or 250 ns westward (3.07 x 80.3 hrs) are therefore of no significance.

Consequently, the actual test results cannot be utilised. Even if the results using portable clocks had been compatible and agreed with the theory, there could be no confidence in them.

Hafele and Keating stated that the tests would be below the detection threshold of the predicted time difference for the eastward test at the height at which the planes were cruising. They showed a graphical proof that any result below about 125 ns could not be used. The fact that they still used the eastward results was not explained. The USNO 1971 report stated that it was *"amusing"* that values for the eastward trip were in excellent agreement with the theory despite expectations that they would not be able to detect any definite effect. The actual results did not support this statement. Any test has a result, but in this case it has no significance. Drawing conclusions from such unreliable tests is anything but amusing – it is downright outrageous.

Hafele and Keating recorded that previous tests reported in 1970 over several weeks had shown results that were normally distributed zero-centred and with a spread of about 60 ns per day of travel. Again, this shows that results in these current tests of less than about 165 ns eastward or 200 ns westward had no significance.

The USNO 1971 report had advocated the future use of better clocks and a circumnavigation with less ground time, which would probably reduce the standard deviation of the results by a factor of ten.

Hafele and Keating concluded by stating that, in any event, *"there seems to be little basis for further arguments about whether clocks would indicate the same time after a round trip, for we found that they did not"*. The clocks certainly altered during the circumnavigations, but the alterations that occurred were random and have no significance.

I offer an apology for making a meal of these Hafele and Keating tests, but they are a hard lesson for the scientific fraternity. What other such scams have been perpetrated in other branches of science?

Some Challenges

There are conceptual difficulties with the Hafele and Keating tests. Under the normal interpretation of SR, an observer on earth would compare time with an observer who flew in the aeroplanes with the clocks. If we believe in one-sided relativity, the observer who remained with the reference-fixed clock in the laboratory should note that the travelling clocks had gone slower. If we believe in symmetrical relativity, the observer who travelled with the travelling clocks should have noted that the clock on the ground had also gone slow with respect to the travelling clocks. Neither of these results was confirmed by the Hafele and Keating tests.

From 1971 to 1974, before the Hafele and Keating tests were done and after the results were published, there was a debate between Schlegel and Hafele. Schlegel wrote in *Nature* (1971):

The kinematic relativistic effect on clock rates is relational, and rests directly on the relative speed between the two coordinate systems of the two clocks. It is not to *be found as a ratio of effects relative to a third system. Thus, if clock A moves with speed v_1 relative to clock C, and clock B moves with speed $v_2 \neq v_1$ relative to C, the rate of A relative to B must be found from the speed of A relative to B, not from the ratio $dt_A \div dt_B$ in the coordinate system of C.*

This latter method is, in effect, what Hafele and Keating had done. Their formula for the slowing of the clock on the aeroplane compared with the ground station clock was to multiply the time on the ground clock by $-(2Rv\omega + v^2)/2c^2$, as quoted at the beginning of this appendix.

Schlegel pointed out that in Hafele and Keating's theory, by choosing the velocity of the aeroplane as $-2R\omega$ and the height as ground level (h = 0) (to eliminate gravitational effects), the ratio of the time kept by the flying clock to the time kept by the ground-based clock is always equal to unity. The speed concerned (v) is less than 1,000 m/s and is therefore a possible speed for an aeroplane. One clock is stationary and the other moving, and the two clocks A and B would read the same. This would not be in accordance with SR. Hafele (1971) made a long, convoluted response in *Nature*, saying that *"it does not depend solely on relative speed in all cases, for if it did there could be no resolution of the clock (or twin) paradox"*. That is a circular argument because we are trying to determine whether or not the twin paradox is true! This admission by Hafele is fairly damning. What he was saying was that to hold on to relativity theory, we have to assume that it is correct and that we must therefore bend our debate to suit that assumption. This is the 'consequences too awful to contemplate' argument. Hafele's response was dotted with the usual *"subtle aspects of the theory"* and *"often lead to confusion"*. He signed off with the meaningless statement that what was needed was *"another spacetime metric which is considerably more complicated than the one used here"*.

There was information to indicate that Hafele and Keating invited Schlegel to inspect their results. They must have confused him with their supposed evidence that their second method was justified. I feel sure that they kept the original test results secret.

This objection by Schlegel to Hafele and Keating's method still stands. At one stage in the debate, Schlegel (1973) retracted what he said earlier on the basis that SR did not apply to motion on a rotating earth. The reader will appreciate that, in this, he was denying something that Einstein had accepted in his first 1905 paper on the transport of clocks around the earth.

Schlegel then erroneously proceeded to introduce the Sagnac effect (see Index), as if that would explain the whole matter. This debate added to the confusion. Schlegel proposed that in an acceleration mode, the *"photons in an atomic clock experience a rate decrease"*. This decrease is deduced to be the same as the relativistic change deduced by Hafele and Keating to occur by the spinning of the clock around on the earth's surface. In 1971 and 1973, Schlegel proposed that there had to be a time loss, no matter which direction was considered. This view is in accordance with the traditional view of SR, whereby the flying clock (going in any direction) will lose time relative to the earth-fixed one. However, in a volte-face, Schlegel (1974) concluded that we can expect atomic clocks carried at a particular ground speed around the world to give the same effect – a loss if carried in an eastward direction and a gain of exactly the same amount if carried westward. This is also not in agreement with Hafele and Keating, whose results predict a magnitude that varies with the direction chosen (east or west).

Schlegel eventually postulated (though he contemplates that most physicists would not agree with him), that maybe there is no change in the time rate of clocks that are not in energy interaction with the observer. He was looking for some way out of the impasse in which the expected results of SR had not been borne out in practice. In the end, he assumes that the changes in time deduced by Hafele and Keating are all due to the general theory and none to the special theory! Schlegel concludes that the Hafele and Keating postulates do not answer the question *"Will any clock undergo a time rate decrease as predicted by the Special Theory"* simply as a consequence of uniform motion at speed *v*?

A paper by Essen (1977) was uncovered when all the above analysis had been done and the papers (Kelly, 1995 and 1996) published on the Hafele and Keating tests. Essen said that his critique was submitted in 1972 to *"a journal that had published something about the experiment, but the note was rejected"*. The journal was *Nature*, which had an editorial lauding the test results and which rejected his article.

The author of this book had a similar experience when trying to have published the current critique of the Hafele and Keating tests in a different journal. Indeed, one reviewer gave a veiled threat that the relatives of Hafele or Keating might institute legal proceedings if such criticism were published. That was a surprising statement and leads to the suspicion that one of the original authors or someone on the original team was consulted before that review was written. Was someone getting scared that eventually, after all these years, the bubble was about to burst? A point made by another reviewer was that the whole episode was so long ago that nobody would be interested today. However, the test results are in all the current texts and are wrong. It does not matter how long ago a currently quoted test was done; if the result is flawed, it should be corrected.

Essen had his note published in 1977 in a more obscure journal. He did not have the original data obtained by this author. He assumed that Hafele and Keating had in some way chosen the time of departure of the clocks on the planes to suit a steady period of their timekeeping. This is very unlikely because the clocks were sent on scheduled flights on which seats were booked to take them. Essen correctly stated that:

All the experiments showed was that the clocks were not sufficiently accurate to detect the small effect predicted; . . . this absurdly optimistic conclusion was accepted and given wide publicity in the scientific literature and by the media as confirmation of the clock paradox.

Essen built the world's first caesium clock in 1955 and spent his life working on time and frequency measurement at the National Physical Laboratory in the U.K. He eventually became director of the Time & Frequency Division. Because he was a world expert on such clocks and their accuracies, he knew what he was talking about. Even so, his studied criticism went unanswered and has been ignored ever since. Essen's estimates from the graphs in the Hafele and Keating paper were somewhat like those originally deduced by this author (and given in Kelly, 1995, before the actual test data was obtained). The fact that the original 1972 paper was published in a reputable journal, which used a peer review system, would have given the paper credibility. Surely estimates made from graphs in that paper and done 25 years later could not be taken as disproof of the veracity of the results! That defence has now been blown out of the water because the original figures are actually worse that those estimated by this author from the graphs. (One is careful to be conservative when estimating from graphs.) Essen's estimates were even less close to the actual data.

In my experience of investigative engineering projects, if evidence such as that presented by Hafele and Keating were to be submitted, it would be immediately rejected.

Ironically, although the Hafele and Keating tests are freely quoted as the final confirmation of SR, they themselves saw the tests as not being relevant to the *"traditional interpretation"* of that theory. By 'traditional', they presumably meant clocks running slow for travel in any direction and relative to any inertial observer.

Appendix 2

Twin Paradox Explanations

The following 54 explanations, presented in chronological order, give a flavour of the myriad attempts that have been made to explain logically the twin, or clock, paradox. In 100 years of trying, nobody has suggested an answer that has stuck. The reason for this is obvious – the paradox is a nonsense!

1. Einstein (1905) gave rise to the problem in his first 1905 paper on Special Relativity (SR) by not making a reciprocal statement on the time recorded on a stationary clock as viewed from the moving frame. This has been discussed earlier in this book. It is surprising that very few authors who discuss the twin paradox refer to this original 1905 Einstein paper, from which the whole puzzle emanated. In this paper, Einstein did not refer to acceleration or deceleration but depended on a large polygonal or orbital path coming back to the same spot.

2. Langevin (1911) seems to be the first proponent of the paradox. He thought the difference was caused solely by acceleration, occasioned by the reversal of the travelling twin when changing direction to come back to earth. *"The most certain experimental facts of physics enable us to confirm that it will be so,"* Langevin asserts. By this he means that relativity theory just has to be correct. While he agrees that *"each of them will see the other age 200 times more slowly than usual,"* he asserts that it is only the travelling twin who ages more slowly. Langevin also states that *"each will see the other live a life which is greatly accelerated – 200 times more quickly than usual"* when the return journey of the traveller is considered. However, from these contradictory facts, Langevin still comes to the strange conclusion that only one twin ages slower. Significantly, he gives no calculations.

    We came across Langevin earlier in the dispute with Dufour and Prunier on their critical tests on the Sagnac effect. In that debate, Langevin had to cease his protestations in defence of relativity theory in the face of the accumulated experimental test results that confounded him (see Dufour and Prunier in Index).

3. Von Laue (1912) said:

    Relativity principles claim that all time scales are the same in all directions. But, the Einstein experiment is presented as a warped worldline, which diverges into two different paths at world spot A, and which is unified together again at world spot B. From all space-time curves or paths, which connect A and B, the straight direct connection has the greatest recorded time; this is what Einstein concluded. In this manner, one of all the 'timewise' directions is a special one; but this particular assumption is not according to universal laws, but only due to our selection of the world spots A and B; that means that this conclusion is due to the particular assumptions in this example. One of the most important perceptions in physics is that all directions, in three dimensional space, have equal behaviour; and one of the most elementary laws in geometry is, that two points define a straight line and therefore a specific direction. These two things prove the above objection to the Theory of Relativity; otherwise one would have to upset this fundamental law of the isotropy of space using this simple geometrical construction.

In this statement, Von Laue did not agree with Einstein.

4. Pauli (1921) said that Einstein's explanation of 1918 was correct and that it could be explained only through the 1916 general theory of relativity. Pauli's book was a review of the then accepted interpretation of relativity theory. It was penned, as he later wrote, *"at the tender age of 21,"* not that that is of any significance in this debate.

5. Born (1922) is quoted in Lovejoy (below) as stating that the paradox is *"in truth a marvellous one, but one which no quibbling can escape. We must simply adjust ourselves to it, as some centuries ago, our ancestors adjusted themselves to the idea of men standing on their heads at the antipodes."* Perhaps we have to stand on our heads to understand the matter!

6. Lovejoy (1931), in relation to the reciprocal relative motion of relativity, says this about twins who never reverse or meet again (an idea such as proposed in this book): *"Paul will be alive while Peter is dead, and also Peter will be alive while Paul is dead – that is to say, Paul will be simultaneously both dead and alive, and Peter will simultaneously be both dead and alive."*

    Lovejoy's analysis demolishes the argument that the relative ages are an illusion or only thought to happen by the parties concerned because being 200 years old means that one is dead! The ploy of planting one twin on the earth, as if that denudes that party of any relative motion in relation to the twin who goes away, is exposed. Instead, Lovejoy sends the twins in opposite directions along parallel tracks for the duration of the test. He does not have them meet ever again and suggests the use of a camera, as suggested (before discovering Lovejoy) in this book. This is a clear exposé of the nonsense involved.

7. Lynch (1932) says, *"I was led to the point where I had to accept the conclusion that a clock would go fast or slow according as it moved relatively to imagined sources of coordinates."*

8. Tolman (1934) states that *"whether we consider A or B to be the clock that moves we obtain the same expression for the relative readings of the two clocks".* He then proceeds to bring in the general theory of relativity and claims to have an explanation of the one-sided ageing. This mirrors Einstein's 1918 attempt.

9. Ives (1937) states:

    Let B be moved to a distant point at the velocity V with respect to A, and back to A. It will on its return be slow with respect to A. But if relative motion is only of significance, A is likewise moving at the velocity V with respect to B, and hence will, when the clocks are together again, be slow with respect to B.

Ives believed that the paradox was inexplicable.

10. Møller (1952), in the textbook *The Theory of Relativity*, says:

> *A clock which is moving with the velocity v relative to S will be slow compared with the clocks in S. When we keep in mind that the systems S and S' are equivalent it is obvious that a clock at rest in S similarly will lag behind the clocks in S'.*

Here Møller clearly says that either clock runs slower than the other! He attributes the difference in ages to the general theory of relativity without saying how or why. He then says that later in the book he will give what he describes as *"the final solution of the clock paradox"*. Some hope! This so-called final solution is the one described in detail earlier in this book and shown to be a nonsense. In contradiction of his earlier statement, it does not rely on the general theory but on the special theory. See Leffert and Donaghue below (no. 15).

11. Brewster (1956), a medical doctor, says:

> *It depends on whether you say the space ship is moving away from the earth or the earth is moving away from the space ship. No matter which twin brother you are, you will see the other as ageing faster. When the two of you are back home, however, one will not be any older than the other.*

This contradicts Einstein.

12. Darwin (1957) gives a mathematical derivation and does not calculate the change in time during the acceleration phase. He switches off the clock before firing rockets on the spaceship carrying the travelling twin. He says that *"the direct effect of acceleration can be disregarded"*. This directly contradicts Einstein's 1918 analysis quoted above. Darwin's analysis was later challenged by Dingle (1960).

13. Frye and Brigham (1957) say that the general theory is needed to explain the matter.

14. Builder (1958) assumes that *"the motions of bodies and clocks through the ether do cause reductions in length and rate"*. He is assuming that it is accelerations that make the difference when he states:

> *. . . the second clock is observationally distinguishable from the first by the fact that its journey, away from and back to the first, requires that it should be subject to accelerations, whereas the first clock remains free from accelerations.*

This is a typical cop-out; no explanation is offered.

15. Leffert and Donaghue (1958) point out that Møller (1952) had not solved the paradox but had introduced another equally intractable problem.

16. Møller (1959) agreed that Leffert and Donaghue (1958) had shown that *"it seems that the solution of the original clock paradox, as presented by the present author, introduces a new paradox as regards the motion of the clocks".* Møller went on to give a more complicated treatise based upon a system *"in which the mass of a particle moving through a gravitational field appears to depend on the gravitational potential as well as on the velocity".* He makes the extraordinary statement that the distance travelled out and back is identical when viewed from the point of view of the stationary clock and also from the point of view of the moving clock. However, is it not that the measured distance changes under relativity theory as viewed by persons in uniform relative motion? Having thus conveniently equated the total distances, Møller (amazingly) concludes that persons travelling with either clock think that the 'moving' one is the only one that goes slow! Also, the mass of a twin is supposed to change suddenly from plus to minus at the reversal. That must be an interesting experience! We have seen earlier that Møller's 1952 analysis, which is one of the few detailed mathematical expositions on the subject in a standard physics textbook, is nonsense.

17. Builder (1959) states (where R is the fixed clock and M the moving clock), *"It has long been supposed that we are therefore forced to conclude that the restricted theory leads to the contrary prediction that the clock R would become retarded relative to the clock M during the experiment."* By the 'restricted theory', Builder means SR. He continues: *"What should have been obvious from the very first, i.e. that the calculations were meaningless because the data were not all expressed in terms of the measures of the same reference frame."*

Contrary to Einstein's 1918 explanation, Builder says that *"It will be assumed that any effects of acceleration and deceleration of M can be neglected."* This contradicts the earlier paper (1958) by the same author!

18. Romer (1959), while setting out the problem, began with the method (independently) advocated in this book of having one of the twins already moving at constant speed at the beginning of the experiment. *"For simplicity, any possible questions about the effect of the initial acceleration are avoided by having B already moving with respect to A at the beginning of the problem."* Romer uses four people, all of the same age, to carry out his analysis. He proves fairly conclusively that A and B are both younger than each other at the end of the experiment. He then gives a rather diffident let-out by saying that, when referring to one pair of his four participants, *"since in the process of turning around, they do not remain in an inertial system, and thus have no assurance that their clocks, if originally synchronised, will remain synchronised".*

19. Sherwin (1960) says that Dingle was a *"pure relativist"* and denied *"the possibility of predicting the time difference of the two clocks solely from the knowledge of their relative motion".* Dingle was accused of believing that *"it is only relative motion between two physical objects which has meaning and what the rest of the universe is doing does not make any difference".* We should certainly agree that Dingle was right! Contrary to many of the other 'experts', Sherwin says that *"all of the phase difference is accumulated during the constant-velocity regions of the path".* He could see that the

acceleration phase could be made tiny and that this period could not be blamed for the one-sided forecast.

20. Lowry (1963) calculated that the traveller's time is really slower than the stationary clock and that the traveller will think that the stationary clock reads less than that again! This doubles the effect calculated by any other author. However, Lowry does not then refer to the ironic reverse situation.

21. Bondi (1964 and 1967) says that the difference is caused by acceleration. He asks, *"How can all this time have got sunk in the relatively short period of acceleration?"* He then claims that there is really no paradox because *"Brian has measured his time and Alfred his time and there is no reason to believe that the two should be the same. There is no universal time, because time is a route dependent quantity."* Vaguely mysterious!

22. Fock (1964) says, *"Such a comparison will show that clock B is running slow compared to A"* and *"the same equations appear to predict also that A should be slow compared to B"*. Of course.

23. Levi (1967) says, *"However, from the astronaut's point of view, the earth twin will have aged more slowly during the trip – and yet, surprisingly, he finds himself older instead of younger."* Indeed that is surprising! To get out of the impasse, Levi then says, *"during the acceleration at the turning point, he will observe himself to age significantly"*. That would be an interesting experience! Watch for this every time you start and stop your automobile.

24. French (1968) is one of the few who refer to Einstein's original 1905 paper. He refers to a *"raging controversy"* that ensued during the years 1957 to 1959, following preliminary skirmishes dating back to 1939. He says that SR explains the paradox because the switching of inertial frames by the travelling twin causes the whole difference. He also says that *"The paradox consists of a one-sidedness that appears to flout the basic tenets of relativity."*

French does not agree with the authors who depend on the general theory to explain the paradox. He gives a supposed explanation based on accelerations and concludes with the optimistic statement that *"one must hope that the matter is finally settled"*. What a hope.

25. Marder (1970) says that *"the general theory adds little to the interpretation of the clock paradox"*. How right he is.

26. Essen (1971) says:

> The argument about the clock paradox has continued interminably, although the way the paradox arose and its explanation follow quite clearly from a careful reading of Einstein's paper. Einstein's result is 'that the time marked by the moving clock viewed in the stationary system is slow' and it follows from the assumption of symmetry that:
> (i) clock B viewed in A is slower than clock A.
> (ii) clock A viewed in B is slower than clock B.

283

There is no contradiction here, but in the next section of his paper Einstein omits the expression 'viewed in A' and reaches the conclusion that clock B is slower than clock A, which contradicts the postulate of symmetry. Einstein calls the result peculiar, but it does not follow from the thought experiment if this is correctly performed. According to Einstein, one clock A moves along a line AB with velocity v to point B. When it reaches B its reading is slow compared with that of the clock which has remained at B and was initially synchronised with A. The result is said to hold good for any polygonal line and also when the points A and B coincide. Finally it is assumed to be valid for a closed curve, so that if a clock makes a round trip from A it will be slower on its return than a clock that has remained at A. Although the clock must be accelerated during its journey, no allowance is made for any effect of the acceleration – which indeed is not mentioned.

This statement is given *in toto* because Essen was the inventor of the caesium clock and was the director of the time-control department at the Greenwich Observatory. He was an expert in this field and knew exactly what was involved.

27. Holstein and Swift (1972) say that *"there is almost universal agreement on the results that would be obtained could the experiment be carried out"*. Well, count this author, Dingle and many others out! Holstein and Swift then say that *"there is something peculiar about the fact that free fall in a gravitational field can turn an inertial frame around"*. There sure is!

28. Greenberger (1972) had a problem with the twin paradox. He says:

If one accepts the postulates of relativity, then one must necessarily accept the twin paradox effect as an essential consequence; . . . there are certain assumptions in special relativity that may well be open to question. One such assumption is that the rate of a clock is independent of acceleration (i.e. that an arbitrary clock runs at the same rate as an inertial one moving at the same velocity). But one must recognise that by altering any of the basic assumptions of the theory one is constructing a different theory.

That is close to an outright challenge to the theory of SR.

29. Muller (1972) says that:

Although the paradox is resolved when one uses the equations of special relativity more carefully, it is surprising how few physicists are aware of the explanation, and think that the explanation lies somewhere in the realm of general relativity. One can resolve the paradox by using general relativity. But general relativity is not really necessary. We can use the equations of special relativity and take actions completely into account simply by assuming that they take place in essentially negligible 'proper time' (i.e. by assuming the acceleration does not cause either the accelerating twin to age, or his local clock to jump suddenly ahead or behind).

284

Muller also says, *"They agree about each other's age only when they are in the same Lorentz frame or separated by zero distance."* All of this contradicts Einstein's own explanation. How about taking photographs every few years and comparing them when the twins eventually meet up?

30. Markley (1973) did not pontificate on the matter but came to the moderate conclusion that *"the twin paradox turns out to be less paradoxical than it originally appeared"*. Only less paradoxical? The reader cannot but be impressed by the frustration of some of the investigators. It is clear that these authors are searching for a non-existent satisfactory explanation of the paradox. Several authors imply that other physicists did not previously appreciate the simple explanation now being put forward with vivid clarity by themselves!

31. Durso and Nicholson (1973) say that *"the asymmetrical ageing of the relativity twins in free fall can be predicted if they do sufficiently sensitive experiments to detect asymmetrical tidal forces which exist in their local reference frames"*. Tidal baloney!

32. Brams and Stewart (1973) use a concept of *"flat space-time which is spatially closed on itself"*. More specifically, they say, *"there are no obvious kinematic, dynamic or geometric distinctions between the two and yet one experimentally verifies that the moving clocks are slowed while the other does not"*. By using the word 'experimentally', Brams and Stewart give the impression that an actual experiment was carried out. This is not so. The whole thing is merely a 'thought experiment'. They conclude that *"the principle of special relativity, although locally valid, is not globally applicable"*. Mysterious! This is the opposite argument to that discussed earlier under the Sagnac effect, where it was claimed that time might be 'locally' different but that generally it was the same.

33. Hall (1976) says, *"Naive use of relativity can make it seem that each twin would expect the other to be younger."* Of Dingle, Hall says that the *"perennial chief skeptic has still not given up his quixotic crusade"*. Name-calling is a sure sign that the caller has lost the debate.

34. Essen (1978) says that *"Students are told that the theory must be accepted although they cannot expect to understand it. They are encouraged right at the beginning of their careers to forsake science for dogma."* Right!

35. Perrin (1979) says that *"the crux of the resolution involves calculating the time that passes on the earth when the travelling twin changes inertial frames"*. All clear as mud!

36. Turner (1979) says that:

> There proves to be no way to maintain that gravity and acceleration equally slow clocks down, or equally slow the ageing process. Gravity slows clocks. Acceleration does not retard clocks. Hence, Einstein's resolution of the twin paradox is not a factual resolution at all.

37. Unruh (1981) came up with another twist to the paradox when postulating that:

. . . during the period of acceleration, the accelerated observer sees the other traveller recede and go backwards in 'time'. This motion completely reconciles the calculations both observers make regarding the reading of each other's clocks when they meet again.

Many authors use the acceleration and deceleration phases as a useful 'cop-out'. By merely saying that these phases are 'not inertial', they seem happy. They do not attempt any further explanation. It seems as if it is sufficient to remark that *"it is not explained thus"*.

38. Rindler (1982) says that the eventual age difference between the twins can be seen to arise during the initial acceleration of the travelling twin away from the stationary twin. How much ageing occurs then? If it is true that this is the period of ageing, why not just accelerate away and then decelerate and come back immediately after, say, one month, without spending 60 years away? Is it harder to justify the strange claims if the traveller is said to be away for a month and to have aged significantly in this short period? If the separation is for 60 years and the acceleration is carried out over the first year, what then happens for the other 59 years? Does the ageing stop for the travelling twin for those years?

39. Desloge and Philpott (1987) comment upon *"the misconceptions which one encounters in many of the standard treatments, and also overlooked facets of the phenomenon"*. They say that the acceleration phase has nothing to do with a solution and that the general theory is also irrelevant. Einstein (1918) says the opposite, as quoted at length earlier, in his paper on this specific subject.

40. Sastry (1987) says, *"Everyone agrees that there is no symmetry in the twins' motion and so no paradox"* but then adds, *"Perhaps the last word on the twin paradox has yet to be said"*. Indeed.

41. Hawking (1988) explains that:

> *. . . it is a paradox only if one has the idea of absolute time at the back of one's mind. In the theory of relativity there is no unique absolute time, but instead each individual has his own personal measure of time that depends on where he is and how he is moving.*

How comforting!

42. Boughn (1989) sent two rockets off with a distance between them at launch. He remarks (in opposition to Einstein's 1918 effort):

> *. . . it is wrong to suppose that the reduced ageing is the direct result of acceleration. The age difference of the twins is proportional to the length of the trip while the period of acceleration is determined only by how long it takes to turn around and is independent of the length of the trip and, hence, the final age difference of the twins.*

So far, so good. Boughn then tries to show that twins who are sent off at the same rate of acceleration age differently.

43. Dray (1990), while postulating what he calls a 'cylindrical universe', says, *"Unlike in ordinary spatial relativity there is a preferred time direction in a cylindrical universe; . . . there are two effects here. The one described above is due solely to special relativity and is called the Sagnac effect."* So here we have an author applying the Sagnac effect to a cylindrical universe! As we saw earlier in this book, the Sagnac effect is not in any way related to relativity. The introduction of a cylindrical universe is suitably mysterious.

44. Low (1990) says that:

> *Unfortunately, one might argue that B can do exactly the same calculation and come to the conclusion that A's clock ought to show less elapsed time than his own after all; . . . the entire technology of using Lorentz transformations is suspect.*

With another example of the cylindrical model of the universe, Low has an amusing explanation:

> *A keeps watching B as B travels away from him. Then he observes B's clock going slower than his own. What he will not expect is that in fact B has come up behind him and is back at x = 0.*

What next? Ironically, if any of the above were to be believed, then the opposite should also apply. Therefore, if the 'traveller' is supposed to be the one who 'really' is found (by both twins) to age to a lesser degree, then, according to the basic tenet of relativity, i.e. that it is solely the relative velocity that is of importance, the reverse should also be true. We are by now sufficiently confused!

45. Winkler (1991), in a paper on the synchronisation of standard clocks around the world, castigated other authors. *"The next step can easily lead to a fatal error, made by many people, even experts, the error of the clock paradox."* In referring to the reverse situation – where the twin who is considered to be moving in the first computation is taken as the 'stationary' one – Winkler comments, *"Claims that 'relativity' means that the relative situation is the same, are false. The situation is clearly not symmetric; the clock that moves nonuniformly is always slow compared to an inertial clock."* However, who says which is the inertial clock? What of the *mutatis mutandi* statement by Einstein? We are listing here all the experts who make such fatal errors!

46. Desloge and Philpott (1991) had a second article in which they say that *"failure to think locally rather than globally are the true sources of difficulty with the twin paradox and most other paradoxes in relativity"*. They say that Boughn's puzzle (1989) *"is pedagogic"*.

47. Young's *Physics* (1992, p. 1079) states that because one of the twins is observing in an inertial frame, the other must have an acceleration with respect to this frame in order to turn around and come back, and that this difference causes the traveller to be really younger on return. The textbook says that *"careful analysis shows this to be*

true". Oddly, it does not give the supposed mysterious 'careful analysis'. Is this the only instance in this university text where such calculations are avoided?

48. Kelly (1995 and 1996) shows that the time does not change aboard a moving object. This dispels the paradox because neither twin ages differently from the other.

49. Debs and Redhead (April 1996) say that the *"direction-reversing acceleration"* has nothing to do with the explanation of the paradox. It is interesting to see the opposing views on this point alone. This long article purports to provide *"a way to settle the often discussed issue"*. They say that there is *"an infinite class of possible accounts, none of which is privileged"*. So, now we know – the above selection of explanations is merely a sample from an infinite series of explanations that will go on forever.

50. Price and Gruber (1996) give an amazing conclusion to their paper, which says:

> *We have given different answers to the question 'where does the differential ageing occur' (i) It all occurs during the twins' rocket trip (ii) Some occurs in the twins early (prerocket) years. The lack of a unique answer shows the lack of meaning of the question. Age difference in relativity has a well-defined meaning, but the origin of age difference cannot be assigned to any specific part of a worldline.*

This explanation is one of the most outlandish of all. It proposes that some of the age difference that is subsequently caused by the high-speed travel actually happens before the travel starts. Will someone put a stop to all this nonsense? There is a small industry producing articles that support the view that only one twin ages. Journals appear to be hungry for any article that will support the lesser ageing of the travelling twin. It does not matter how daft are the reasons given.

51. Blau (1998) continues the nonsense as follows:

> *If the space in which the twins live is a circle, then the sister can return to her brother without accelerating. Each twin sees the other moving uniformly and might claim the other's clock runs slowly. Of course this cannot be so, which is the twin paradox on the cylinder. One says 'cylinder' instead of circle because the topology of the two-dimensional space-time is cylindrical.*
>
> *On a space-time cylinder, the principle of relativity breaks down; it is not so that all sets of observers in uniform motion with respect to each other should expect to see the same physics. There is a unique set of privileged observers, all at rest with respect to each other, who see light circle the cylinder in either direction in the same amount of time. Twins at rest with respect to these privileged observers always age more than their siblings who travel around the cylinder and meet them.*

What a statement!

52. Cranor et al. (2000) use the example of two rotating rings that rotate in opposing directions. Each twin is on a ring. The twins pass by each other as the rings counter-rotate. Cranor et al. try to explain that each twin will see the other as ageing slower,

while the symmetry of the setup demands that they will agree on the time elapsed each time they meet. That is a difficult task! Cranor et al. consider that, in the limit, the motion is straight-line motion at any place on the circle. This is the very point that is denied in relation to the Sagnac effect (see Sagnac in Index). They propose that there is a 'discontinuity' in synchronisation at the position of one twin – like 'jumping time' instead of jumping frames!

53. Dolby and Gull (2001) bemoan that *"the description of 'when events happened according to the traveling twin' seems never to have been fully settled"* and that one twin *"assigns three times to every event"* and also that *"distant planets sweep backwards and forwards in time"* every time that twin moved. They say that GR is not needed for an understanding of the problem. They must never have read Einstein's 1918 paper on the subject! They refer to one twin as having *"hypersurfaces of simultaneity 'sweep around'"* or being *"overlapping"*. This is another of the 'frame jumping' brigade. Dolby and Gull have the usual complement of words, such as 'wrongly', 'common misconceptions' and 'misrepresented', when referring to previous papers on the paradox.

54. Hawking (2001), in a sequel to *A Brief History of Time*, again describes the matter as follows: *"Although it seems against common sense a number of experiments have implied that the travelling twin would indeed be younger."* This is complete with lovely colour diagrams, which give the statement a sense of importance. At least Hawking says that the experiments just 'imply' and do not prove – I wonder if he is having heretical doubts.

Watch out for the next published 'explanation' – such papers comprise a minor industry. Will the editor of the *American Journal of Physics* (which published over half of the above references) read this book and never again publish a paper on the paradox? That would be a coincidence!

. . . these consequences hold mutatis mutandi, for every system of reference.

Albert Einstein (1922)

I consider it quite possible that physics cannot be based on the field concept i.e. on continuous structures. In that case nothing remains of my entire castle in the air, gravitation theory included (and the) rest of physics.

Albert Einstein (1954) in a letter to Besso

References

Abolghasem G H et al. 1989 *J. Phys. A Math Gen.* **22** 1589-97

Aharonov Y and Bohm D 1959 *Phys. Rev.* **115** No 3 485-491

Airy G B 1872 *Phil. Mag.* 310-13 & 472-3

Allais M 1959 *Aerospace Eng.* **18** 46

Allais M 1998 *21st Century Science & Technology* Spring 26-34

Allan D W et al. 1985 *Science* **228** 69-70

Allen C W 1973 *Astrophysical Quantities* (The Athlone Press: London)

Alley C O 1979 *Proc. Ann. Symp. Freq. Control (33rd)* 4-39

Anderson D Z 1986 *Scientific American* **254** 86-91

Anderson et al. 1994 *Am. J. Phys.* **62** (11) 975-85

Antoni G 1953 *Inst. Nazionale di Ottica Arcetri Firenze* S **IV** N 143 1-4

Arditty H J and Lefèvre H C 1981 *Opt. Lett.* **6** (No 8) 401-3

Arfken G et al. 1989 *University Physics* (Academic Press: London)

Arp H 1987 *Quasars, Redshifts and Controversies* Interstellar Media (Cambridge Uni. Pr.)

Arp H 1999 *Seeing Red: Redshifts, Cosmology and Academic Science* (Aperion: Montreal)

Ashby N and Bertotti B 1987 *Phys. Rev.* **D34** 2246-58

Aspden H 1981 *Physics Lett.* **85A** No 8 & 9 411-14; 1972 *Physics Without Einstein* (Subberton Publications: Southampton)

Assis A K T 1994 *Weber's Electrodynamics* ((Kluwer: Dordrecht)

Assis A K T and Thober D S 1994 In: *Frontiers of Fundamental Phys.* (Plenum Press: New York; edited by M Barone and F Selleri) pp 409-14

Assis A K T and Neves M C D 1995 *Astroph. Space. Sci.* **227** 13-24

Assis A K T and Neves M C D 1995 *Apeiron* **2** (No 3) 79-84

Assis A K T 1999 *Relational Mechanics* (Apeiron: Montreal)

Assis A K T et al.1999 *Found. Phy.* **29** 729-53

Babcock G C and Bergman T G 1964 *J. Opt. Soc. Am.* **54** (2) 147-151

Barnett S J 1908 *Phys. Rev.* **36** 425-72; 1912 **35** No 5 323-36; 1913 **2** 323-6; 1915 **6** No 4 239-70; 1918 **12** No 2 95-114; 1920 **15** 527-8; *Phil. Mag.* 1922 1112-28

Bartocci U 1999 *Albert Einstein & Olinto De Pretto* (Societa Editrice Andromeda: Bologna)

Bates H E 1988 *Am. J. Phys.* **56** (8) 682-7

Beckmann P 1987 *Einstein Plus Two* (Golem Press: Colorado)

Beehler R E et al. 1965 *Meterologia* **1** (No 3), 114-31

Beiser A 1991 *Physics* 5th ed. (Addison-Wesley: Reading) p 747

Bergson H 1907 *Creative Evolution* (Dover Publications: New York)

Bernstein J 1991 *Einstein* (Fontana: London)

Bewley L V 1929 *AIEE Trans.* **48** 327-37

Bilger H R and Zavodny A T 1972 *Phys. Rev. A* **3** (No 2) 591-6

Bilger H R and Stowell W K 1977 *Phys. Rev. A* **16** (No 1) 313-9

Bilger H R et al. 1993 *IEEE Trans* IM **42** (No 2) 407-11; 1995 IM **44** (No2) 468-70

BIPM Bureau International des Poids et Mesures; International Bureau of Weights and Measures; Pavillon de Breteuil, F-92312 Sévres Cedex, France

Bjerknes C J 2002 *Albert Einstein the Incorrigible Plagiarist* (XTX Inc.: Illinois)

Blanchard A et al. 2003 *Astron. Astroph.* **412** 35-44

Blatt F J 1992 *Modern Physics* (McGraw-Hilt: New York) p 25

Blau S K 1998 *Am. J. Phys.* **66** (3) 179-184

Block D and Wainscoat R 1997 *Astronomy Now* **1** 6

Blondel A 1915 *The Electrician* 364-6

Bodily L N and Hyatt R C 1967 *Hewlett-Packard J.* **19** (No 4) 12-20

Bondi H 1964 *Relativity and Common Sense* (Doubleday: New York); 1967 *Assumptions and Myths in Physical Theory* (Cambridge Uni. Pr.)

Born M 1963 *Nature* March **19** No 4874 1287

Boughn S P 1989 *Am. J. Phys.* **57** (9) 791-3

Bowler M G 1986 *Lectures on Special Relativity* No 8 (Pergammon Press: Oxford) p 58

Brams C H and Stewart D R 1973 *Phys. Rev. D* **8** (No 6) 1662-6

Brewster W R 1956 15th Dec. *Sci. News Lett.* 371

Brillet A and Hall J L 1979 *Phys. Rev. Lett.* **42** (No 9) 549-52

Brown G B 1958 *Sci. Prog.* **46** 15-29

Brown W 1968 *Nature* **219** 791-3

Browne W 1996 *Letter to Irish Times*

Brush S 1967 *ISIS* **58** 230-2

Builder G 1959 *Am. J. Phys.* **27** 656-8; 1957 *Aust. J. Phys.* **10** 246-62; 1958 **11** (3) 279; 1979 *Spec. Sci. & Tech.* **2** (No 3) 230-42; (No 4) 421-37

Buller A H R 1923 *Punch*

Burt E G C 1973 *Nature Phys. Sci.* **242** 790-1

Cambridge Atlas of Astronomy 1980

Cannon W and Jenson O 1975 *Science* **188** (No 4) 186 & 317-28; 1976 **191** 490-1

CCIR 1990 *International Telecommunications Union,* Reports of the CCIR Annex to Vol 7 150-4; *Recommendation 536* 1978 p 21 of the ITU-R TF Series1997

CCDS 1980 Comité Int. des Poids et Mesures, Comite Consultatif pour La Def. de la Seconde 9th Sess., S14-17

Chappell J E 1979 *Spec. Sci. & Tech.* **2** (No3) 313

Clarke R W 1984 *Einstein: The Life and Times* (Avon Books: New York)

Cocke W J *Phys. Rev.* 1966, **16** 662-4

Cohen M H et al. 1977 *Nature* **268** 405-9

Cohn G L 1949 *Elect. Eng.* 441-447

Colella R, Overhauser A and Wernar S *Phys. Rev. Lett.* 1975 **34** (No 25) 1472-4

Conklin E K 1969 *Nature* **222** 971-2

Consoli M and Costanzo E 2003 *Astro-ph* 0311576 v1 p1-16

Consultative Committee for the Definition of the Second (CCDS) – see CCTF

Consultative Committee for Time and Frequency (CCTF), new name of CCDS from 1997

Cowen R 1998 *Science News* 139-41

Cramp W and Norgrove E H 1936 *IEE Journal* **78** 481-91

Cranor M B et al. *Am. J. Phys.* 2000 **68** (1) 1016-20

Crooks M J et al. 1978 *Am. J. Phys.* **46** (7) 729-31

Cullwick E G 1966 *The Fundamentals of Electromagnetism* (Cambridge Uni. Pr.)

Cutnell J D and Johnson K W 1995 *Physics* 3rd ed. (Wiley: New York)

Dabbs J W T et al. 1965 *Phys. Rev.* **139** (No 3B) 756-60

Darwin C J 1957 *Nature* **180** 976-7

Das Gupta A K 1963 *Am. J. Phys.* **31** 428-30

Davies P C W 1995 *Physics* 4th ed. (Prentice Hall: Essex)

Debs T A and Redhead L G 1996 *Am. J. Phys.* **64** (4) 384-92

De Pretto O 1903 *Ipotesi dell' Etere nella via dell' Universo,* presented 29th November 1903-4 *Proc. Veneto Roy. Inst. Sci. Lett. Arts A.A.* **63** Pt. 2 439-500

De Sitter W 1913 *Proc. Amsterd. Acad.* No 15 1297-8

Desloge E A and Philpott R J 1987 *Am. J. Phys.* **55** (3) 252-61; 1991 **59** (3) 280-1

Dewan E and Beran M 1959 *Am. J. Phys.* **27** (7) 517-8

Dieks D and Nienhuis G 1990 *Am. J. Phys.* **5** (7) 650-5

Dingle H 1956 *Nature* **177** No 4513 782-4; **178** 680-1; 1957 *Aust. J. Phys.* **10** 418-23; 1963 *Nature* **197** No 4874 1248-9 & 1287-8; 1979 **277** 584-5; 1960 *Br. J. Phil. Sci.* **11**, 11-31 & 113-129

Dingle H 1972 *Science at the Crossroads* (Martin Brian & O'Keefe: London)

Dolby C and Gull S 2001 *Am. J. Phys.* **69** (12) 1257-61

Dray T 1990 *Am. J. Phys.* **58** (9) 822-5

Dufour A 1935 *Compt. Rend.* **200** 894-7 & 1283-5

Dufour A and Prunier F 1937 *Compt. Rend.* **204** 1332-4 & 1925-27; **205** 658-9; 1939 **208** 988-90; 1941 **212** 153-4; 1942 *J. de Phys.* **3** No 9 153-61

Durso J W and Nicholson H W 1973 *Am. J. Phys.* **41** 1078-80

Eddington Sir A 1929 *The Nature of the Physical World* (Cambridge Uni. Pr.); 1933 *The Expanding Universe* (Cambridge Uni. Pr.); 1926 *The Internal Constitution of the Stars*, (Cambridge. Uni. Pr.)

Edmunds M G 1982 *Nature* **297** 284-5

Ehrenfest P 1909 *Phys. Zeitsch* **10** No 23 918

Einstein A 1905 *Ann. der Phys.* **17** 891-921

Einstein A; see translation of 1905 and 1916 papers by Perrett and Jeffery 1952 *The Principle of Relativity* (Dover Publications: New York)

Einstein A 1905 *Ann. der Phys.* **17** 891-921; 1906 *Ann. der Phys.* **20** 627-633; 1914 *Astron. Nachb.* 7-10; 1918 *Die Naturwissenschaften* **48** 697-702

Einstein A and Infeld L 1938 *The Evolution of Physics* (Cambridge Uni. Pr.)

Einstein A 1920 *Relativity (*authorised translation by R Lawson: Methuen & Co: London)

Einstein A 1920 *'Meine Antwort' Berliner Tageblatt u. Handels-Zeitung (27th August)*: English translation in Tauber G E 1979 *Albert Einstein's Theory of General Relativity* (Crown: New York) p 97-9

Einstein A 1922 *The Meaning of Relativity* (Methuen & Co: London)

Einstein A 1935 *The World As I See* It (Bodley Head: London)

Ellis R et al. 2000 *Astron. Geophys.* **41** 2-10

Escangon E 1927 *Comp. Rend.* **185** No 26 1693-5

Essen L 1971 *The Special Theory of Relativity: A Critical Analysis* (Clarendon Press: Oxford)

Essen L *Nature* 1964, **21**, 396; **202**, No 4934, 787; *Creat. Res. Soc. Quart.* 1977, **1**, 46; *Wireless World* Oct 1978, 44-5; Electr. and *Wireless World* Feb. 1988, 126-7

European Space Agency 1999 *Report No 15ISO Sees the Golden Age of Galaxy Formation*

Fadner W L 1988 *Am J. Phys.* **56** (2) 114-22

Faraday M 1832 *Phil. Trans. Roy. Soc.* **122** 125-194; 1852 **143** 25-43

Fehrle K 1913 *Ann. der Phys.* **62** 1109-28

Feldman L M 1971 *Am. J. Phys.* **42** 179-81

Ferguson A 1999 Camberley Surrey U.K. *Private correspondence*

Feynman R P 1963 The Feynman Lectures on Physics Vol. 2 (Addison-Wesley: Essex)

Feynman R P 1990 *QED* (Penguin Books: London)

Finlay-Freundlich E 1954 *Phil. Mag.* 303-8; 1986 *Astrophys. J.* **221** 544-53

Fitzgerald G F 1889 *Science* **13** (No 328) 390

Fizeau H 1851 *Comp. Ren.* **33** 349-55

Fock V 1964 *The Theory of Space Time & Gravitation* (Pergammon: New York) pp 234-7

Fox J G 1962 *Am. J. Phys.* **30** 297; 1965 **33** (No 1) 1-17

Freedman R and Kaufmann W 2002 *Universe* 6th ed. (W H Freeman: New York)

French A P 1968 *Special Relativity* (Chapman & Hall: London)

Frisch D H and Smith J H 1963 *Am. J. Phys.* **31** 342-55

Frye R M and Brigham V M 1957 *Am. J. Phys.* **25** 553-5

Gamow G 1961 *The Creation of the Universe* (Viking: London)

Gaposchkin E M 1971 *E O S Trans Am. Geophys. Un.* **52** 30-33

Gehrcke E 1913 *Die Naturwissenschaften* **1** No 3 62-6

Gehrcke E 1924 *Kritik der Relativittätstheorie* (H Meusser: Berlin) (lecture of August 24th 1920 in Berlin Philharmonic reproduced *Berliner Tageblatt u. Handels-Zeitung (27th August)*

Gerber P 1898 Zeitschrift f. Math. U. Phys. Leipzig **43** 93-104

Gerber P 1898 *Ann. der Phys.* **22** 529-30; 1917 S4 **52** 415-41

Gerber P 1902 *Programmabhandlung des städtischen Realgymnasiums zu Stargard in Pommerania* (reproduction of 1898 paper)

Geroch R 1978 *General Relativity* (University of Chicago Press)

Giancoli D C 2005 *Physics* 6th ed.(Prentice Hall: Essex)

Giannoni C and Øyvind G 1979 *Am. J. Phys.* **47** (5) 431-35

Graneau P March 1997 *The Missing Magnetic Force Law, Galilean Electrodynamics* 1-2

Graneau P and Graneau N 1996 *Newtonian Electrodynamics* (World Scientific: New Jersey)

Graneau P and Graneau N 1993 *Newton Versus Einstein* (Carlton Press: New York)

Green C 1976 *Decline and Fall of Science* (Hamilton: Corby)

Greenberger D 1972 *Am. J. Phys.* **40** 750-4

Grøn Ø 1975 *Am. J. Ph.* **43** No 10 869-76

Guinot B 1997 *Meterologia* **34** 261-90

Haffle J C 1970 *Nature* **227** 271; 1971 *Nature Phys. Sci.* **229** 238; 1971 *Proc. 3rd Ann. Dept Def. PTTI Meet.* 261-88

Haffle J C and Keating R E 1972 *Science* **177** 166-7; 168-70

Hall D E 1976 *Am. J. Phys.* **44** (No 12) 1204-8

Halliday D et al. 2005 *Fundamentals of Physics* 7th ed (Wiley: New York)

Harada M 2002 *Science Journal Kagaku* **72** (No 8) 769-71

Harress F 1911 *Die Geschwindigkeit des Lichtes in Benigten Körpern* Thesis (unpublished), Jena University

Harwit M 1981 *Cosmic Discovery* (Basic Books: Colorado) p 27

Harzer P 1914 *Astron. Nachr.* Band 198 **20** No 4748 377-84

Hasselbach F and Nicklaus M 1993 *Phys. Rev. A* **48** No 1 163-151

Hatch R, 2004 *GPS Solutions* **8** No.2 67-73

Hawking S W 1988 *A Brief History of Time* (Bantam Press: London); 2001 *The Universe in a Nutshell* (Bantam Press: London)

Hayden H C 1991 *Physics Essays* **4** No 3 361-7

Hehl F W and Ni W T 1990 *Phys. Rev. D* **42** No 6 2045-8

Hering C 1923 *Trans. AIEE* **42** 311-40

Highfield R and Carter P 1993 *The Private Lives of Albert Einstein* (Faber & Faber: London)

Hill C M 1995 *Gall. Electrod.* **6** (No 1) 3-6

Hils D and Hall J L 1990 *Phys. Rev. Lett.* **64** No 15 1697-700

Hoffmann B 1961 *Phys. Rev.* **121** (1) 337-42

Hoffmann B 1975 *Relativity and Its Roots* Ch. 5 (Scientific American Books: New York)

Holstein B R and Swift A R 1972 *Am. J. Phys.* **40** 746-50

Howe G W O 1935 *The Electrician* Jan. 4th

Hoyle F 1980 *Steady-State Cosmology Re-visited* (Uni. Coll. Cardiff Press)

Hubble E 1953 *Monthly Not. Roy. Astrom. Soc.* **113** No 6658-66

Holme N 1800 *Phil.Trans.* 161

Hurley W V 1980 *Spec. Sci. Tech.* **3** No 4 423-38

Ideström A 1948 *The Relativity Theories of Einstein Untenable* (Almquist & Wiksells Boktryckeri: Uppsala)

Internat. Telecom. Union CCIR 1990 *Internat. Radio Consult Comm. Report* Annex to Vol **7** No 439-5 Geneva 150-54; 1997 *ITU-R Recommendations* No TF 1010-1

Ives H E J: see Turner and Hazlett for a book of his many papers

Ives H E J 1937 *Opt. Soc. Am,* **27** No 5 177-80; 263-73, No 9 305-9, 310-11 & 389-92; 1938 **28** 296-99; 1952 **42** No 8 540-43

Ives H E J and Stilwell G R 1938 *J. Op. Soc. Am.* **28** 215-26; 1941 **31** 369-74

Jaseja J S et al. 1964 *Phys. Rev.* **133** No 5A 1221-5

Kantor W 1971 *Spectr. Lett.* **4** (5) 99-110 & 111-21; 1981 *App. Opt.* **20** No 23 3993

Katz R 1964 *An Introduction to the Special Theory of Relativity* (Van Nostrand: New Jersey)

Kelly A G 1965-6 *Proc. I Mech E* **180** Pt 1 No 42 981-97 *Hydraulic Design of Syphons*

Kelly A G 1995 *Inst. Engs. Irel.* Monogr. No 1 *Time and the Speed of Light – A New Interpretation*

Kelly A G 1996 *The Sagnac Effect & Relativity PIRT* London 6-9 Sept. 149-54

Kelly A G 1996 *Inst. Engrs. Irel.* Monogr. No 2 *A New Theory on the Behaviour of Light.*;

Kelly A G 1997 *Inst. Engrs. Irel.* Monogr. No 3 *Reliability of Relativistic Effect Tests on Airborne Clocks*

Kelly A G 1997 *Inst. Engrs. Irel.* Monogr. No 4 *Rules for Einstein Synchronisation of Clocks Challenged*

Kelly A G 1998 *Inst. Engrs. Irel.* Monogr. No 5 *Experiments on the Relative Motion of Magnets and Conductors*

Kelly A G 1998 *Inst. Engrs. Irel.* Monogr. No 6 *Faraday's Final Riddle?; Does he Field Rotate with a Magnet?*

Kelly A G 1998 *Experiments on Faraday's Law and the Relative Motion of Conductors & Magnets PIRT VI* London 11-18 Sept. 298-3089

Kelly A G 1998 *Synchronisation of Clock-Stations and the Sagnac Effect Proceedings Conf. Relativistic Phys.* June 25-28 Athens, Greece; in *Open Questions in Relativistic Physics* (Apeiron: Montreal)

Kelly A G 1999 *The Sagnac Effect and the Synchronisation of Clock-Stations, Galileo Back in Italy II* Bologna 26-28th May 149-63

Kelly A G 1999 *Experiments on Unipolar Induction, Physics Essays* **12** No 2 372-82

Kelly A G 1999 *Experiments on Unipolar Induction, Galileo Back in Italy II* 164-179 (26-28 May)

Kelly A G 2000 *Does the Field of a Magnet Rotate about its North-South Axis? PIRT VII* 170-86 (London 15-18 Sept.)

Kelly A G 2000 *Hafele and Keating Tests: Did They Prove Anything? Physics Essays* **13** (4) 616-21

Kelly A G 2000 *Special Relativity Right or Wrong? Electronics World* **106** 722-3 (Sept.)

Kelly A G 2001 *Inst. Engrs. Irel.* Monogr. No 7 *Whither Galaxies?* (All monographs post-free from Inst. Engrs Irel, 22 Clyde Rd, Dublin 4.)

Kelly A G 2001 *Sagnac Effect Contradicts Special Relativity, Infinite Energy* Issue **39** 24-8

Kelly A G 2003 *A Potential Source of Dark Matter, Physics Essays* 2003 **16** No 4

Kelly A G 2004 *Unipolar Experiments Ann. De la Foundation Louis de Broglie* **29** No 1-2 119-148

Kelly A G 2004 *The Location of the Missing Dark Matter; PIRT* IX London 3-6 Sept.

Kelly A G 2004 *The Sagnac Effect and Uniform Motion; PIRT* IX London 3-6 Sept.

Kelly A G 2004 *Tired Light and the Shape Effect in Cosmology, Meta Res. Bull.* **13** No 217-21

Kelly A G 2005 *Big Bang or Full Stop? Galilean Electrodynamics* **16** No 6 106-8

Kennard E H 1916 *Phys. Rev.* **7** 339-400; 1912 *Phil. Mag.* **23** 937-41; 1917 **13** 179-90

Kennedy R J and Thorndyke E M 1932 *Phys. Rev.* **42** 400-18

Keswani G H 1965 *Br. J. Phil. Sci.* **16** 19-32

Kiang T 1995 *Irish Astron. J.* **22** (2) 159-63

Kosowski S 1978 *Il Nuovo Cimento* **458** 98

Kristian J et al. 1978 *Astroph. J.* **221** 383-94

Langevin P 1911 *Scientia* **10** 31-54; 1921 *Compt. Rend.* **173** 831-4; 1935 **200** 48-51, 1161-5 & 1448-50; 1937 **205** 304-6

La Violette P A 1986 *Astrophy. J.* **301** 544-53

Lecher E 1895 *Ann. der Phys.* **54** 276-304

Leeb W E et al. 1979 *App. Opt.* **18** (No 9) 1293-5

Leffert C B and Donaghue T M 1958 *Am. J. Phys.* **26** No 8 915-23

Lerche I 1977 *Am. J. Phys.* **45** (12) 1154

Levi L 1967 *Am. J. Phys.* **35** No 10 968-9

Lewis G N 1908 *Phil. Mag.* S6 **16** (95) 705

Lodge Sir O J 1893 *Philos. Trans. R. Soc. London* **184** 727-804; 1897 **189** 149-66

Longair M 1976 *Roy. Astron. Soc. Quarterly J.* **17** No 4 422-47

Longair M 1998 *Astron. Geophys.* **39** Pt 2-10

Longair M 2000 *The Determination of Cosmological Constants IAU Symposium* **202** 1-12

Lorentz H 1952 Original 1904 paper in *The Principle of Relativity* (Dover Publications: New York)

Lovejoy A O 1931 *Phil. Rev.* **40** 48-68

Low R J 1990 *Eur. J. Phys.* **11** 25-7

Lowry E S 1963 *Am. J. Phys.* **31** 59

Lynch A 1932 *The Case Against Einstein* (Philip Allen: London) p 185

Macek W M and Davis D T M 1963 *App. Phys. Lett.* **2** No 3 67-8

Macek W M et al. 1964 *J. App. Phys.* **35** 2556-7

MacRoberts D T 1980 *Spec. Sci. & Tech.* **3** No 4 365

Maddox J 1990 *Nature* **346** 103; 1995 **376** 385

Malykin G 2000 *Physics - Uspekhi* **43** (12) 1229-52

Marder L 1971 *Time and the Space Traveller* (Allen & Unwin: London)

Marinov S 1977 *Eppur Si Muove* (East-West, Graz) 77-86,122-6 & 143-6; 1990 *Nature* **346** 103

Markley F L 1973 *Am. J. Phys.* **41** 1246

Markowitz W 1968 *Science* **162** 1387-8

Martin G J 1986 *Scien. Am* **254** 86-91; 1986 *IEEE Spectrum* Feb. 48-53

McCrea W H 1951 *Nature* **167** 680; 1956 **177** 784-5; **178** 681-2

Mencherini L 1993 *Phys. Ess.* **6** (1) 45-51

Metz A 1952 *Compt. Rend.* **234** 597-9 705-7

Metz A and Prunier F 1952 *Comp. Rend.* **234** 185-7

Michelson A A 1881 *Am. Jour. Sci.* (3) **22** 120-9; June 1897 *Am. Jour. Sc.* **3** 475-8; 1904 *Phil. Mag* **6** Part 8 716-9; 1913 *Astrophys. J.* **37** 190-3

Michelson A A and Gale H G 1925 *Nature* **115** No 2894 566

Michelson A A 1925 *Astroph. J.* (Pt 2 with Gale H G) **61** 3 137-45

Michelson A A and Morley E W 1886 *Am. Jour. Sci.* 3rd Ser. **31** 377-86; 1887 *Phil. Mag.* S5 **24** No 151 449-66

Michelson D (Livingston) 1973 *The Master of Light* (Scribner: New York)

Miller D C 1922 *Am. Phys. Soc.* **19** No 4 407-8; 1926 *Science* **63** No 1635 431-48; 1933 *Rev. Mod. Phys.* **5** 204-42

Misner C W et al. 1973 *Gravitation* (W H Freeman: San Francisco)

Møller C 1959 *Am. J. Phys.* **27** No 1 491-3; 1952 *The Theory of Relativity* (Oxford Uni. Press: New York) p 48

Montgomery H 2004 *Eur. J. Phys.* **25** 171-83

Monti R A 1996 *Physics Essays* **9** No 2 238-60

Moody R 2005 *Infinite Energy* **59** 34-8

Moon P and Spencer D E 1955 *J. Frank. Inst.* **260** 213-26; see also references in Spencer D

Moore W 1989 *Schrödinger* (Cambridge Uni. Pr.)

Morgan H B 1930 *J. Op. Soc. Am.* **20** 225-9

Morley E W 1905 *Phil. Mag.* 669-80

Morley E W and Miller D C 1905 *Phil. Mag.* S6 **9** No 53, 669-680 & 680-685

Morris R 1992 *The Edges of Science* (Fourth Estate: London)

Müller F J 1990 *Gall. Electrody.* **1** No 3, 27-31

Müller F J 1999 (formerly on the NPA site) *An experimental Disproof of Special Relativity theory (Unipolar Induction)*

Muller R A 1972 *Am. J. Phys.* **40** 966-0

Múnera H A 1998 *Apeiron* **5** No 1-2 37-54

Murray W A S 1982-3 *Wireless World* 10 articles *"A Heretics Guide to Physics"*

Musser G 2003 *Scientific American* (Nov.) 14-15

Nature 1967 *Nature Editorial* **216** 113-4; 1971 **233** 519; 1972 **238** 244-5; 1979, **239** 242

Nernst W 1938 *Ann. der Phys.* **32** 44-8

Nicols E F and Hull G F 1903 *Phys. Rev.* **17** 26-50 91-104

Nodland B and Ralston J P 1997 *Phys. Rev. Lett.* **78** No 16 3043-6

Ockert C E 1968 *Am. J. Phys.* **36** 158-161; 1969 **37** (No 3) 335-6

Ohanian H A 1989 *Physics* 2nd ed. (Norton: New York) p 1006

O'Rahilly A 1938 *Electromagnetics* (Longmans Green: London)

Pagels H R 1983 *The Cosmic Code* (Ml. Joseph: London)

Panofsky W and Phillips W 1964 *Classical Electricity and Magnetism* (Addison-Wesley: Essex)

Pauli W 1921 *Theory of Relativity* (Dover Publications: New York)

Peebles P J E et al. 1991 *Nature* **352** 769-76

Pegram G B 1917 *Phys. Rev.* **10** No 6 591-600

Penzias A and Wilson R 1965 *Astroph. J.* **142** 419-21

Perlmutter S el al. 1998 *Nature* **391** 51-4

Perrin R 1979 *Am. J. Phys.* **47** (4) 317-9

Petit G and Wolf P 1994 *Astron. Astroph.* **286** 971-7

Phipps T E 1989 *Am. J. Phys.***57** (6) 549-51

Pogany B 1926 *Ann. der Phys* **4** No 11 Band 80 217-31; 1928 S4 **85** 244-51

Popper K 1972 *The Logic of Scientific Discovery* (Hutchinson: London)

Post E J 1965 *Phys. Rev. Lett.* **15** No 5 177-8; 1967 *Rev. Mod. Phys.* **39** No 2 475-93

Pound R V and Rebka G A 1960 *Phys. Rev. Lett.* **4** (7) 337-41

Pound R V and Snider J L 1965 *Phys. Rev.* **140** No 3B 788-803

Preston S Tolver 1885 *Phil Mag.* **19** No 17 131-140 & 215-7; 1891 **31** 100-2

Price R H and Gruber R P 1996 *Am. J. Phys.* **64** (8) 1006-8

Prokhovnik S J 1979 *Spec. Sci & Tech.* **2** No 3 323

Prunier F 1925 *Compt. Rend.* **200** 46-48

Reasenberg R D et al. 1979 *Astroph. J.* **234** L219-21

Regener E 1933 *Zeit. für Phys.* **32** 66-9

Renshaw C 1999 *Proc. IEEE Aerosp. Conf.* 59-63

Riess A et al. 1998 *Astron. J.* **116** 1009-38

Rindler W 1982 *An Introduction to Special Relativity* (Clarendon Press: Oxford)

Ritz M 1908 *Ann. De Chim. Et de Phys.* 8th series v **XIII** 145-275

Romer R H 1959 *Am. J. Phys.* **27** No 3 131-5

Rothmann M A 1960 *Scien. Am.* July 142-52

Rudefer M 1979 *Spec. Sci & Tech* **2** No 4 405

Russell B 1925 *The A.B.C. of Relativity* (Keegan Paul: London)

Saburi Y 1976 *J. Radio Researdh Labs.* **23** No 112 255-65

Saburi Y et al. 1976 *IEEE Trans* **IM25** 473-7

Sachs M 1998 *Dialogues in Modern Physics* (World Scientific: Hong Kong)

Sadeh D et al. 1968 *Science* **161** 567-9

Sagnac M G 1910 *Compt. Rend.* **150** 1302-5 & 1676-9; 1913 **157** 708-10 & 1410-13; 1914 *J. de Phys.* 5th series1914 **4** 177-95

Sama N 1972 *Am. J. Phys.* **40** 416-8

Sandage J and Sandage M 1975 *Galaxies & The Universe* (University of Chicago Press)

Sastry G P 1987 *Am. J. Phys.* **55** (10) 943-6

Saxl E and Allen M 1970 *Physics Rev. D* **3** 825

Scaife W G 2000 *From Galaxies to Turbines* (Inst. of Phys.: London)

Scanlon P J and Hendriksen R N 1979 *Am. J. Phys.* **47** (10) 917-8

Scientific American Editors 2002 *Understanding Cosmology* (Warner Books: New York)

Schilling G 2004 27th November *New Scientist* 28-31

Schlegel R 1971 *Am. J. Phys.* **42** 183-7; 1971 *Nature Phys. Sci.* **229** 237-8; 1973 *Nature* **242** 180; 1973 *Found. Phys.* **3** No 2 169; 1974 *Am. J. Phys.* **42** 183

Schwinger J 1986 *Einstein's Legacy* (Scientific American Books: New York) Ch. 6

Shadowitz A 1975 *The Electromagnetic Field* (McGraw-Hill: New York)

Shankland R S 1955 *Rev. Mod. Phys.* **27** 167-78

Shama U: see Spencer D.

Shapiro I I et al. 1977 *J. Geophys. Res.* **82** No 28 1129-34

Sherwin C 1960 *Phys Rev.* **120** 17-21

Silberstein L J 1921 *Opt. Soc. Am.* **5** No 4 291-307

Silvertooth E W and Whitney C K 1992 *Physics Essays* **5** No 1 82-9

Smith M S 1960 *Modern Physics* (Longman: Harlow)

Smoot G F et al. 1977 *Phys. Rev. Lett.* **39** No 14 878-901

Spencer D, 2001 *Jour. New Energy* **5** No 356-67; referenced articles by Spencer, Moon, Shama.

Speziali P (ed.) 1979 *Correspondence avec Michele Besso 1903-1955* (Hermann: Paris)

Stachel J 1980 *General Relativity & Gravitation* ed. A Held (Plenum Press: New York) pp 1-15

Stokes G G 1845 *Phil Mag.* 9-15 & 76-81; 1846 6-10

Stebbins J and Whitford A 1948 *Astro. J.* **108** 413-36

Sunday Times Supplement 2001 *The A to Z of the Universe* Sept. 13th & 20th

Synge J L 1968 *Nature* **219** 793

Synge J L 1960 *Relativity – The General Theory* (North-Holland: London)

Tauber G E 1979 *Albert Einstein's Theory of General Relativity* (Crown: New York)

Taylor E F and Wheeler J A 1992 *Space Time Physics* 2nd ed. (W H Freeman: New York) p 133

Terrell J 1959 *Phys. Rev.* **116** No 4 1041-5

Then J W 1960 *Am. J. Phys.* **28** No 6 557-9; 1962 **30** 411-5

Thompson D C et al. 1978 *App. Phys. Lett.* **33** (11) 940-1

Tilley D R 1968 *Am. J. Phys.* **36** 458

Tolman R C 1987 *Relativity Thermodynamics and Cosmology* (Dover Press: Toronto); 1934 (Oxford Uni. Press: Oxford)

Trocheris M G 1949 *Phil. Mag.* **40** 1143-54

Turner D 1979 – see book edited by Turner D & Hazlett R for section by Turner

Turner D and Hazlett R (eds). 1979 *Einstein Myth and the Ives Papers* (Devin-Adair Old Greenwich: Connecticut)

Unruh W G *Am. J. Phys.* 1981 **49** (6) 589-92

Vali V et al. 1977 *App. Opt.* **16** (No 10) 2605-7

Valone T 1994 *The Homopolar Handbook* (Integrity Research Institute: Washington, D.C.)

Van Flandern T 1992 *Quasars: Near v Far; Meta. Res. Bull.* **1** 28-32

Van Flandern T 1993 *Dark Matter Missing Comets & New Comets,* (North Atlantic Books: California)

Van Flandern T and Yang S 2003 *Phys. Rev. D* **67** 022002

Vessot R F C 1979 *Rad. Sci.* **14** No 4 629-47; 1984 *Contemp. Phys.* **25** No 4 335-80

Vigier J P 1990 *IEEE Trans Plas. Sci.* **18** (1) 64-72; 1997 *Phys. Lett. A* **234** 75-85; 1997 *Phys. Lett. A* **235** 419-31

Von Laue M 1920 *Ann. der Phys.* **62** 448-63

Von Laue M 1912 *Phys. Zeit.* **123** 118-20

Von Mettenheim C 1998 *Popper versus Einstein* (Mohr Siebeck: Tübingen)

Walker J S 2004 *Physics* 2nd ed.(Pearson Education: Essex)

Wang R et al. 2003 *Phys. Lett A* **312** 7-10

Wang R 2005 *Gall. Electrodyn.* **16** No 2 23-30

Weber T A 1997 *Am. J. Phys.* **65** (6) 486-7; **65** (10) 946-53

Weber W 1841 *Pogg. Ann.* Bd **52** 354

Webster D L 1963 *Am. J. Phys.* **31** 590-7

Werner S A 1979 *Phys. Rev. Lett.* **42** No 17 1103-6

Wesley J P 1991 *Selected Topics in Advanced Fundamental Physics* pp 220-237 (B Wesley: Blumberg)

Whitaker E T 1960 *History of the Theories of Aether & Electricity* (Harper & Row: New York)

Willick J and Batra P 2001 *Astrophy. J.* **548** 564-84

Wilson D B 1987 *Kelvin and Stokes* (Adam Hilger: Bristol) pp 129-54

Winkler G M R 1970 *Proc. 2nd Ann PTTI Meeting* **1** 129

Winkler G M R et al. 1970 *Meterologia* **6** No 4 126-33
Winkler G M R 1991 *Proc IEEE* **79** No 6 1029-39
Young H D 1992 *University Physics* (Addison-Wesley: Reading, Mass.)
Young H D and Freedman R A 1996 *University Physics* (Addison-Wesley: New York)
Zeeman P 1915 *Proc. R. Acad. Amsterd.* **18** 398-408
Zernike F 1947 *Physics* **13** No 4-5 279-88
Zukav G 1979 *The Dancing Wu Li Masters* (Rider: London)

. . . the obstacles to the acceptance of my argument are mainly psychological; my communication has been read, not to see if what I say is right, but to see where it is wrong. If my critics could only manage to conceive the possibility that it might be right, I think they would at once see that it is; it is so very simple.

Herbert Dingle (1963)

Index

Brewster W R · 281
Brillet A & Hall J L · 119–20, 125, 126, 259
    and Aspden · 119–20, 126, 259
Brown G B · 249
Browne W · 177, 248
Brück M
    meeting with Pope John Paul II · 222
Brush S
    Fitzgerald publication in *Science* · 6
Builder G · 114, 131–32, 281, 282
Buller R · ii
Burt E G C · 98

C

C + O = Fe · 262
caesium clocks · *See* clocks, caesium
Cannon W & Jensen O · 111, 112, 246–48
CCDS · 57, 95–100, 104–10, 120, 124. *See also*
    CCTF
    correspondence with author · 108–9
CCIR · 57, 95–110, 115, 124
    error in angular velocity of earth · 102
CCTF · 95, 100, 106. *See also* CCDS
CERN · 82
Chappell J E · 62, 171
circular motion applicable to SR · 53–56
Clarke A C · 20
Clarke R W · 78
clock paradox · *See* twin paradox
clocks
    and acceleration · 163, 246–48
    caesium · 31–34, 111, 150, 167, 170, 265–78, 284
    drift rate · 266–75
    Einstein synchronisation · 93–94
    moving, run slow · 11–12, 24–26, 248
    on aeroplanes · *See* Hafele & Keating
    portable, accuracy of · 267–68, 275
    presetting of satellite clocks · 110
    rod · 11–12, 137–38, 167
    run slow with respect to geocentre · 33–34, 95–97,
        100, 109–15, 150
    slower at poles · 95
    stability · 267
    standard · 31, 33, 111, 157, 247, 287
    synchronisation · 93–115
Cocke W J
    atomic clocks, timekeeping · 31, 112, 113
Cohen M H et al. · 141
Cohn G L · 187, 191, 203
Colella R et al. · *See* COW experiment
comparison of theories · 125

Conklin E K · 80
Consoli M & Costanzo E · 80
contemporaneous, definition of
    Russell · 74, 130, 228
contraction of length with speed · 14, 27, 144,
    146
Cooney J · 177
Coriolis effect · 62–63
cosmic rays · 248
COW experiment · 70
Cowen R · 214, 219
Crab nebula · 141
Cramp W & Norgrove E H · 182, 186, 192, 200
Cranor M et al. · 288–89
Crooks M J · 200
Cullwick E · 187
Curie M · 34
    Langevin · 45
    Solway conference · 45
Cutnell J D & Johnson K W · 31

D

Dabbs J W T et al. · 123
dark energy
    Cowen · 219
    Perlmutter et al. · 218
    refuted by Blanchard et al. · 219
    Riess et al. · 218–19
dark matter · 217–30, 264
    located · 222–25
    matter not yet seen · 225–29
Darwin C J · 281
Das Gupta A K · 182, 199
Davies P C W · 31
De Pretto O
    discoverer of $E = mc^2$ · 15–22, 72, 251, 263
    links to Einstein · 15–22
    murdered · 19
De Sitter W · 139
Debs T A & Redhead L G · 288
density of matter in universe · 230
    critical value · 217–19
Desloge E A & Philpott R J · 286, 287
Dewan E & Beran M · 146–47
Dieks D & Nienhuis G · 57, 58, 179
Dingle H · 24, 149–60, 164–74, 261, 281, 282,
    284, 285, 300
    and Born · 153, 155, 160
    and Lovell · 159
    and Synge · 159
    British Association · 159

303

K

Kantor W · 69
Katz R · 9, 12, 14–15, 28, 65–66
Kelly A G · 153, 176–79, 261, 268, 277, 288
Kennard E · 182, 186, 199, 208
Kennedy R J & Thorndyke E M · 119
Keswani G H · 172
Kiang T · 141
kinetic energy · 145–46, 218
Kissane B · 189
Kosowski S · 90
Kristian J · 216

L

La Violette P A · 242
Langevin P · 43, 58, 279
   Curie M · 45
   Dufour & Prunier · 43–45
Lecher E · 182
Leeb W · 67, 69
Leffert C B & Donaghue T M · 281, 282
length contraction · *See* contraction of length
  with speed
Lerche I · 69
Levi L · 283
Lewis G N · 146
Liebnitz · 17
light
   and gravity · 123–24, 245–46, 264
   escaping from influence of earth · 127–28
   extinction theory of · 88–91, 128
   faster than · 85–86, 140–44, 242, 264
   frequency · 28, 114, 120, 148–50, 250–51
   in medium · 67–70
   in outer space · 75, 118, 127
   measurement of speed · 117
   moves with earth's centre on orbit · 117
   nature of · 84
   not moving with earth's daily spin · 118
   orbital angular motion · 84
   polarisation · 81–85, 210
   signals from Mars, behaviour of · 124, 252, 255
   slit experiment · 80–85
   speed affected by velocity of observer · 3
   speed affected by velocity of source · *See* Ritz
   speed not constant · *See* Sagnac
   speed of · 120–21
   wavelength · 28, 120, 213, 250–51
lightning bolts · 9–10, 20, 76
light-year · 29, 213

M

Limerick, University of · 180
Lodge, Sir O J
   and Sagnac formula · 61
Longair M · 221, 230
Lorentz equations
   derivation · 68, 91, 139–40
Lorentz H · 43, 135, 136, 173
   Fitzgerald · 6, 139
   priority on contraction · 6
Lovejoy A · 280
Lovell, Sir B · 159
Low R J · 287
Lowry E S · 283
Lynch A · 173

Macek W M & Davis D T M · 51
Macek W M et al. · 69
MacRoberts D T · 167
Maddox J
   Dingle · 171
magnet
   effect on light · 210–11
   field of · 187–89
   lines of force rotate · 192–203, 264
magnetic field of earth · 123, 266
magnetism · 123, 144–46
Malus · 82
Malykin G · 56
Marder L · 283
Marinov S · 90, 170
Markley F L · 285
Markowitz W · 111
Mars · 124, 251, 255
Martin G J · 52
mass · 14
   of photon · 28–29, 114, 145, 246
   paradox · 28
mass-energy equivalence · 19–22
Maxwell · 135, 139, 144, 146, 149, 206, 207, 263
McCrea W H
   versus Dingle · 153–60
Medawar, Sir P · 152
medium
   light in · 67–70
Mencherini L · 187
Mercury, perihelion of
   calculation of · 249
   Einstein incorrect · 250
   Gerber priority · 249
meson · 146

shape of galaxies · *See* galaxies, shapes explained

Shapiro I I et al. · 124

Sherwin C · 111, 282

shortening, apparent · *See* apparent shortening under UR

Silberstein L J · 42, 49

Silvertooth E W & Whitney C K · 80

singularities · 256

siphon, lifts water higher · 153

Smith M S · 66

Smoot G F et al. · 78

Soddy · *See* Essen (1988) and Fadner (1988)

Somers C · 178

sound, speed of · 3, 7, 74, 75, 222–23

space, expanding · 221, 232–33, 240

space-time
   relativistic · 130
   universal relativistic · 130

Special Theory of Relativity · 3–22
   explanation of · 7–9
   motion on a circuit · 52–56
   problems with · 23–30
   Sagnac effect · 34–39, 56–57
   straight-line motion · 52–56

speed of light · *See* light, speed of

speed, absolute · *See* absolute speed

Spencer D · 260

spin of earth · *See* earth, spin of

spiral galaxies · *See* galaxies

Stachel J · 43, 146

stars, fixed · *See* fixed stars

steady-state universe · 215–16, 220–21, 229–30, 242, 243
   and Bondi · 127, 216
   and Hoyle · 216
   and Kelly · 215

Stebbins J & Whitford A · 241

Stokes G G · 6, 87

Sunday Times supplement · 227

superluminal objects · 140–41

swans are white · 1

synchronisation of clocks · *See* clocks, synchronisation

Synge J L · 28, 88, 159

T

tachyons · *See* superluminal objects

Tauber G E · 249

Taylor E F & Wheeler J A · 33, 88

tellurium, speed of light in · 127

Terrell J · 135–36, 232

Then J W · 182, 186, 199–200

Tilley D · 204–6

time
   absolute · *See* absolute time
   accelerating field · *See* Schlegel
   proper · 247, 284
   relative · 113

tired light theory
   Assis · 240–43
   Hubble · 213, 240–43

Tolman R C
   twin paradox · 23, 153, 280

Tolver Preston S · *See* Preston S Tolver

train
   ball bouncing · 76–77

Trocheris M G · 58

Tuite M · 176

Turner D · 43, 74, 285

Turner D & Hazlett R · 19, 74, 150

twin paradox · 23–27, 279–89
   American Journal of Physics · 166, 171, 289
   Dingle · 24, 160, 164–74, 281, 282, 284, 285
   Einstein · 24–27, 160–66, 279
   Maddox · 171
   McCrea · 153–60
   Nature · 155–56, 159, 171
   Royal Society · 154, 160
   Science · 159
   Synge · 159
   Tolman · 23, 153, 280

U

unipolar induction · 181–212
   experiments · 183–203
   magnet tests · 183–88
   proof that the field rotates · 202–3
   solenoid tests · 184–86, 188–89, 198–203, 205–6, 210–11

universal
   energy · 144–46
   length · 144
   space-time · 132–33
   time · 129

universal clock · 128, 132

universal relativity · 117–51

universe
   accelerating away · 220–21
   age of · 214, 220
   expanding · 217–22
   size of · 215
   steady state · *See* steady-state universe

University College Dublin · 41, 84, 177, 260

Printed in the United Kingdom
by Lightning Source UK Ltd.
108673UKS00003B/47-580